A MILLION YEARS OF MAN

A MILLION YEARS
OF MAN

*The Story of Human Development as
a Part of Nature*

Richard Carrington

THE WORLD PUBLISHING COMPANY

CLEVELAND AND NEW YORK

Published by The World Publishing Company
2231 West 110th Street, Cleveland 2, Ohio

Library of Congress Catalog Card Number: 62–15712

FIRST EDITION

901.9
C318

CONTENTS

v

CONTENTS

PART 4: CIVILISATION

PART 5: MAN'S PLACE IN NATURE

ILLUSTRATIONS

PLATES

III. THE LIVING RACES OF MAN

Between pages 136 and 137

IV. FROM PREHISTORY TO HISTORY

Between pages 176 and 177

LINE DRAWINGS

ILLUSTRATIONS

TABLES AND CHARTS

PREFACE

I HAVE attempted in this book to recount as simply and directly as possible the history of our species, and to relate it to its universal setting. Until the rapid growth of evolutionary biology in the middle of the nineteenth century it was customary to regard man and other life forms as belonging to separate orders of nature. Man, it was believed, was the creation of a personal and supernatural deity who would watch over his chosen *protégé* like a benevolent father watching over a son. If this privileged creature conducted himself according to certain authoritarian tenets, or duly repented of any failure to observe them, he would be rewarded by an indefinitely prolonged happiness in Heaven. According to this view, the so-called 'brute creation' had been summoned into existence by God especially for the benefit of man, and the physical universe was to be regarded simply as a setting in which he could conduct his inevitable progress towards divine estate.

The last century has seen a dramatic revolution in this somewhat self-centred concept of man. Darwin and his immediate successors proved conclusively that we have evolved by the same basic laws of nature which govern the growth of all other organisms. More recently it has come to be understood that even the physical universe is part of the same process, and that life has developed as logically and naturally from inorganic matter as man has emerged from the ranks of the Mammalia to become the dominant species on earth.

The implications of this new world view offer an extraordinarily exciting challenge to the human mind. Man must now cut away the dead wood of traditional beliefs and approach the whole problem of his role in nature with a new humility. To some people this still seems at best a depressing and at worst a sacrilegious task but, as I hope to show in this book, it can offer us a far grander vision of our nature and destiny than any that we have conceived before. The new world view rejects the idea that we alone have special significance in the universe; it challenges us to a compassionate understanding of our close relationship not only with every other living thing, but with the very stuff of the earth and the laws that move the stars in their courses.

The title *A Million Years of Man* has not been chosen without some thought. In a sense any definition of man's age is arbitrary, for it must depend on one's interpretation of the word 'man'. Certainly our own species, *Homo sapiens,* cannot claim even the brief antiquity of a million years and has existed for at most 200,000 generations. Man did not spring full-armed into the world, however; he grew upon it slowly. The figure we have chosen is therefore intended to define not just the last few millennia of man's development, but the whole period of hominid evolution since our ancestors first acquired the power of conceptual thought.

I have divided the unfolding of this long and complex story into five parts. In Part 1 I deal particularly with man's home on the planet earth, the laws which have led to his evolutionary emergence, and some living and extinct members of the great mammalian order known as the Primates to which he belongs. In Part 2 I tell the story of human origins in the early Pleistocene epoch, and describe the man-like creatures who were man's cousins or possible ancestors at that time. In Part 3 the focus is reduced to the early history of *Homo sapiens* himself, and I detail the stages by which our immediate ancestors grew from being simple hunters and food-gatherers to the high degree of social organisation known as civilisation. In Part 4, which is in some ways the most ambitious, I survey the contributions made by the earth's major civilisations to man's evolving mind, and try to relate these to the biological principles which have governed the whole of evolution. Finally, in Part 5, I make some attempt to relate the human adventure to the totality of nature, and to offer a tentative view of what man's role in the universe may be.

The large field covered by this book makes it quite impossible for me to detail the sources of every individual fact, but the bibliography between pages 309 and 320 lists the works to which I have mainly referred. In addition I am deeply grateful to the following friends, colleagues and mentors who have read and commented on the whole or part of the typescript, or given me advice on specific points:

Dr F. R. Allchin, Lecturer in the Institute of Oriental Studies, University of Cambridge; Professor E. N. da Costa Andrade, F.R.S., formerly Quain Professor of Physics, University of London; Dr R. D. Barnett, Keeper of Western Asiatic Antiquities, British Museum; Mr C. A. Burland, Department of Ethnography, British Museum; Mrs Sonia Cole, Member of Council, Royal Anthropological Institute; Professor K. de Burgh Codrington, Professor of Indian Archaeology, University of London; Dr W. C. Osman Hill, Prosector, Zoological Society of London; Professor H. D. F. Kitto, Professor of Greek, University of Bristol; Dr L. Harrison Matthews, F.R.S., Scientific Director, Zoological Society of London; Dr Margaret Murray, formerly Assistant Professor of Egyptology, University College, University of London; Dr Stephen Toulmin, Director, Nuffield Foundation Unit for the History of Ideas, London; and Dr J. S. Weiner, Reader in Physical Anthropology, University of Oxford. The responsibility for the final presentation of the book of course remains entirely my own.

My acknowledgements are also due to the following for illustrative material:

Mr Maurice Wilson for the original half-tone and line illustrations he has contributed to this work; Mrs Sonia Cole and Illustration Research Service for their energetic assistance in obtaining photographs and line drawings; and Miss Jane Mackay for invaluable assistance with the lay-out. For the photographs not taken by myself or under my direction my special thanks are due to the following individuals, agencies and institutions: Frank Lane for Plates 1, 8, 11 and 15; Frank Lane and San Diego Zoo for Plates 16 and 17; the British Museum for Plates 59, 60, 61, 64, 65, 66, 68, 69, 70, 71, 73, 74, 76, 77, 78, 79, 80, 81 and 82; the British Museum (Natural History) for Plates 2, 23, 25, 27 and 44; Paul Popper for Plates 3, 4, 5, 6, 7, 9, 10, 12, 14, 30, 31, 33, 34, 35, 36,

37 and 38; Topix for Plate 13; Dr John Napier and the Editor of *Discovery* for Plate 18; the Shell Petroleum Co. Ltd for Plates 28, 29 and 58; the National Film Board of Canada for Plate 32; Australia House for Plate 39; British Overseas Airways Corporation for Plate 40; Messrs George Weidenfeld and Nicolson for Plates 41, 45 and 51; the Chicago Natural History Museum for Plate 43; Professor D. Berciu for Plate 48; Professor J. G. D. Clark and Messrs Methuen & Co. Ltd for Plate 49; Dr Kathleen Kenyon for Plate 50; the Ministry of Works for Plates 52 and 53; the Radio Times Hulton Picture Library for Plates 54, 67, 75 and 92; Dorien Leigh Ltd for Plate 62; India House for Plate 63; Fox Photos Ltd for Plates 84 and 91; The United States Information Service for Plates 85 and 90; the Imperial War Museum for Plates 86, 87, 88 and 89; Camera Press for Plate 93; and Lady Epstein for Plate 94. Mr John Curtis saw the book most efficiently through the press.

Finally, my deepest gratitude goes, as always, to Mary Eden, with whom every chapter was discussed, and who typed the successive drafts and checked the bibliography. It was largely through her constant encouragement that the work was completed as originally planned.

R.C.

London, Nice and Aix-en-Provence,
    December 1959–September 1962

AUTHOR'S NOTE, APRIL 1963

While this book was in the press new work in geochronology began to suggest that the antiquity of the australopithecines may shortly be put back by at least another half-million years, and that the Pleistocene epoch and the Great Ice Age may occupy a longer span than was previously thought. The datings for early fossil hominids given in Part 2, and also the earlier figures given in the Chart of Quaternary Time appearing on pp. 50 and 51, should therefore be treated with caution while the matter is *sub judice*.

Part 1

SPACE, TIME AND EVOLUTION

Chapter One

MAN'S HOME, THE EARTH

MAN AND ALL his works cling precariously to the surface of a spinning sphere of concentrated matter which is rushing through space at a rate of approximately eighteen miles, or thirty kilometres, per second. This sphere has an equatorial diameter of about 7,900 miles, a surface area of about 197 million square miles and a weight of rather more than 6,000,000,000,000,000,000,000 or 6×10^{21} tons. In spite of the apparently respectable nature of these figures our earth is one of the most physically insignificant bodies in the universe. Even within the solar system it is exceeded in size by four of the nine planets that circle the sun. Jupiter, the largest planet, has a diameter ten times larger than that of the earth, and its volume is greater by some 1,390 times.

Apart from its smallness our earth's insignificance is emphasised by its isolation in the immensity of space. Matter at the degree of concentration found in the heavenly bodies is a rare phenomenon in the universe, and the size of even the largest stars is as nothing compared to the vast distances that separate them. The earth's isolation is shown even by reference to its parent star, the sun, and its planetary neighbours in the solar system. Thus if we were to make a model of the sun's family, representing the sun by a tennis ball, then the earth would be comparable to a small pea orbiting at a mean distance of 25 feet. The farthest planet, Pluto, on the same scale would be the size of a single grain of sand orbiting about a fifth of a mile away.

Placing the earth, and indeed the whole solar system, in the vast context of the universe itself, the puny nature of man's home can hardly be imaginatively conceived. The sun and its family are part of a disc-shaped agglomeration of stars known as the galaxy, which is so vast that light travelling at approximately 186,000 miles a second takes about a hundred thousand years to cross it. Similar star cities are spread out in space at distances of between $1\frac{1}{2}$ and 2 million light years from one another to the observable horizon of the universe. In comparison with its spatial environment our earth is thus seen to be far smaller and less noticeable than a speck of dust floating in the Pacific Ocean.

After contemplating such facts it is a relief to turn to the comparatively familiar and manageable features of our planet itself. This consists essentially of five interacting zones or spheres, known respectively as the atmosphere, the lithosphere, the hydrosphere, the centrosphere, and the biosphere. The first four lie within the province of geophysics, the fifth within the province of biology.

The atmosphere is the gaseous envelope in which the earth is enclosed. This extends several hundred miles from the surface, but after 50 miles or so it becomes extremely attenuated. If our planet had lacked an atmosphere there would have been no human history at all, for this envelope of 'air' is, of course, essential to the existence of life itself. Less basically the atmosphere has also become particularly important to man in recent years by providing the medium for his swiftest method of transportation in flying machines of various kinds.

The lithosphere (from the Greek *lithos,* a stone) is the crust of the earth, which has formed the main theatre of man's activities. This mantle of solid rock is about 40 miles thick, which sounds a reasonably large figure, but in comparison with the earth's diameter the lithosphere is thinner than the skin of an apple. Although appearing very stable, with its mountains and valleys and plains, the crust is in fact constantly changing its outline, as we shall shortly see.

The hydrosphere is the name given to all the waters that lie on the face of the earth, whether these be lakes, rivers, or seas. Man, as a land animal, is not naturally associated with the hydrosphere, but it has played an important role in his history; in the early days it was a barrier to his migrations, and it later became a highway for his ships. The hydrosphere is also the place where life itself originated on earth, and is therefore the source of the whole vast evolutionary process of which man at present forms the culminating point.

The centrosphere comprises the great bulk of the earth lying beneath the crust. This region is still largely mysterious, and can never be directly examined, although the behaviour of earthquake waves passing through the earth's interior suggests that it may consist partly of peridotite and partly of nickel-iron in a plastic state. Although of great interest to geologists, this aspect of our home has played no direct part in the story of man and we need not consider it further.

Finally we come to the biosphere, which is the only zone of our earth which cannot be described in purely physical terms. This is simply because, by definition, it consists of the whole of the earth's life, including man. It may seem odd to suggest that the biosphere should be regarded as just another zone of the earth, comparable with the physical zones we have just described. Yet this is much more logical, and also more in accord with the evidence, than the alternative view that life is some special and mysterious phenomenon belonging to a different order of nature. Later, when I talk about the general development of life on earth, I hope this proposition will become acceptable even to those readers who may at first be inclined to regard it with suspicion.

The age of the earth is now reckoned at some 4,500 million years, but the exact way it came into being is still unknown. One popular modern theory is that it is a fragment of a star of the type known as a supernova, which exploded and flung the earth into the sun's gravitational field. Our earthly home may therefore not be, as was once thought, a child of the sun, from which it was torn by the attraction of a passing star. We may be occupying a fragment of matter thrown into proximity with the sun from a quite distant part of the star city around us.

Next we must give a few facts about the evolution of the lithosphere, which has had an exceptionally important effect on the evolution of life, and therefore on man's own history. Poets of the pre-scientific age were inclined to wax lyrical on occasion concerning the stability of the eternal hills. In fact few natural phenomena, except the lives of individual organisms, are more impermanent than the earth's physical features. The shape of our planet's crust is constantly being changed by deep-seated forces acting both at the centre and the surface of the sphere. The erosive action of wind, rain and frost is continually wearing away the raised lands and spreading their substance over surrounding areas as level plains. At the same time lateral forces in the crust, produced by the shrinking of the core, are breaking up these plains and raising them in jagged and fantastic shapes into new mountain ranges. This slow but inevitable process is accompanied by successive advances and regressions of the hydrosphere, so that areas that were high tablelands at one stage in earth history may at a later stage be covered by sea. Similarly the sea-bed of one age may be upraised to form the mountain peaks of another. As an example of this process, the peak of Mount Everest, the highest piece of land at present existing on the earth's surface, is largely composed of the fossilised remains of marine invertebrates from the bed of an ancient sea.

These changes in the physiognomy of the earth's surface through time have led to corresponding changes in the direction of ocean currents and the circulation of the atmosphere, and have thus constantly affected the nature of the climate in any given region. The earth's climates are likewise related to the action of cosmic forces, such as an intensified or reduced sunspot activity and the filtering effect of dust particles or clouds of gas far out in space. Fluctuations of climate on this grand scale have naturally had a strong influence on the distribution of life and the tempo and direction of evolution. Man's present state and the whole of his history are thus closely related not only to changes in the aspect of the earth's crust but to the subtlest fluctuations of physical conditions in the outer universe.

The facts and figures given above must at first seem very doubtfully related to the course of events during the forty-odd thousand years of purely human history. In fact, however, every event of our daily lives is entirely dependent on them It may help us to a salutary detachment if we realise that the whole of man's existence, from the most misguided machinations of his politicians to the highest achievements of his greatest artists and thinkers, is indissolubly bound up with the slightest physical change in the sun and the movement of the stars in their courses.

Chapter Two

LIFE BEFORE MAN

ALTHOUGH, AS WE have seen, both man and his planetary home are ultimately the product of cosmic forces, we can only understand our species in its immediate context by considering the sequence of more parochial events on the earth itself. Man is a member of the whole vast family of living things, and his present state is the direct result of the evolutionary processes that have operated over the last two thousand million years.

Of the five zones, or 'spheres', composing our earth the biosphere was the latest to evolve. The phenomenon we know as life did not appear until our planet had been in existence for nearly half of its present life-span. Then, probably rather more than two thousand million years ago, strange events began to occur along the meeting places of water and land. There appeared, it seems, a new kind of matter – or rather, for the distinction is important, a new state of the formerly existing matter at a higher level of organisation. Life as we know it was born.

For many years now scientists have been investigating the mechanism of life's origin. Although the ultimate secret of manufacturing self-reproducing organisms from non-living matter has so far eluded them, great progress has been made, and the general principles of the process are daily becoming clearer. The basic particles of living things can now be synthesised by biochemical processes in the laboratory, and the commonly accepted distinction between 'life' and 'non-life' has been recognised as artificial and arbitrary.

This is not, of course, to say that there was no difference in quality or degree of maturity between the chemically charged particles lying where land and water met and the protoplasmic froth that began to stir there some two thousand million years ago. It is simply that a new potential of development had been realised. Recent studies have shown that the simplest organisms, lying just this side of the so-called border-line between life and non-life, have an astonishing resemblance to the larger and more complex molecules of inorganic chemistry. For instance, many of the qualities supposed to be characteristic of life, such as renewal and repair of substance, the use of fuel to perform work, growth, and response to environment, are just as evident in such inorganic entities as crystals as they are in the most primitive living things. The need to think in terms of some miraculous 'creation' of life has been removed, and a far grander concept has taken its place. It is already clear that 'living' matter has evolved as logically and inevitably from 'dead' matter as man has evolved through a succession of invertebrate and vertebrate forms from this very froth on the fringes of the primeval seas.

Now what has been happening to the earth's biosphere between the time it first began to develop and the emergence of man? This is a long and complicated story which I cannot do more than touch upon here, but the main sequence of events must be briefly outlined and a few general principles stated.*

Our main clues to the nature of life before man, and also to the course of man's own early development, are fossils. These are the remains of animals and plants which, by a variety of processes, have become embedded in the rocks of the earth's crust. Laymen are sometimes inclined to think of fossils as rather dull and lifeless objects, and the term 'old fossil', as applied to elderly and boring members of our own species, well suggests the disrespect in which they are held. When imaginatively considered, however, fossils become extremely exciting objects. They are the keys which unlock the secrets of the past.

*Readers especially interested in evolution and its mechanisms are referred to the brilliant book by Professor G. G. Simpson entitled *The Meaning of Evolution,* and also to my own *A Guide to Earth History,* where several of the questions raised in this and the preceding chapter are more fully discussed. Both these books are listed in the selected Bibliography at the end of this volume.

Usually only the bones and other hard parts of animals are preserved as fossils, although the imprint of the skin, and also the outlines of such soft-bodied organisms as plants and shell-less invertebrates, may in some cases leave fossil traces too. This is because the softer tissues normally rot away very fast, so that there is no time for the process of fossilisation to take place. This process is itself very interesting, and consists in most cases of the filling of minute cavities in the bone with the mineral particles usually present in water-borne sediments. There are other types of fossilisation too, but it will be sufficient if I explain here how a large pre-historic animal might become 'permineralised', as this typical example of fossilisation is called.

To make matters clear I must first ask the reader to accompany me in imagination to the banks of some great river of, say, a hundred million years ago. At this time we should find ourselves in the culminating millennia of the so-called 'Age of Reptiles' when the famous dinosaurs were the rulers of the earth. On the river bank a ferocious battle is raging between a giant carnivorous dinosaur and one of its harmless but no less gigantic vegetarian relations which it has ambushed on its way to the water. The vegetarian dinosaur is fatally wounded but, just as the victor is about to deliver the *coup de grâce,* its prey topples backward into the river and is carried away by the swift-flowing current. The carnivore, thus robbed at the last minute of the spoils of victory, follows the floating carcase for a mile or more along the river bank uttering frustrated roars. Eventually, however, the carcase floats far out into the estuary and it has to abandon the chase.

Now before the body of the slaughtered dinosaur can reach the sea, it is caught by an eddy and drifts slowly against a sandbank, where it comes to rest. During the next few weeks its bones are picked clean by small water reptiles and scavenging birds, and the skeleton sinks deeper and deeper into the sandy ooze. Eventually it is entirely covered by the river-borne sediments and then, over many centuries, the process of fossilisation occurs. After a further long interval the geological processes already described upraise this whole section of the earth's crust with its enclosed fossil until it forms a new mountain range. Finally erosion gets to work, and in due course a scientist working in the area may be rewarded by seeing the fossilised bones of the skeleton beginning to weather out of the rock.

Using fossils of this kind as clues, what picture can we build up of the evolution of life before man? For the very earliest ages in the history of life we have to go on circumstantial evidence, for the first micro-organisms to develop from the primeval protoplasmic froth had no hard parts to

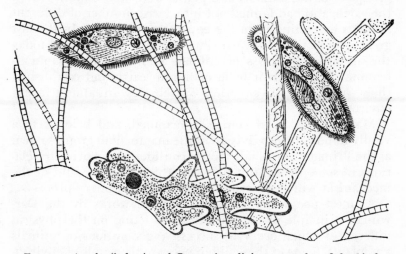

FIG. 1.   *Amoeba* (below) and *Paramecium*, living examples of the kind of simple organisms that flourished in the primeval seas. *From 'Animals without Backbones' by Ralph Buchsbaum, Chicago, 1948, p. 11*

leave traces on the rocks. Nevertheless we can deduce by analogy with primitive organisms alive today what some of them were like. For instance, the amoeba and the paramecium shown in the accompanying drawing probably resemble very closely the type of microscopic organisms that swarmed in the waters of the ancient earth (Fig. 1).

When the fossil record itself begins between five hundred and a thousand million years ago we find that still only very simple kinds of organisms had evolved. These were either primitive plants such as seaweeds, or animals without backbones such as jellyfish and worms, and none of them had yet learnt to leave the water and take to life on land. But as million upon million of years went by many more advanced forms began to evolve. The back-boned animals slowly developed from invertebrate ancestors, and by about three hundred million years ago several of these, as well as some of their plant and invertebrate cousins, had embarked on the conquest of land life. First came the amphibians, then the great army of prehistoric reptiles, and finally the mammals and birds. By some sixty million years ago all the major groups of living animals and plants were well established on the earth, and had fanned out into a vast number of different habitats extending from the equator to the poles. In the last great span of time between sixty million years ago and today the all-important class of animals known as the mammals became the dominant form of life on earth and established their superiority over other vertebrates in almost every environment.

Man himself is, of course, a mammal, and belongs to a vitally important subdivision of the mammalian group known as the Primates. We shall shortly consider man's primate relations in some detail, but first something must be said of the mechanism which governs the whole evolutionary process.

As most people now know, evolution works by the Darwinian principle of natural selection acting on the physical differences which occur in successive generations of animals and plants. Some of these differences are the result of environmental factors operating during the individual's lifetime, but such 'acquired characteristics', as they are called, cannot be inherited, and are therefore of only minor evolutionary significance. From time to time, however, more basic changes, known as 'mutations', occur in the germ cells of an organism, and the variations caused by such changes are transmitted to the next generation. These are the variations on which natural selection mainly acts. Thus in any one generation in a given area the organisms whose characteristics fit them best for life in that environment are more likely to stay alive and breed than their less well-equipped cousins. They can therefore be said to have been 'naturally selected' for survival.

Now it is clear that as this process goes on generation after generation, certain characteristics making for survival will continually be emphasised. At the same time others of no survival value will either remain unchanged or, if they should become a positive handicap to the animal, will be gradually eliminated. But as the value of the selected or discarded qualities will constantly vary with changes in the environment, different strains of organisms are eventually established, each with its own answer to the problems of living in a particular ecological niche. It is by a process as grand and simple as this that the whole family of living things, in all its beauty and variety, has become spread across the face of the earth.

Another fairly obvious point is that one of the most valuable survival qualities on a long-term view is adaptability. An animal or plant that becomes highly specialised for a single environment will be able to survive there only while the environment itself remains stable; as soon as change occurs it must either adapt, move to a new and more favourable environment, or perish. Too often in the history of life the very specialisations made by organisms to one way of life have been their undoing when change occurs. They have become too rigid in their physical or mental attributes, or both, either to survive the change or to move elsewhere, and have thus become extinct. One of the causes of the remarkable success of the human species has been that it has remained physically very unspecialised except in the superior development of its brain. And the brain is fortunately the very organ which enables the advantages of a flexible way of life to be grasped, and allows man either to adapt to changing conditions on the spot or to move to a new area.

One other general question we shall eventually need to face is, of course, why evolution should have occurred at all. But to tackle this problem of problems we shall obviously need to bring in the evidence of the human story, and the question must therefore be postponed until the very end of this book. At present only two points need be made. The first is that biological science alone does not provide any evidence whatever that evolution has a discoverable purpose or goal, and that the meaning of the whole process, if it exists at all, must therefore probably be sought in a synthesis of all the sciences with the evidence derived from such higher products of evolution as religious and artistic experience. The second is that the record of life's development on earth, including the appearance of man, shows that there must be a vast source of energy operating in the universe which is driving the whole process along. It remains to be seen whether this scientific concept of universal energy can be squared with man's various speculations on the nature of God. But before we can even consider the matter we must first inform ourselves as fully as possible about our own origins and the course of our history.

Chapter Three

THE PRIMATE ORDER

MAN, AS WE HAVE SAID, belongs to the group of mammals known as the Primates. This contains not only man, but all the living apes, monkeys, lemurs and tree-shrews, a little creature known as the tarsier, and a number of fossil predecessors of all these forms dating back in some cases for over 60 million years.

The mammals themselves are the most advanced group of animals to have evolved on earth. They are descended from the reptiles and, by some 60 million years ago, had quite superseded them in importance. Mammals had then spread to nearly every part of the world, and in every region they were the dominant form of life.

When natural selection led to the divergence of the reptilian and mammalian stocks increasing differences naturally began to develop between the two classes of animals. It would not be relevant to talk about all these here, but three can be mentioned as specially important.

First, mammals have larger brains than reptiles of the same body size, and in some types the brain-body ratio, which is one of the factors determining intelligence, is increased to a spectacular extent. This generally gives the mammals a great evolutionary advantage in demanding situations.

Second, mammals have a much more efficient metabolism than reptiles, and are thus able to maintain their body temperature at a fairly constant level in greater extremes of heat and cold. The body temperature of reptiles is much more rigidly controlled by that of the environment, and they are therefore largely at the mercy of climatic change.

Third, mammals typically bring forth their young alive, and look after them for varying periods during the first part

of their lives. Reptiles typically lay eggs, and although sometimes these may be incubated or buried for protection, little
post-natal care is given to the newly-hatched young. The less
common species of reptiles that bring forth their young alive
likewise leave them to fend for themselves from the moment
of birth. The young of mammals therefore have in general a
higher chance of survival compared with the young of reptiles
when both types of animals are competing for the same
environment.

Among the mammals, as among other groups of animals,
the differences produced by natural selection have led to the
creation of species of varying types and varying degrees of
success. Some mammals, such as the elephant, have concentrated on size as an aid to survival; some, such as the gazelle,
on speed. The bats, to take another example, have become
highly specialised to a night-flying life, and their mammalian
fore-limbs have become modified into wings, while the members of the cat family have become especially efficient predators. Whatever the nature of the adaptation, however, all
these mammals are unconsciously striving like every other
living thing to solve a single basic problem; how to remain
alive and reproduce themselves, and thus achieve the survival
of their own species. Before we consider the particular solutions attempted by man to this problem, we must say a little
about the primates in general, their classification, and how
they have evolved. In this chapter we shall be mainly concerned with living primates; in the next we shall look at some
of the primates that have lived in the past.

Most readers of this book will be familiar with the way
naturalists order the living world by giving its members
scientific names and placing them in a number of different
categories, or 'pigeon holes', such as phyla, classes, orders,
families, genera, species, and so on, but to refresh their memo-
ries I will give a few words of explanation about the Table
on the opposite page. This Table, although it should not be
regarded as definitive, provides a simple working basis for any
discussion of the primate group. It will be seen that the Primates, which are themselves one of the thirty major divisions
or 'orders' of the class Mammalia, are comprised in two sub-
orders named respectively the Prosimii and the Anthro-

CLASSIFICATION OF THE PRIMATES

ORDER Primates

SUBORDER Prosimii (the prosimians, or lower primates)
>   FAMILIES: about 12. Six include respectively the living tree-shrews; lemurs; indris and woolly lemurs; aye-aye; lorises and galagos; and *Tarsius* (as well as some extinct forms). The remainder are represented only by extinct forms, mainly from the early Tertiary.

SUBORDER Anthropoidea (the higher primates)
>   SUPERFAMILY Ceboidea (primates of the New World)
>   FAMILY Cebidae (New World monkeys)
>   FAMILY Callithricidae (marmosets and tamarins)

>   SUPERFAMILY Cercopithecoidea
>   FAMILY Cercopithecidae (Old World monkeys)
>>   SUBFAMILY Cercopithecinae (macaques, mangabeys, baboons, drills, guenons, etc.)
>>   SUBFAMILY Colobinae (langurs, colobus monkeys, etc.)

>   SUPERFAMILY Hominoidea
>   FAMILY Pongidae
>>   SUBFAMILY Hylobatinae (the gibbons)
>>   SUBFAMILY Dryopithecinae (about seven genera of extinct apes from the Miocene and Pliocene)
>>   SUBFAMILY Proconsulinae (*Proconsul* only)
>>   SUBFAMILY Oreopithecinae (*Oreopithecus*)
>>   SUBFAMILY Ponginae (the living great apes and at least one extinct form)

>   FAMILY Hominidae
>>   SUBFAMILY Australopithecinae
>>>   GENUS *Australopithecus*
>>>   GENUS *Paranthropus*
>>>   ?GENUS *Zinjanthropus*
>>   SUBFAMILY Hominae
>>>   GENUS *Pithecanthropus*
>>>   GENUS *Homo*
>>>>   SPECIES *Homo neanderthalensis*
>>>>   SPECIES *Homo sapiens*

Modified by the author after Simpson (1945) and Howells (1960).

poidea. The second of these is in turn divided into three 'superfamilies' known as the Ceboidea and Cercopithecoidea (derived from two Greek words for a long-tailed monkey) and the Hominoidea, meaning 'man-like types'. Of these, the Hominoidea, which is the group which most closely concerns our present story, is divided into the two 'families' Pongidae, or apes, and Hominidae, or 'men', both represented during the last million years by several different genera and species.

The close relationship of all these animals to one another is proved mainly by studies of their skeletal anatomy and embryonic development. A comparison of the bones of, say, a man, a monkey and an ape, shows that their structure and arrangement are so astonishingly similar as to be inexplicable unless all these creatures shared a common ancestor a few million years back in the geological past. The likenesses between the embryonic young of primates are even more remarkable. In fact laymen, and even some professional biologists, would find it very difficult to distinguish the embryo of a man from that of, say, a gorilla or a chimpanzee. Even without technical studies, however, the fact that monkeys and men are closely related could scarcely be doubted by an unprejudiced mind. The chimpanzee and other pongids especially are so reminiscent of ourselves in appearance and behaviour that we must immediately recognise them as our kin.

Of the various divisions shown on the Table the first main group, the suborder Prosimii, contains a mixed collection of lower primates, including the tree-shrews, lemurs, lorises, pottos, galagos and, according to some authorities, the tarsiers. All these are attractive furry creatures of small or moderate size, and are of particular interest in suggesting by analogy with certain fossil forms what our own early ancestors may have been like. (Plates 1–6.)

We will begin with the lowliest group, the tree-shrews, which until recently have not been generally regarded by scientists as primates at all. These are small insect-eating and fruit-eating animals, which for many years were placed in the order Insectivora, the group which also includes the ground-shrews, water-shrews, moles, tenrecs and hedgehogs. But it seems now that their points of resemblance to primates are more important than their differences, and that they must therefore be accepted for membership of our own order of animals.

To the more conventional person in western Europe a hundred years ago (and many of them existed there at the time) it came as a big shock to learn from Darwin and Huxley that man was the not-too-distant cousin of the amusing but definitely 'brutish' monkeys he was accustomed to tease at the zoo. What would he have said, we may wonder, if it had then been fully realised that at a comparatively recent epoch our ancestors bore a startling resemblance to long-nosed squirrels? For there is a strong, though superficial, resemblance between tree-shrews and squirrels, even though the latter belong to quite a different order of animals.

The five genera of living tree-shrews are distinguished mainly by size and the colour and length of their fur. Their range is restricted to south-east Asia, where they are found in India, Pakistan, Burma, Malaya, Sumatra, Java and Borneo. The smaller species live high in the treetops, while the larger species live among the lower branches and are found in bush country as well as forests. All are diurnal and exceptionally active, and nearly all have bushy squirrel-like tails which act as stabilisers as they make their way through the trees and leap from bough to bough. Another resemblance to squirrels is their habit, when feeding, of sitting on their haunches and holding their food between their fore-paws. Several species are very distinctively coloured, bearing vivid stripes and other markings similar to those found in some oriental squirrels. Their most obvious external differences when compared with the squirrels are their pointed snouts and smaller ears, the latter often being quite strikingly human in shape. Less immediately obvious, but also very important, are the differences in tooth structure. Squirrels, being rodents, or gnawing animals, have the highly specialised chisel-like incisors of their order, whereas the tree-shrews, with their comparatively soft insect and fruit diet, have much simpler incisors. One other important difference concerns the feet. These still have clawed digits, as in the squirrels, but in the tree-shrews the digits corresponding to the human thumb and big toe are far more flexible than in the squirrels, enabling them to grasp branches with considerable effectiveness. This trend towards an opposable thumb and more efficient grasping mechanisms becomes increasingly marked as one ascends the primate scale and, as we shall see later, was one of the more important anatomical factors leading to the present dominance of man.

Our second prosimian group contains the lemurs and their close relatives, the lorises, pottos and galagos. The true lemurs are entirely restricted to Madagascar and some of the small nearby islands, and are represented by many different genera. Almost all are arboreal and nocturnal animals, with large eyes and comparatively immobile features. The name lemur derives from the Latin *lemures,* meaning 'spirits of the dead', and the lemurs move about the dense Madagascan jungles as elusively as ghosts.

A typical Madagascan lemur, such as the common lemur or the ring-tailed lemur, is about the size of a domestic cat. It has a pointed face, a muzzle with a moist, naked tip, and eyes directed somewhat to the sides. Its body is covered with thick fur, which contrasts with the generally rather sparse coats of higher primates, and it has a long furry tail. The thumb and big-toe digits on the foot are widely separable from the other digits, so that the animals have a grasping mechanism comparable to that of the more advanced members of their order. The claws of all but one digit on each foot are reduced to the nails typical of man, monkeys and apes. On the second digit in each case, however, a claw, sometimes known as the 'toilet digit', is retained for scratching. The animals vary a great deal in their markings, and in some species there are considerable colour differences between the male and the female. They live on a mixed diet, which includes birds, reptiles, eggs, insects and fruit, and the lower incisor and canine teeth are modified into a kind of 'dental comb' which is used by the animals for grooming their fur.

Apart from the typical lemurs described above, several species have a wide range of size and other specialisations. For example, the mouse lemurs, as their name suggests, are very much smaller than the average, with elongated bones in the feet which enable them to move by hopping. Larger forms include the sifakas and indris which may have a body length of over two feet. Another genus, known from its characteristic cry as the *aye-aye,* has a number of particularly interesting specialisations. These include rodent-like incisors and an elongated third finger, enabling the animal to scoop the grub which forms its favourite diet from holes and fissures in the bark of trees. Among other Madagascan lemurs are species with such charming names as the gentle lemurs, the weasel lemurs and the sportive lemurs, each adapted to its own particular ecological niche.

Related lemuroid primates are found on the mainlands of tropical Africa and Asia. The typical lemuroids of tropical Asia are the slow and slender lorises. These are both very sluggish creatures with much reduced tails which creep about the branches with a deliberate crawling gait, as if they were being seen on a slow-motion cinematograph film. The slender loris from Ceylon and southern India is the smaller of the two. It is an animal of great strangeness and beauty, but according to the British naturalist, Sir James Emerson Tennent, this did not prevent the natives of the region holding it in front of a fire until its large and lustrous eyes burst so that their juices could be used as a supposed remedy for ophthalmia.

Two other genera of lorises live on the mainland of Africa, where they are known as pottos. One of these, the angwantibo, or Calabar potto, is distinguished by the complete absence of a tail. The other, scientifically known as *Perodicticus,* or 'maimed pointer', is distinguished by the aborted condition of the index finger. The only other lemuroids, which are also found in Africa, are the galagos, or bush babies. These are widely distributed in forest districts over the greater part of the continent south of the Sahara. Like most lemuroids, they are nocturnal and largely arboreal, and when they come down to the ground they resemble the mouse lemurs in their ability to progress by hopping. Both lorises and galagos are more advanced in structure than the typical Madagascan lemurs, particularly in their comparatively flattened faces and more forward-facing eyes, developments which foreshadow the condition found in the higher primate groups.

The last group of prosimians are the tarsioids, represented by only one living genus. This is the spectral tarsier (*Tarsius*) found in Borneo, the Philippines, Celebes, Sumatra, and a number of smaller islands in the Malay Archipelago. The animal is very small, its body being little bigger than a man's clenched fist, but it has many characters that make it an exceptionally interesting member of the primate order. Anatomically it seems to be about midway between the lemurs and the higher primates, and possesses an unusual mixture of primitive and advanced characters. Its rat-like tail and elongated hind-legs show that it lies well off the main evolutionary line leading to man, but at the same time it has a much better-developed brain than the lemurs, and a greatly improved visual apparatus. In its breeding arrangements the structure and function of the placenta, which is the organ by which mammals feed their embryonic young, show a far greater affinity with monkeys, apes and man than with the lemurs and other primates at a comparatively low level of development.

Like most other living prosimians the tarsier is a nocturnal tree-dweller. Its fur is brownish-fawn and, apart from its immense eyes and elongated ankle bones, its most characteristic features are its large ears and the disc-shaped adhesive surfaces on the digits, which assist it in clinging to the boughs of trees. It feeds mainly on insects, small reptiles, and birds, and is usually found only singly or in pairs. Only one offspring is produced at a time and it has been observed to carry its young in its mouth like members of the cat family. It seems probable that the spectral tarsier has changed remarkably little during the last fifty million years or so of evolution, and therefore has a very good claim to be regarded as a 'living fossil'.

We turn next to our second great group of primates, the suborder Anthropoidea. This, as I have said, is divided into three great superfamilies. The first of these, the Ceboidea, consists entirely of South and Central American forms. The second, known as the Cercopithecoidea, contains only Old World forms such as the macaques, rhesus monkeys, mangabeys, baboons, langurs, and colobus monkeys. Third comes the Hominoidea, also of Old World origin, which consists of the four man-like apes – gibbons, orangutans, chimpanzees, and gorillas – and man himself. (Plates 7–17.)

The ceboids are sometimes referred to as the platyrrhines, or 'broad snouts', because the two nostrils are generally, but not universally, separated by a comparatively wide partition, and open more sideways than forward or downward. This differs from the condition generally found in the cercopithecoids of the Old World, where the nostrils are generally closer together and more downward pointing, causing these monkeys to be called 'catarrhines', or 'down snouts'. Another more technical distinction between New and Old World monkeys is that the former have three premolar teeth in each half of the jaw whereas the latter have only two.

The living ceboids, or platyrrhine monkeys, of the New World fall into seven main groups. The first six (family Cebidae) are the douroucoulis and titis, the uakaris and sakis, the howlers, the capuchins and squirrel monkeys, the spider and woolly monkeys, and the callimicos (although the cebid status of the last-named group is questioned by some authorities). The seventh group, which forms the family Callithricidae, contains the marmosets and tamarins. There would be no point in considering each of these groups in detail here as none of the American monkeys is closely related to the human stem, but the reader may be interested in a few generalisations to fill in his picture of the primate group.

The marmosets and their allies are superficially squirrel-like in appearance, with thick fur and bushy tails. More typical of the ceboids are the capuchins, the organ-grinders' monkeys of a less sophisticated age, which are still commonly kept as pets. The woolly monkeys, spider monkeys, and howlers are more specialised, the latter having a bony resonating chamber in the throat which enables them to make their characteristic howling sounds. The douroucoulis are unique among monkeys in their nocturnal habits, their exceptionally large eyes and specially constructed retinas being evidence of this specialisation to night-time activity.

All the New World monkeys are strictly arboreal, and several have developed prehensile tails, which act as a kind of 'fifth limb' to assist their progress through the trees, and even for grasping food. In some species, such as the spider monkey, specialisation to arboreal life is carried to great extremes by the development of exceptionally long spidery limbs. If one were asked for a quick verdict on the status of the ceboid monkeys in the evolutionary story, there would be a temptation to say that they represented an intermediate stage between prosimians and the higher primates, but this would be quite untrue. During the past sixty million years the Old and New Worlds have been separated by a vast tract of sea, and it is clear that the ceboids could never have lived anywhere but on the American continent. Thus instead of representing an intermediate stage in the primate story, they must be regarded as an intriguing example of parallel evolution. The New World and Old World monkeys must have diverged at some distant point in time from a common ancestral primate group and then made comparable adaptations to their environment in different geographical settings.

The living cercopithecoids have a wide range in tropical and sub-tropical regions of Africa and Asia, and a solitary species, the so-called 'Barbary ape' (*Macaca sylvana*), still exists in a semi-domesticated state on the Rock of Gibraltar. These monkeys have made a much wider range of specialisations to their environment than their New World cousins, and include both tree-dwelling and ground-dwelling forms. They are usually divided into two subfamilies, the Cercopithicinae, with distensible cheek pouches for the storage of food, and the Colobinae, with rather complicated stomachs which are adapted, like those of ruminants, to a particular kind of vegetable diet.

The macaques are a typical genus of the cheek-pouched group, and include not only the Barbary ape, but the rhesus monkey, kra, wanderoo and toque. They are of moderate size, in general rather stoutly built, and are sufficiently hardy to have invaded many different habitats, such as the oppressive and humid tropical jungles of the East, the snow-covered foothills of the Himalayas and other Asiatic mountains, and the arid slopes of the Atlas range in north-west Africa. Although they are good climbers they are also very much at home on the ground. Another group are the guenons, the typical small monkeys of Africa, such as the green monkey, mona monkey, vervet and talapoin, which are more strictly arboreal than the macaques. Many guenons are unusually coloured, and this, combined with their vivacity, makes them popular exhibits at zoos. A related African group are the mangabeys,

I. Man's nearest living relatives

1 Living tree-shrews, which have a superficial likeness to squirrels, closely resemble the ancient primates from which man is descended. **2** The spectral tarsier (*Tarsius spectrum*) is another tree-dwelling relative of man.

3

The living lemurs and the
lorises, pottos and galagos
depicted on this and the
following page belong to
evolutionary lines that
branched off from the main
human stem some
50 million years ago.

3 An albino slow loris
(*Nycticebus coucang*)
from south-east Asia.

4 The slender loris
(*Loris tardigradus*)
of Ceylon and southern India.

5 The ring-tailed lemur
(*Lemur catta*) of Madagascar.

6 A galago, or 'bush-baby'
(*Galago moholi*),
of tropical Africa.

4

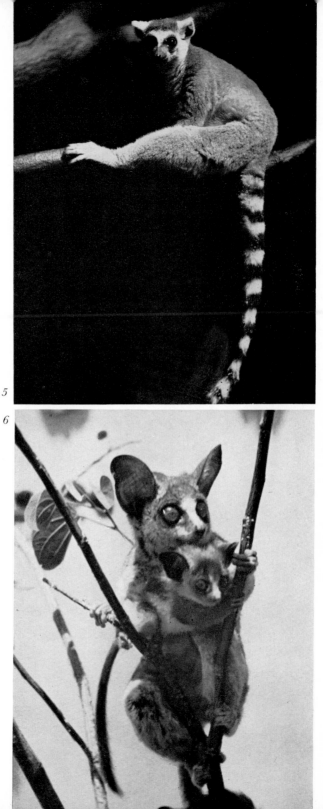

5

6

7

8

The pictures on these two pages show typical monkeys of the New and Old Worlds, all cousins of man.

7 The pinché marmoset (*Oedipornidas oedipus*) of Columbia. **8** Geoffroy's spider monkey (*Ateles geoffroyi*) from Central and South America. Note the prehensile tail. **9** The vervet monkey (*Cercopithecus pygerythrus*), a typical African cercopithecoid. **10** The purple-faced langur (*Pithecus senex*) of Ceylon.

9

10

11

11 A female rhesus monkey (*Macaca mulatta*) and her young. The rhesus monkey, found in India and parts of China, is a typical macaque.

12 The chacma baboon (*Papio porcarius*) of southern Africa.

12

Man's closest living relations are the great apes of the subfamilies Hylobatinae, containing the gibbons, and Ponginae, containing the orangutan, gorilla and chimpanzee. They are depicted on this and the following two pages. Gibbons and orangutans are almost completely arboreal; gorillas and chimpanzees spend much of their time on the ground.

14

15

13 A gibbon.

14 A mature male gorilla.

15 A young gorilla.

16 The orangutan, although a close relative of man, is lower
in the evolutionary scale than either the gorilla or chimpanzee.

17 Chimpanzees rank second to man in the hierarchy of animal intelligence. The lively expression of this young specimen resembles that of a mischievous human child.

which have longer than average tails and can also be distinguished by conspicuous white markings on the eyebrows and upper eyelids. These, like the guenons, are more generally arboreal than the macaques and this is correlated with a lighter and slenderer build. The drills, mandrills, and baboons represent heavier ground-dwelling forms which are nevertheless closely related to the genera mentioned above.

Our second cercopithecoid subfamily, the Colobinae, is made up of the colobus monkeys, or guerezas, of equatorial Africa, the langurs of southern Asia and the East Indies, and the extraordinary proboscis monkey of Borneo. The latter is distinguished by a fleshy nose, or proboscis, which hangs down some three or four inches over the mouth of the male animal. There has been much speculation about the function of this dubiously attractive organ, which does not apparently enhance the sense of smell. As it is much reduced in the female, the most favoured solution (however unlikely it may seem in terms of human aesthetics) is that it appeals to the female eye, and is therefore a factor in sexual selection.

All the Old World monkeys are of catarrhine type; that is to say, they have nostrils which are normally separated by only a narrow bridge, and open forward and down. This is a more advanced type of structure than is found in the platyrrhines of the New World. The catarrhines are also in general less strictly arboreal than the platyrrhines, and some types, notably the drills and baboons, spend most of their time on the ground. They walk on all fours, on the flat of the palm and sole, and in some species the common adoption of a sitting posture is associated with callosites, or patches of hardened skin, on the buttocks.

The cercopithecoids are the largest group of Old World primates, but in the story of private evolution they are far outweighed in importance by the hominoids. This is the third of our three anthropoid superfamilies, and includes the living man-like apes and modern man himself. The hominoids, like the cercopithecoids, are of catarrhine type, but they represent a fairly early divergence from the development of other primate groups. The popular superstition about Darwinism, that 'man is descended from monkeys', is therefore seen to be based on a misconception. Man certainly shares a *common ancestor* with all living members of the primate order, but the idea that he is the descendant of any existing species of monkey is quite untrue.

The smallest and most primitive of all living hominoids are the gibbons. These are the only living representatives of a single subfamily, the Hylobatinae, which also contains a number of important fossil forms. The living gibbons are contained in two very active and vocal genera which are now confined to various parts of Malaya and the East Indies. They are almost completely arboreal, with extremely long arms but, like all the man-like apes, are without tails. On the rare occasions when they descend to the ground they walk upright on their hind-legs, with their arms stretched out sideways as balancers. No other hominoid except man habitually adopts the erect posture on the ground.

The other three genera of living man-like apes are grouped together in another subfamily, the Ponginae, comprising the orangutan, chimpanzee and gorilla. They greatly exceed the gibbon in size, and the gorilla, which is the largest, is much more massive and powerful than man himself. These three hominoids are our nearest living relations in the animal world, sharing with us many common characters not only in structure, but in intelligence, behaviour, and even in such details as similarity of blood-groups. For this reason alone each of them requires a fairly extended description.

The orangutan, from the jungles of Sumatra and Borneo, is a large, ponderous, arboreal creature covered with a sparse coat of reddish-brown or carroty hair. The males weigh on the average about the same as a man, but because of their extremely short legs they seldom measure more than $4\frac{1}{2}$ feet from head to foot. The body is very massive and the girth in mature specimens averages almost two-thirds of the height. The females are much smaller, with an average weight of between 80 and 90 pounds.

The arboreal habits of orangutans are suggested by their long arms which, when fully extended, reach to the feet if the animal is made to stand erect (a position not naturally adopted). The hand is exceptionally narrow, and the elongated fingers and reduced thumb show that it is more specialised as a hook for swinging through the boughs than as a grasping organ, although it can also hold on to things quite efficiently. All the digits may have the flattened nails so characteristic of the higher primates, although these are commonly lost on the big toe.

The head is large, with a protrusive face, heavy projecting jaws and tusk-like canine teeth. The forehead is high and domed, but this is not correlated with an exceptionally high degree of intelligence. In fact the brain is only about a third of the size of an average western man's.

The orangutan, although a cousin of man, is not so high in the evolutionary scale as the two man-like apes of tropical Africa, the chimpanzee and the gorilla. Chimpanzees especially are inclined to prompt the remark that they are 'almost human', and although this is not a scientifically valid comment as it stands, many details of their anatomy, physiology and behaviour certainly show significant parallels.

There are at least three species of chimpanzee, of which the common chimpanzee, with its pale-coloured face and sparse black fur, is the best known. This animal, which may be taken as the typical member of the genus, is smaller than both the orangutan and man, an average male weighing about 110 pounds. Compared with the orangutan the arms are reduced and the legs considerably longer, a condition which suggests a less exclusively arboreal way of life. This is in fact the case, for although chimpanzees are expert and agile climbers, they also spend part of their time on the ground. At these times they go on all-fours, only raising themselves on their hind-legs for some special reason, such as looking over an obstruction. As in the orangutan, the hands are long and narrow with a comparatively small thumb; the foot has an opposable big toe like a thumb, and is as well adapted as the hand for use as a grasping organ. The chimpanzee does not have the same intellectual appearance as the orangutan, for its forehead is low and there are heavy and brutish brow-ridges. It is, however, more intelligent, and is the closest of all animals to man in this respect.

The gorilla, as we have seen, is the largest of the living primates. Like the chimpanzee, it lives in tropical Africa, but its range is far more restricted. Whereas the chimpanzee is found from Gambia in the north to Angola in the south, and from the Atlantic seaboard to Uganda, the gorilla inhabits only two limited equatorial areas separated by a region over 600 miles broad. The western, or lowland, gorilla is found chiefly in the dense rain forests of Gabon and the Cameroons; the mountain gorilla, distinguished by its narrow skull, longer trunk, shorter limbs and other important characters, lives in the mixed bamboo forests of the east Congo at altitudes up to 12,000 feet, or even more.

An adult male gorilla is an extremely formidable animal which may weigh between 500 and 600 pounds and measure over six feet in height. The powerful body is covered with black hair, and the massive skull is equipped with enormous brow-ridges and a network of bony crests which serve as points of attachment for the muscles supporting and working the lower jaw. The legs are relatively short, and although the foot has a fully opposable big toe like the chimpanzee, its proportions, and particularly the reduced length of the lesser toes, show an approximation to the human form. In habits the gorilla is even less arboreal than the chimpanzee, and although it can climb quite easily it spends the greater part of its life on the ground. It also habitually sleeps there, although the sleeping nest may sometimes be built in the low-lying branches of a tree. The animal walks on all-fours, with the sole of the foot on the ground but with the shoulders supported by the knuckles and not the flat of the hand.

In absolute size the brain of the gorilla is larger than that of the chimpanzee, and is nearly half that of the most primitive human races now alive. This is not as significant as it appears, however, for it is not the absolute size of the brain that determines mental capacity, but its size relative to the size of the body, and also the areas in which it is developed. Thus in spite of its larger brain the gorilla does not possess greater intellectual powers than the chimpanzee, and of course comes nowhere near man in this respect. In descending order of mental capacity the hominoid series runs: man, chimpanzee, gorilla, orangutan, and gibbon.

The intelligence of both chimpanzees and gorillas is nevertheless exceptionally high, and seems to approximate closely in type, if not in amount, to that of man. Their memory is good, and they also show the beginnings of reasoning power as we know it. For instance, chimpanzees have been known to fit two sticks together to obtain a coveted banana through the wires of their cage, or to make a pile of boxes to reach food hanging in an otherwise inaccessible position (see Chapter 6, pp. 65–6). Recently experiments made by Dr Desmond Morris at the London Zoo have shown that, given paints and a piece of paper, a chimpanzee may even produce a picture, suggesting some rudimentary sense of colour and design.

The only other representative of the living hominoids is man himself, the highest of all the primates. But before we go on to describe the origin and development of our own family we must briefly consider some of the major features of primate evolution as a whole.

Chapter Four

PRIMATES OF THE PAST

THE EVOLUTION of the primates has occurred over approximately the last fifty to sixty million years. This estimate is arrived at by a number of scientific techniques based on the behaviour of radioactive minerals in the rocks. The relative age of different fossils can also be determined by measuring their fluorine content, which is higher in older specimens. In order that the sequence of events can be made clear to him the reader may wish to be reminded of the kind of 'calendar' used by historical geologists to order the vast periods of time with which they are concerned.

The 4,500 million years of earth history can be logically divided into a whole series of eras, periods and epochs based on geological events. Here we need only be concerned with the very latest of these, which cover the story of primate evolution. The Chart on pages 32 and 33 shows their layout and approximate duration in millions of years.

The reader will see that the mammals as a whole began to evolve from the reptiles in the penultimate, or Jurassic, period of the Mesozoic era, but that the first fossil insectivores which may be ancestral to the primates do not appear until the Cretaceous. The main events of primate evolution took place in the various epochs of the so-called 'Tertiary' period, while the whole history of our own species and its immediate predecessors occupied only the million years of the Pleistocene and Holocene epochs at the very top of the chart.

Our knowledge of primate evolution is based on both direct and indirect evidence. The direct evidence comes from the science of palaeontology, which deals with the actual remains of fossil primates buried in the rocks. The indirect evidence comes from the study of evolutionary mechanisms in general, and of living representatives of the primate order whose development seems to have become partially stabilised at different phases of the evolutionary process.

The fossil record of the primates is unfortunately poorer than that of many other mammals. This is not simply due to chance, but to several factors of which only three need be mentioned here. First, primates are more intelligent than other animal groups, and therefore seldom meet death by drowning, which is one of the most common accidents leading to fossilisation. Second, the great majority of primates are tree-dwellers, and their fossils rarely survive in the rock strata which form in forested areas. Third, it so happens that nearly all the known beds of fossiliferous strata of Tertiary age occur in temperate zones, so that primates, which are mostly tropical animals, do not leave their remains in them. Nevertheless, a number of primate fossils are known which, when considered in relation to the evolutionary principles governing the history of other vertebrates with a better fossil record, allow us to build up a fairly good picture of the primate story. Our deductions from these sources are reinforced by a study of the living primates, which form a kind of graded series reminiscent of an actual scale of evolutionary development. This is not to suggest, of course, that *living* tree-shrews, lemurs, tarsiers, ceboids, cercopithecoids and apes actually evolved one from the other, but some of them do represent phases roughly equivalent to the phases in the true evolutionary line leading to man.

Before I try to draw a picture of our early relations from this kind of evidence the reader may like to consider some of the general adaptations primates have made to the problems of living. As a group they have been remarkably successful, and I have already emphasised their intelligence, which is one of the main reasons why they have done so well. But *why* should primates be more intelligent than other mammals? *Why* did they show this particular emphasis on brain rather than brawn? A study of some of their other physical adaptations may help to suggest an answer.

As we have seen in the last chapter, one of the characteristic features of most primates is their adaptation to a tree-dwelling life. The little shrew-like insectivores that were

ERA	PERIOD	EPOCH	YEARS AGO IN MILLIONS	EVOLUTIONARY EVENTS
PSYCHOZOIC, OR AGE OF MAN	QUATERNARY	HOLOCENE ('wholly recent')	(Began 10,000 years ago)	Recent human history
		PLEISTOCENE ('most recent')	1	Evolution of man (see Chart of Quaternary Time, pp. 50 and 51).
CENOZOIC, OR AGE OF MAMMALS		PLIOCENE ('more recent')	12	Few hominid fossils. The most notable is *Oreopithecus* from Italy, probably an extinct great ape but just possibly on the line leading to man.
	TERTIARY	MIOCENE ('less recent')	26	Division of the lines leading to the great apes, sub-men and man. *Proconsul* of Africa may be ancestral to the living gorillas and chimpanzees and near the ancestry of man. *Pliopithecus* and *Limnopithecus* were closely related to the gibbons. *Dryopithecus* was probably a specialized side-branch of the hominoid stock.
		OLIGOCENE ('few of the recent')	34	Division of the lines leading to monkeys on the one hand and great apes, sub-men and man on the other. *Parapithecus* of Egypt may be near the dividing point. *Propliopithecus*, also from Egypt, may be ancestral to modern gibbons.

ERA	PERIOD	EPOCH	YEARS AGO IN MILLIONS	EVOLUTIONARY EVENTS
CENOZOIC, OR AGE OF MAMMALS	TERTIARY	EOCENE ('dawn of the recent')	58	First definite fossil evidence for primate evolution. Tree-shrews, lemurs and tarsioids well established. Typical Eocene lemurs were *Adapis* in Europe and *Notharctus* in North America. The tarsioids *Necrolemur* and *Microchoerus* may have been close to the human stems.
MESOZOIC, OR AGE OF REPTILES	CRETACEOUS		125	Apotheosis of the ruling reptiles followed by their total extinction. Fossil remains of small insectivores foreshadow the evolution of the primates.
	JURASSIC		180	Reptiles rule the earth – dinosaurs on land, pterosaurs in the air, and ichthyosaurs, plesiosaurs and mosasaurs in the seas. Mammals begin to evolve from reptiles.

Note: This Chart shows the sequence of events in the history of the primates. It should be read from bottom to top, and is continued on the facing page. None of the divisions is to scale. Readers interested in the general history of life in former ages are referred to the author's book *A Guide to Earth History* (Chatto and Windus, 1956).

their ancestors probably took to the trees towards the end of the Mesozoic to escape the competition of the more physically formidable reptiles that lurked in the undergrowth below. Up in the treetops new means of livelihood would have been open to these animals, and they would have been largely out of the way of predators. Moreover, as time went on, they would have become better and better adapted to their environment, and natural selection would have led to a radiation of types, each suited to a particular ecological niche in the forests.

Now the first essential of efficient climbing is radical modification of the limbs. Most ground-dwellers are quadrupeds, their four limbs acting simply as supports to the body, a pair forward and a pair aft. Although the fore-limbs may show some considerable differentiations from the hind-limbs according to the animal's way of life, these are seldom as extreme as those found in tree-dwellers. The hook-like hands of some primates, specially adapted to swinging through the trees, have already been mentioned, but modifications in the limbs of primates are much more varied than this, and some have played an important role in producing man's evolutionary success.

The fore-limbs and hind-limbs of the early tree-climbing mammals ancestral to the primates were very little differentiated, but as primates themselves evolved, the contrast between them became more marked. The need for the hind-limbs to take the whole weight of the body in the climbing position, and to project it forward in leaps from bough to bough, caused them to become thicker and stronger than the fore-limbs. The latter, on the other hand, became adapted to reach forward and upward to find new holds while the hind-limbs supported the body weight, and thus developed in general a greater flexibility. Of course there were many exceptions to this trend, and in such primates as the living lemurs and ceboids, and even in the orangutan, the hind-limbs also have a suspensory and grasping function. It is, however, extremely interesting to note how the differentiated limbs of man (whose legs are essentially supporters and whose hands are flexible organs which, in conjunction with his brain, have given him the power of making and using tools) can be traced back to the early adaptations made by primitive mammals to an arboreal life.

An even more fundamental modification concerns the relative importance of the sense organs, and the organisation of the brain, two features which are so closely interrelated that they must be considered together. To a small land-living

animal the sense of smell is of the greatest importance, whether
for finding food or in distinguishing between enemies
and friends. But if it takes to a tree-dwelling life smell is
much less useful, and the senses of sight and touch become
more important. There is no longer any need to go sniffing
through the undergrowth in search of a living; a greater evolutionary advantage is conferred by well-developed vision, increased co-ordination of the complex movements necessary
for treetop locomotion, and an efficient grasping mechanism
to avoid the unpleasant experience of falling on one's head.

This changing emphasis is reflected in anatomical structure. The typical ground-dwelling mammal has a long snout
with highly developed organs of touch and smell at its ex-
tremity. These give the first information about any object
encountered, and the eyes, which follow after, give only a
confirmatory account. In tree-dwelling forms the inquisitive
snout is progressively reduced. The face becomes gradually
flattened, and the eyes, previously forced by the configuration of the muzzle to look out one on either side, are given
the benefit of a new mounting so that both can look forward.
This not only brings them into a better position for the primary investigation of the environment, but also confers the
tremendous advantage of binocular vision. The co-ordination
of the field of vision, and especially the accurate determination of the spatial relationships of objects, is immensely increased by this double and complementary viewing apparatus. Like the specialisation of the limbs it thus contributes
to a great extent to the survival potential of the animal.

The new balance of sensory mechanisms is reflected in
evolution in important changes in the organisation of the
brain. The primitive vertebrate brain simply consists of three
hollow expansions of the organ known as the 'neural tube',
each specialised for different activities and referred to respectively as the fore-brain, the mid-brain and the hind-brain.
Overlying these, like the skin of an orange, is the 'cerebral
cortex', which is the seat of the co-ordinating mechanisms
which determine the total effectiveness of the organism in
relation to its environment. The development of higher types
of brains from lower types consists very largely in an increase

in elaboration of the cerebral cortex, which sorts out impressions from the various sense organs and weighs them one against the other before the motor nerves set in train the appropriate response. Tree-dwelling life obviously demands a response based on a greater degree of co-ordination between impressions from different senses than one which is mainly based on the reports from a single sense, such as that of smell. The co-ordinating mechanism, or cortex, of the brain therefore normally shows a progressive increase in size in primates at the expense of the areas limited to receiving sensory impressions alone.

Now all this is extremely significant. The enlargement of the primate cortex which resulted from the demands of a tree-dwelling existence not only gave the animal greater efficiency in its physical environment, but also provided an instrument for the evolution of far more complex patterns of thought. Man's capacity for understanding abstract ideas, and for deducing general principles from particular instances, is a direct result of this development in our arboreal forbears. The 'intelligence' of the primates, including man, is therefore seen to be a beautiful example of the evolutionary process leading a particular group of organisms from the mainly physical to the mainly mental plane, and thereby producing a new technique of survival.

I shall return to this fascinating topic in dealing with the emergence of man himself to his present state of domination. In the meantime I must refer to one other especially interesting connection between the arboreal habits of our ancestors and our own condition. This concerns the typical reduction of the numbers of offspring produced by humans and other primates at a single birth compared with the numbers produced by most other members of the animal kingdom.

As we ascend higher in the evolutionary scale there is a tendency for reproduction to become less wasteful. The significance of this phenomenon in all its ramifications would require a book in itself, and I must therefore confine myself here to the observation that the reduced number of offspring at a single birth among mammals is correlated with an increased degree of post-natal care. Here again, however, there are differentiations. Primitive ground mammals often produce litters of twelve or more individuals, despite the fact that the young receive protective attention during the early part of their lives. Even comparatively advanced mammals such as dogs and cats likewise produce fairly numerous offspring at each birth. But it is obvious that large litters would be quite incompatible with arboreal life. For one thing the carrying by the female during pregnancy of a heavy burden of young would be a serious disadvantage in the active life of the typical tree-dweller. Moreover, a tree is hardly the place for a harassed mother to give numerous offspring all the care and protection they need. Thus as we go higher up the evolutionary scale of primates we find that the number of young at each birth is progressively reduced. Tree-shrews produce three or four young compared with the large litters of their closest ground-dwelling relations. Lemurs and the most primitive ceboids, such as marmosets, have two or three. Higher ceboids, cercopithecoids, apes and man normally produce only a single offspring, twins being a rarity, and larger numbers so uncommon as to be quite atypical.

This progressive decrease in the number of young must obviously be correlated with a higher degree of intelligence in our arboreal ancestors so that qualitative rather than quantitative breeding determined survival. We may also note in passing that this reduction of offspring was paralleled by a reduction in the number of breasts. Some species of lemurs still have four breasts, two in the normal human position and two lying just below them. But the reduction to two is in general symptomatic of higher intellectual capacity – a fact from which chorus girls as well as schoolmistresses are fully entitled to take comfort.

I do not wish to labour this particular subject by enumerating all the significant correlations that can be made between arboreal life and the eventual emergence of man. The story of our origins can be more profitably illuminated by describing some of the actual fossils of the primates of the past. As we have seen, the first fossil evidence for primate evolution occurs between 60 and 50 million years ago in the early Tertiary period (see Chart on pages 32–3). Considerable diversification had already occurred at that time, however, for not only tree-shrews but true lemurs and an exceptionally large variety of tarsioids already existed in Eocene strata. Eocene tree-shrews are unfortunately not well known from the fossil record, but a number of teeth, jawbones and limb fragments of the families known as the Plesiadapidae and Apatemyidae show that animals of this type were well established at the time. This view is confirmed by the remains of an animal known as *Anagale,* whose fossil remains were found in Oligocene strata in Mongolia. This animal was more specialised than typical tree-shrews, suggesting evolution from primitive generalised ancestors living at an earlier date. It is particularly interesting in having certain lemuroid characteristics, such as flattened nails instead of claws on the hind-feet, and may therefore be regarded as a kind of connecting link between the two groups. During the second half of the Tertiary

FIG. 2. The tree-shrew *Anagale,* from the Oligocene of Mongolia.
Reconstruction by Maurice Wilson

period no tree-shrews, or animals closely resembling them, are known as fossils, although the existence of various living forms shows that there must have been an unbroken sequence from the Oligocene epoch to the present day.

Lemuroids themselves were represented by some fourteen Eocene genera, after which there is a gap until the Pleistocene of Madagascar, which has produced seven other examples of the group. The best-known Eocene forms are *Adapis* ('rabbit-like one') of Europe and *Notharctus* ('false bear') of North America. Both these animals were about the size of living lemurs, but had smaller brains and were not so specialised in some of their characters. For instance, they did not have teeth modified into the dental comb which most modern genera of lemurs use for grooming their fur.

The fossil remains of both tree-shrews and primitive

lemurs in the early Tertiary are greatly exceeded by those of tarsioids. No fewer than five subfamilies are known, comprising in all some twenty-five genera. Most of these fossil

FIG. 3. The lemuroid *Adapis*, from the Eocene of North America. *Reconstruction by Maurice Wilson*

tarsioids are from the Eocene epoch, although a few are known from the Oligocene. After this there is another gap

FIG. 4. An Eocene tarsioid. *Reconstruction by Maurice Wilson*

until the modern spectral tarsier appears in the Holocene, or 'recent' epoch. Unlike the modern tarsier, which is restricted to a comparatively small region in south-east Asia, the early tarsioids had a very wide range, including vast tracts of the

North American and European continents. The various genera differed greatly among themselves, some being similar to the modern tarsier, others being very much more specialised, and others again being more primitive with comparatively small brains. It seems most probable that some members of this last more generalised group represent a transitional evolutionary phase between the tree-shrews and the higher monkeys and apes. Particularly significant in this respect are a little creature known as *Necrolemur* ('extinct lemur') from the Eocene of France, and another, called *Microchoerus* (literally 'small pig' – a pleasing, if inaccurate, scientific name for a primate!), which flourished some 50 million years ago in the region which is now the English county of Hampshire. Whether these animals passed through a lemuroid phase in their development from the earlier tree-shrews cannot be definitely decided until the fossil remains of transitional forms have been found. In the meantime we can certainly say that creatures closely resembling *Necrolemur* and *Microchoerus* were very close to the main evolutionary line leading to monkeys, apes – and man.

The next phase of human ancestry is reached in the Oligocene epoch, which lasted from about 34 million to 26 million years ago. This represents a particularly important stage in the evolution of the primates, as it seems probable that it saw the divergence of the lines leading on the one hand to the existing monkeys of the ceboid and cercopithecoid groups, and on the other to the Hominoidea, the group to which we and the living man-like apes belong. The fossil material is too scanty for us to give a very definite picture of the primates of the time, but a word must be said about two remarkable Oligocene fossils which seem to be nearer the hominoid than the monkey line of descent.

The first of these, known as *Parapithecus,* or 'near ape', was found in the Fayum region of Egypt in the strata surrounding the ancient Lake Moeris. This region is a famous fossiliferous locality, which has also produced the remains of several spectacular early Cenozoic mammals, including ancestral elephants and the almost complete skeleton of the horned monster *Arsinoitherium.* Unfortunately *Parapithecus* did not yield such lavish evidence, and the animal is in fact only known from a single lower jawbone. Nevertheless, this was sufficient to show that it was about the size of the tiny squirrel-monkey of today, and probably stood on or near the line between primitive tarsiers and modern anthropoids. In the absence of limb bones it is impossible to say whether it was a strictly arboreal form, but the fact that the Fayum region is now a treeless desert would not be evidence against this view. The climate in Oligocene times was very different from what it is today, and this part of Africa probably consisted largely of swamps and jungle. The terrain would have been as well suited to a tree-dwelling primate as modern equatorial Africa.

The second Oligocene fossil primate is known as *Propliopithecus*, or 'before the more ape-like one'. This rather complicated name is derived from the fact that it preceded in time a fossil known as *Pliopithecus* ('the more ape-like one'), to be referred to in the next paragraph. *Propliopithecus* came from rather later strata in the same region of Egypt, and was about the size of a modern gibbon. It is likewise known only by a single jaw, which is far from satisfactory. But a study of its teeth suggests that it represents a more advanced stage than *Parapithecus*, although on a line leading to the gibbons rather than to the more man-like hominoids such as the gorilla and chimpanzee.

Pursuing the descent of the Hominoidea, we come next to the Miocene epoch, which lasted from about 26 million to 12 million years ago. By the dawn of this epoch primates had entirely disappeared from North America, but in the Old World fossils begin to appear in greater numbers, and at least four Miocene genera have been described. Two of these, known respectively as *Pliopithecus* ('the more ape-like one') and *Limnopithecus* ('marsh ape'), were gibbon-like in character, and already too specialised to be directly ancestral either to the Ponginae (the family containing the orangutan, chimpanzee and gorilla) or to man. But two others, known respectively as *Proconsul* ('before Consul' – Consul being a famous chimpanzee at the London Zoo) and *Dryopithecus* ('tree-ape') are much more significant and demand fuller consideration.

The jaws and teeth of *Proconsul* were discovered in 1931

on Rusinga Island, Lake Victoria, by the wife of Dr L. S. B. Leakey, the enthusiastic prehistorian, and many other remains of the animal, including a skull, have since come to light. The genus is now represented by a number of species of different size, the smallest being comparable to a small chimpanzee, the largest to a large gorilla. It was a remarkably generalised creature with many features much more closely related to the living apes than to the cercopithecoid monkeys. It is in fact quite possible that the different species of *Proconsul,* or creatures closely resembling them, were the ancestors of the living chimpanzee and gorilla. It has never been seriously suggested that any of these Miocene species was directly ancestral to man, but *Proconsul* was certainly close to his line of descent. The reconstruction on Plate 18 will give us a good idea of the general type of animal from which we may all be descended.

Remains of *Dryopithecus* are not known in Africa, but the animal was widespread in western and central Europe in Miocene times, and in the Pliocene extended its range to India. Several fossilised jaws and teeth and two limb bones show that it was roughly the size of a chimpanzee. At one time it was believed, on the basis of the cusp pattern of the molars, that *Dryopithecus* might have been ancestral both to man and the living great apes. But today the animal is regarded as more specialised than primitive, and seems unlikely to be the father of us all. It is nevertheless a most interesting creature closely related to the main human stem.

We come now to the Pliocene epoch, which lasted from about 12 million to one million years ago – to the threshold, in fact, of the story of man's own physical history as a family. During this epoch the world began to assume its modern form. The changing outlines of continents and oceans became recognisably as we know them today. The climate was very like our own except that the temperate zone was somewhat broader, and a gradual retreat of the various plant assemblages towards the equator showed that the earth was becoming cooler. Even so, it was not until the end of the epoch that the glacial conditions which, as we shall see, were to play such an important part in the human drama began to supervene.

During the eleven million years of this last epoch of the Tertiary period primates continued to pursue their evolutionary destiny. The cercopithecoids are particularly well represented, and various fossil genera are known from France, Greece, Czechoslovakia, Persia, Egypt and elsewhere. The most controversial fossil is *Oreopithecus*, the 'mountain ape', from Italy which may be rather closer to the hominid line than was once supposed. Fossil remains of this creature have been known for many years, and it has generally been classified as a cercopithecoid despite the fact that some authorities have preferred to regard it as a generalised type of anthropoid ape, or even as a member of the human family. Then in 1958 Dr Johannes Hürzeler of Basle discovered an almost complete skeleton of the animal in a coal mine at Baccinello in Tuscany. When this remarkable fossil has been fully studied it may yet appear that the hominid school was right, and that the animal is a much closer cousin of ours than the earlier evidence seemed to suggest. At the time of writing the matter is still undecided, and I have taken the middle line of grouping it with the great apes rather than with man. (See 'Classification of the Primates', p. 17, and Plate 19.)

Hominoids in general are not particularly well represented in the Pliocene. Eight fossil genera are listed in the current 'bible' of mammalian classifications, Professor G. G. Simpson's *The Principles of Classification and a Classification of Mammals* (1945), but of these one is *Dryopithecus*, which already existed in the Miocene, and the remainder seem to be so closely affiliated to *Dryopithecus* that only the most determinedly individual expert on fossils (of whom, incidentally, there are quite a few) would be able to recognise the difference. This scanty Pliocene record of the Hominoidea occasionally tempts the diminishing band of anti-evolutionary cranks (who always make up in zeal what they lack in intellectual discipline) to question the whole validity of man's primate ancestry. There is, of course, no reasonable basis whatever for these criticisms, and as man continues to seek for the truth about his origins the family tree of his Pliocene ancestors will be progressively filled in. In the meantime the processes that have gone to the making of man are abundantly

43

clear to all those who have made an honest effort to understand the principles of evolutionary change, even though the fossil evidence is still incomplete. In the next part of this book we shall pick up the human story as it appears in the Pleistocene epoch, when our ape-like forbears were evolving into the human species as we know it today.

Part 2

THE EMERGENCE OF MAN

Chapter Five

THE PLEISTOCENE WORLD

THE EXTRAORDINARILY significant phase in organic evolution which saw the rise of the advanced primate known as man, and culminated some 40,000 years ago in the emergence of our own species, *Homo sapiens,* is entirely comprised in the million-odd years of the Pleistocene epoch. Before we begin to piece this story together from the fossil remains of our ancestors and subhuman cousins, we must briefly describe the setting in which these dramatic events took place.

When the Pleistocene dawned the climate of the earth was roughly comparable to that of the modern world, but as the epoch advanced conditions became gradually colder. From about 600,000 until between 15,000 and 10,000 years ago the more northerly parts of Europe, Asia and North America were subjected to successive waves of arctic and near-arctic cold. The polar ice-cap spread southwards over what is now the temperate zone, and great glaciers ground down from the high mountain ranges to invade the previously warm and fertile land. Similar changes must have occurred in southern latitudes, but owing to the absence of large continental masses in those regions the geological evidence is limited.

This period of intense cold which characterised so much of the Pleistocene epoch is popularly known as the Great Ice Age. The term is misleading, however, for there was not one single continuous period of cold, but four quite distinct glacial phases, each separated from the next by mild, and even subtropical, conditions. These oscillations of climate naturally had a great effect on the flora and fauna of the time, which tended to migrate north and south with the alternating phases of heat and cold. The challenge of the cold had a particularly strong effect on man's development, but before coming to this (Chapter 11) we must first ask why such harsh conditions should have occurred at all.

The Pleistocene glaciations are by no means unique in the history of the earth. Equally severe episodes of glaciation occurred at several other periods in the geological past, and have left evidence in the rocks of more than 500 million years ago. Numerous ingenious theories have been put forward to explain these events, but if we are honest we cannot yet say that any is definitely correct. One suggestion has been that ice ages are due to the upraising of new mountains, leading to a new pattern of circulation of the atmosphere; another that the changing outlines of continents and oceans (always a feature of geological evolution) have led to changes in the direction of the prevailing currents and winds, which have in turn altered the climate of the lands. It is certainly true that geological events have a marked effect on climate, but the objection to these suggestions in connection with the successive phases of the Pleistocene glaciation is that the periods of heat and cold occurred far more rapidly than could be accounted for by such slow-moving processes. The climate changed in a fundamental way without any corresponding major change in the geological aspect of the earth.

More convincing than the above are the various astronomical hypotheses, especially that based on the relation between climate and sunspot activity. It is well known that at certain times the sun's surface is disrupted by a rash of spots which may cause the solar heat reaching the earth to be increased by as much as 3 to 5 per cent. At the first incidence of this additional heat the earth tends to warm up, and an exceptionally warm summer may be experienced, but in succeeding months the increased evaporation from the sea causes the formation of unusual amounts of cloud. It has been suggested that prolonged sunspot activity might thus lead not to a general heating up of the earth, as might be expected, but to widespread glaciation resulting from the masking effect of a vast cloud canopy. Although this is an attractive theory, there is still no one completely convincing explanation of the extreme Pleistocene climate which formed the environment of early man.

In spite of this, the various phases into which the Great

Ice Age is divided are well defined from geological data. To appreciate their relative length and importance, and also how they are correlated with the sequence of Pleistocene animals and the development of man, the reader may find it helpful to study the Chart of Quaternary Times on pages 50 and 51, which attempts to combine the geological, climatic, faunal and human events of the period in one picture. Although the vast amount of data available means that the Chart has had to be greatly over-simplified, it helps to give a bird's-eye view of the world in which our ancestors lived.

To begin with climate, the reader will see that the Pleistocene is divided into nine main phases. After an extended pre-glacial prelude, a cycle of glacial and interglacial phases occurs which lasts altogether for nearly 600,000 years; a short transitional stage then leads directly to the Holocene epoch in which we now live. The four glacial phases are known respectively as the Günz, Mindel, Riss and Würm. Their names are taken from sites in the Alps where geological evidence of each phase occurs, and which were selected from among others because they conveniently follow an alphabetical sequence. In Europe the three interglacial phases separating them are usually referred to simply by number, as First, Second and Third (although the Second is so exceptionally long that it is sometimes called the Great Interglacial). In North America the glacial and interglacial phases are all known by name, as shown on the Chart, these names being based on states and localities in which their characteristic deposits are found.

Three main ice-sheets are recognised in the northern hemisphere. These are: (1) the North American ice-sheet, itself subdivided into the Cordilleran glacier complex of western Canada and Alaska, the Laurentine ice-sheet, which covered central and eastern Canada and the northern United States, and the Greenland ice-sheet; (2) the northern European ice-sheet, centred on Scandinavia, which at the height of the glacial phases covered the plains of north Germany, north Russia and much of the British Isles; and (3) the Siberian ice-sheet of eastern Russia. When these ice-sheets were at their greatest extent they covered regions in the central United States where present summer temperatures of 100° F.

Ch

				Geological Divisions			Years Ago	Main Climatic Ph...

Time Scale

UPPER PLEISTOCENE	▨	Holocene (10,000→)
		Transition Phase (15,000–10,000)
		Fourth Glacial Phase
		80,000
		Third Interglacial Phase
		190,000
MIDDLE PLEISTOCENE	▨	Third Glacial Phase
		240,000
		Second Interglacial Phase
		440,000
LOWER PLEISTOCENE, OR VILLAFRANCHIAN	▨	Second Glacial Phase
		480,000
		First Interglacial Phase
		550,000
	▨	First Glacial Phase
		600,000
		Pre-glacial Phase
		1,000,000

Geological Divisions			Years Ago	Main Climatic Ph...
HOLOCENE OR RECENT EPOCH				Modern Clima...
			10,000	
QUATERNARY PERIOD	PLEISTOCENE EPOCH	UPPER PLEISTOCENE	15,000	Transition Phas... gradual retreat... the ice-sheets
			80,000	Fourth, or Wür... Glacial Phase (Wisconsin Pha... in North Americ...
		MIDDLE PLEISTOCENE	190,000	Third Interglac... Phase (Sangam... Phase in Nort... America)
			240,000	Third, or Riss... Glacial Phase (Illinoian Phas... in North Americ...
			440,000	Second, or Grea... Interglacial Pha... (Yarmouth Pha... in North Americ...
		LOWER PLEISTOCENE OR VILLAFRANCHIAN	480,000	Second, or Mind... Glacial Phase (Kansan Phase... in North Americ...
			550,000	First Interglaci... Phase (Aftonia... Phase in North... America)
			600,000	First, or Gunz,... Glacial Phase (Nebraskan Phas... in North Americ...
			1,000,000	Pre-glacial Phas... transition from... Pliocene Epoch

This chart has been devised to give a general picture of the geological, climatic and archaeolo...
phases of the Quaternary Period, with their associated fossils and human cultures. Most of the ...
are still speculative and recent research suggests a rather greater antiquity for the Australopithe...

Quaternary Time

Characteristic European Fauna	Archaeological Divisions	Main Cultures	Main Human and Subhuman Types	Years Ago
Existing species First domestic animals	Modern urban society AGE OF METALS NEOLITHIC	Metal cultures and civilisation. Advanced stone cultures	Modern races of *Homo sapiens*	
Steppe fauna REINDEER AGE (tundra fauna)	MESOLITHIC	Campignian Erteböllian Maglemosian Tardenoisian Azilian		10,000
E OF WOOLLY MAMMOTH olly mammoth (*Mammuthus* *rimigenius*) olly rhinoceros (*Rhinoceros* *chorhinus*) e bear (*Ursus spelaeus*) e lion (*Panthera leo spelaea*)	UPPER PALAEOLITHIC	Magdalenian Solutrean Gravettian Aurignacian Chatelperronian	Fossil races of *Homo sapiens:* Cro-Magnon Grimaldi and Chancelade	40,000
AGE OF THE ANCIENT ELEPHANT	MIDDLE PALAEOLITHIC	Mousterian	Neanderthal Man (*Homo neanderthalensis*)	160,000
Ancient elephant (*Palaeoloxodon antiquus*) *Mammuthus trogontherii*		Levalloisian		
Merck's rhinoceros (*Rhinoceros mercki*)		Acheulian	Heidelberg Man (*Homo heidelbergensis*)	
Hippopotamus major	LOWER PALAEOLITHIC	Clactonian		
te:—During this period the nperate and subtropical natic belts with their asso- ted faunas moved frequently rth and south with the vance or retreat of the ice- ets. The above are four aracteristic mammals of the ne.		Abbevillian Choukoutienian	Java Man and Pekin Man (*Pithecanthropus*)	
		Oldowan	Australopithecinae and *Telanthropus*	
			?*Zinjanthropus* (exact status and date of this fossil is still speculative)	600,000
AGE OF THE SOUTHERN ELEPHANT uthern elephant (*Elephas* *eridionalis*) ruscan rhinoceros *Rhinoceros etruscus*) bre-toothed cat *Machairodus*)	?Origin of tool-making tradition		? Pre-Australo- pithecine sub-hominids (no known fossil evidence)	1,000,000

is shown here (see Author's Note, p. xvi). The time scale on the left gives an approximate indi-
on of the duration of the various phases; the remainder of the chart is diagrammatic only and is
drawn to scale.

are by no means uncommon. In Europe the ice-sheet extended into Wales, the English Midlands, and East Anglia, while the Thames valley and much of France and southern Germany was a desolate tundra region of semi-frozen ground. In the warmer interglacial phases when the ice retreated temperatures rose rather higher than the characteristic averages in the various regions today. While glacial and interglacial phases were alternating in the present temperate zone it seems that they were paralleled by what are known as 'pluvial' and 'arid' phases in tropical and subtropical regions. The evidence for these is particularly strong in Africa, but whether they exactly coincided with the advance and retreat of the ice-sheets in Eurasia and North America is not certainly known.

An important consequence of widespread glaciation was a considerable lowering of the sea level throughout the world. Rain, which in warmer times ran off the continents to augment the content of the world ocean, fell as hail, sleet or snow, and was trapped on the land surfaces in the form of glaciers and snow-fields. As a result, many parts of the present sea-bed were then exposed, and regions now separated by water were intermittently connected by bridges of dry ground. For example, at the height of the glacial phases England formed part of the main European land mass, the Mediterranean was joined to Africa between Italy and Tunisia and at the Straits of Gibraltar, and there was a land bridge between Asia and America across the present Bering Straits. Conversely, at the height of the warm interglacial phases, when the Arctic and Antarctic snows had withdrawn beyond their present boundaries, the sea level was much higher than it is today. Clear evidence of this is provided by the remains of ancient raised beaches which can still be seen in many regions, and which, by comparative studies, can be ascribed to one or other of the interglacial phases.

Compared with the long millennia of the Pliocene epoch, when little climatic change occurred, the geographical background of man's Pleistocene evolution was therefore particularly unstable. The fluctuations of climate caused constant changes in the environment which were expressed not only in fluctuations of temperature but in the cyclical creation and removal of actual physical barriers such as seas and ice-fields. These geographical and climatic changes naturally had a widespread effect on organisms, and the ecological pattern was in a constant state of flux. Plant life was particularly influenced by the changing climate, and the belts of tundra, steppe and forest moved with the ice-sheets to the north or south. This had an immediate effect on the herbivorous animals which depended on particular kinds of plants for their food; either they had to migrate with the plants or adapt themselves to a new type of vegetable diet. It had an equally profound effect on the predators, who in turn had to follow the migrating herbivores or discover a new form of prey in their existing habitat. The geographical barriers alluded to above often prevented the obvious solution of migration, and many kinds of animals succumbed to the sudden intensification of the environmental pressure. Others went through rapid phases of evolution which enabled them to assimilate the new conditions, so that the Pleistocene saw a widespread replacement of ancient animal types by new species better equipped to survive in the struggle for existence. Among the successful ones, of course, were the hominids, and our own species in particular may be said to owe much of its present character to the challenge of the Pleistocene Ice Age.

I do not wish to complicate the main story by giving a full account of the floral and faunal successions of Pleistocene times, but something must be added to amplify the over-simplified picture given on the Chart. I have there called the earliest faunal division of the Pleistocene the Age of the Southern Elephant, but of course many other remarkable animal fossils are known from that time. The most important of these from the point of view of human history were likewise mammals, but before coming to them a brief word must be said about the flora.

The Age of the Southern Elephant lasted from approximately one million until 600,000 years ago. We are thus still in preglacial times, and this phase is essentially a continuation of the comparatively mild and stable Pliocene epoch. The flora, as we would expect, is therefore characteristic of a temperate and fairly equable climate. In Europe the familiar trees of today, including oak, beech, maple, poplar, walnut and larch, all flourished, together with several genera such as the locust, honey-locust, tulip tree, sweet gum and sour gum, which are now confined to temperate North America. The plains were covered with a lush carpet of grasses, mostly of modern type, and there was a profusion of bushes and low trees from which the browsing animals could take their food.

The typical mammal of the time, after which the period is here named, was the southern elephant (*Elephas meridion-alis*), which had short tusks, a peculiarly flattened forehead, and a peaked cranium. The Etruscan rhinoceros (*Rhinoceros etruscus*), a browsing animal with short-crowned teeth, was also common, and the young of both these species were probably preyed on by the last of the great sabre-toothed cats (*Machairodus*). Woodland areas were well populated with deer; herds of horses, bison, and wild cattle roamed the plains; and at the opening of the period there may even have lingered some of the strange Pliocene mammals, such as the short-necked giraffe *Samotherium* and the herbivorous ungulate known as *Chalicotherium*, which had hooves modified into great bird-like claws.

The next faunal phase, which I have called the Age of the Ancient Elephant, covers the first three glacial phases, with the interglacial phases which followed them. The flora and fauna were thus constantly migrating north and south with the changes in climate, and nowhere did the pattern of life remain stable throughout the period. Nevertheless, a number of forms can be singled out as typical, even though their range fluctuated with the alternating phases of heat and cold. One of the best-known mammals of the time was the ancient, or straight-tusked, elephant (*Palaeoloxodon antiquus*). This animal seems to have been mainly a forest-dwelling form, and probably played the same role in the ecology of the Middle Pleistocene as the forest elephant does in the ecology of Africa today. It was among the giants of its order, some specimens standing over 14 feet at the shoulder. Yet in spite of its size and formidable tusks it was almost certainly one of the animals hunted by early man. A related form, *Mammuthus trogontherii,* was distinguished from the ancient elephant by its tooth structure, and probably lay close to the ancestry of the famous woolly mammoth of the last glacial phase. It may also have been ancestral to the Asiatic elephant (*Elephas maximus*) of modern times.

Merck's rhinoceros is another animal typical of the Middle Pleistocene. Like the ancient elephant it was a forest-dwelling form, and both animals may have been captured in pits by man. Other representatives of the fauna included the giant deer, or so-called 'Irish elk' (*Megaceros*), a primitive species of wild boar (*Sus scrofa ferus*), the spotted hyena, the hippopotamus, an early form of lion, and monkeys very similar to the living macaques. All these species are now either extinct or restricted entirely to the more exotic environments of Africa and southern Asia, but there were also representatives of the fauna associated with temperature regions in our own times. If we could transport ourselves back to the world of a quarter of a million years ago we should already be able to wander through a landscape inhabited by such familiar creatures as the brown bear, the wolf, the hamster, and the red and roe deer. Martens would climb in the trees, while bison, wild horses and wild cattle would roam the plains. The rivers would be barricaded with the dams of beavers, while otters would gambol in the shallows at sunset, and bright-eyed water voles would peer from the dense jungle of reeds on either bank.

Following the Age of the Ancient Elephant come two faunal periods which complete the transition to modern times. They are often named the Age of the Woolly Mammoth and the Reindeer Age after the two most typical mammals associated with them. The Age of the Woolly Mammoth coincides with the peak of the Fourth, or Würm, Glacial Phase, which lasted from about 80,000 to 15,000 years ago; the Reindeer Age covers the gradual decline of glacial conditions in northern Europe and the dawn of the modern world. The second of these is particularly important to our story as it saw the first consolidation of human society and culture.

The woolly mammoth was smaller than the ancient elephant and quite different in appearance. It was covered with a thick, shaggy coat of reddish hair and its back sloped steeply from front to rear. Unlike the two living species of elephant, some parts of its body were probably covered with subcutaneous fat as a thermal reservoir against the cold. Its tusks were quite different from those of both the ancient elephant and modern forms in that they curved so strongly inwards that in middle-aged and elderly specimens the tips sometimes crossed. These animals were commonly depicted in the cave paintings and engravings of early man, and certainly formed an important item in his diet.

Often associated with the remains of the woolly mammoth are those of the woolly rhinoceros (*Rhinoceros tichorhinus*). As its name suggests, this animal also had a thick, shaggy coat as an adaptation to the icy conditions of the Fourth Glacial Phase. Its head was long and narrow and supported two horns, the front one enormously long, the hind one much shorter but still a formidable weapon. The nearest living relation of this remarkable creature is the white rhinoceros of Africa, with whom it probably shared a common ancestor in Middle Pleistocene times. Like the woolly mammoth, it is a favourite subject in Upper Palaeolithic art, and rhinoceros steak probably figured largely on the menu of the cave kitchens of the time.

These two great animals shared the bleak tundra fringing the ice-sheets with a variety of less spectacular but nevertheless most interesting creatures. The reindeer was already common, and became increasingly so as time went on. The arctic fox, the arctic hare, the banded lemming and the arctic ptarmigan all flourished. In alpine regions ibex and marmots were numerous, while the lynx and brown bear shared forested areas with the wolf and several species of deer. The steppes to the south of the tundra still supported their population of horses and cattle, and there was a characteristic cave fauna, including the giant cave bear (*Ursus spelaeus*), the cave lion (*Panthera spelaea*), and a cave hyena and a cave leopard. (For reconstructions of Pleistocene fauna see Plates 20 and 21.)

As the ice retreated, the belts of tundra and steppe moved gradually northward. Reindeer were the most characteristic animals of the higher stages of Old Stone Age, or 'Palaeolithic' culture, in northern Europe, and their hides and horns were widely used in manufacturing clothing and weapons, implements and ritual objects. The woolly mammoth and woolly rhinoceros were dying out, and horses, cattle, sheep and goats gradually came under direct human control as domesticated animals.

This, then, was the environment in which the human adventure took place, and these were the animals with whom early man shared his world. Later we shall return to the subject matter of this chapter and describe some of the different ways in which man interacted with his environment. But first we must consider the question of human beginnings as revealed by the record of Pliocene and Pleistocene geology, and particularly the characteristics which have conferred on man his present position as the star character in the evolutionary drama.

Chapter Six

HUMAN BEGINNINGS

In the previous chapter I tried to draw a general picture of the Pleistocene world, especially of its climatic background and the various kinds of animals who then shared with the first men the tenancy of the earth. I made no more than a passing reference to our own ancestors at this time, or to the Pleistocene hominids closest to us in the evolutionary scale. This was because I felt that the stage should be suitably dressed before the entry of the main actors. In this chapter, however, I intend to reduce the focus and say something about the nature of our own forbears and collaterals.

I have stated earlier (Chapter 4) that we are greatly handicapped in the quest for our earliest ancestors by the shortage of fossil remains between the Miocene skeletons of *Proconsul* and *Dryopithecus* and the later part of the Lower Pleistocene when near-human primate fossils first begin to appear. All the same, general evolutionary principles, and the pattern of primate evolution in particular, do allow us to make some reasonable deductions about what was happening during this gap in the fossil record. Before we can speculate on the subject, however, we must first try to devise a simple working definition of man. This will not only help us to frame our assumptions concerning progress towards the human condition in the early Pleistocene, but will be useful in later chapters as a standard against which the various types of early man can be measured.

Man, we can say, is a large ground-dwelling primate possessing six main characteristics and interrelated attributes: (1) a limb structure suitable to an erect stance and the manipulation of objects; (2) an exceptionally well-developed brain;

(3) highly specialised social habits; (4) the power of speech; (5) the ability to make and use tools; and (6) the faculty of conceptual thought. The last of these, as we shall see, is the key to our definition of man, but each plays a part in determining his nature. Bearing them all in mind, we must now consider how our primate ancestors and nearest relations were probably developing in the early Pleistocene world of a million years ago.

The first two attributes of the human species listed above were evolving for at least eighty million years before man as we know him appeared. Driven into the trees during the Mesozoic by the pressure of competition with their larger and more powerful reptilian contemporaries, our ancestors there acquired all-important specialisations of limb and brain which enabled them at a later stage to reinvade the ground with greatly increased chances of success. To amplify the points already made, we may say that the limb and brain specialisations of the early primates were as follows: (1) an exceptionally flexible hand adapted to grasping such objects as branches and food, instead of having the purely locomotory function of most mammalian fore-limbs; (2) well-developed hind-limbs which, from their primary use in supporting the body weight in trees, could be easily adapted to supporting the body weight in the upright posture on the ground; and (3) an exceptionally well-organised cerebral cortex, arising first from the need for a high degree of co-ordinated movement in the trees, but ready for adaptation to much more advanced functions when these were required.

It is clear that as long ago as the Miocene certain groups of ancestral apes were using their highly evolved evolutionary equipment to return to a terrestrial habitat. *Proconsul* itself was at least partly terrestrial, and the later *Oreopithecus*, although likewise doubtfully in the direct human line, was probably as much at home on the ground as in the trees. Several kinds of monkeys were also coming down to earth at the same time, but it is interesting to note in passing that this movement was entirely confined to the cercopithecoids of the Old World. The New World ceboids have always been strictly arboreal, and remain so to this day.

59

Now can we say how the characteristic primate limb specialisations mentioned above became adapted to the new conditions of ground-dwelling life? Two alternative solutions were open to the returning tree-dwellers and, if we are to judge by living primates, both of these were in fact adopted by different groups. In some groups, such as the baboons, a return was made to a modified kind of four-legged gait. This plan was also followed by the ancestral gorillas (which almost certainly spent as much time on the ground as their modern descendants), and to a lesser extent by the chimpanzees. But in the group of hominoids ancestral to man an entirely new solution was devised. It seems that when these animals returned to the ground, selection went to work on them in such a way that their hind-limbs became more and more specialised for carrying the whole weight of the body in the upright position. The return to a new kind of four-legged progression, as exemplified by the modern baboons and gorillas, as well as by the less arboreal genera of living monkeys whenever they descend from the trees, was entirely rejected. Instead, the sole became larger in area and more flattened, and the digits of the hind-limbs progressively shorter and less prehensile until they were transformed into typically human toes. At the same time the legs became more pillar-like and muscular to fulfil their locomotory function, and longer to confer the advantage of height. As a result of the tendency towards an upright stance, the fore-limbs were freed for other uses. They became still more generalised than in the tree-dwellers, while retaining their flexibility for such characteristically human activities as grasping food and manipulating objects. This total emancipation of the fore-limbs from their locomotory function is one of the key events in the line of evolution leading to modern man.

The reader may well inquire at this point what caused certain groups of primates to descend from the trees at all. The answer to this question lies in the general principles governing evolutionary change. We have seen in Chapter 2 that the ability to adapt to the physical environment is essential to the survival of any organism. If it cannot deal with the challenges of its own chosen region, whether these result from climatic change or the pressure of competition from other organisms, it must either move to a new area more favourable to its survival or perish. But as we ascend higher in the evolutionary scale it seems that an additional factor comes into play. Quite apart from the necessity of survival, there is a tendency for organisms to fan out of their own volition into new and unexplored environments. It is almost as though the mysterious force which drives evolution forward were constantly pressing these creatures into the vacua of unrealised possibilities. Through their mental attributes survival as such has become reasonably assured, and the evolutionary energy is utilised in more creative and adventurous ways. It seems probable that some such factor played a part in the evolution of the primate ancestors of man.

In a sense, of course, the ground was not a 'new' environment to those primates who returned there, as it was the place of their origin many millions of years before. But it must be remembered that in the meantime the pattern of interaction between the various forms of life and their physical environment had been revolutionised. The great reptiles were all extinct, and the primates themselves had acquired an almost unrivalled evolutionary advantage in the development of highly organised brains. Thus the biological balance was quite different, and the primates could return to the ground with an entirely new set of survival techniques. Their groundward movement was also probably correlated with the reduction of tropical forests which was taking place during the Pliocene epoch and continued into the Pleistocene. As usual, change of habitat occurred as a result of a number of distinct but interrelated factors. The reduction of the arboreal *lebensraum* introduced a greater pressure of competition in the trees, while at the same time the physical and mental equipment of certain groups of primates was already enabling them to embark on a more adventurous type of evolutionary development.

We may therefore recapitulate the prelude to the human story as follows. The Mesozoic primates took to the trees to avoid direct competition with ground-dwelling reptiles. Their arboreal life led them to make particularly significant specialisations in their limbs and brains. Their limbs became differentiated so that the fore-limbs were mainly specialised for grasping food, boughs and other objects, while the hind-limbs were mainly specialised to support their body weight in the trees. Their brains meanwhile responded to the need for a greater co-ordination of movement by an immense development in the cortical region, which is also the seat of an organism's general intelligence. By Miocene times certain groups which excelled in these directions were ready for a reinvasion of the ground, a reinvasion which was eventually triggered off by a reduction in the forest habitat and the tendency of evolution to press suitably equipped organisms into regions where there are still biological possibilities to be realised. Of the invading groups, some, such as the ancestral baboons and gorillas, adopted a modified form of four-legged gait, but others, such as the ancestors of modern man and his Pleistocene cousins, adopted an upright stance. Before further discussing the significance of this latter development we must turn to the third characteristic of man enumerated above – his tendency to socialisation.

The combination of biological units into a social structure is one of the oldest and most fundamental characteristics of life. Single-celled organisms tend to combine with others of their kind into clusters or colonies, and at a higher level of evolution many different kinds of animals associate in groups, variously known as flocks, packs, herds, and so on, which favour the survival of the species. At all levels, however, socialisation is of two main types. The first type is a purely additive one, based on the principle of 'safety in numbers'; the second is based on the specialisation of different individuals in the group for different functions, an arrangement which in certain circumstances makes for a far higher survival potential for the group as a whole.

A herd of elephants or antelopes is an example of the first type of socialisation. Such a herd may, and often does, have a leader, and may even show evidence of other types of role specialisation, such as the posting of sentinels, the sending out of scouts and so on. At this level of aggregation, however, no higher degree of individual specialisation to different functions in the community is achieved. The survival potential of the herd is mainly based on its size and numbers – the principle of collective security we might call it – not on a marked differentiation of function and skills.

The second type of socialisation, based on the specialisation of the group's individual members for different tasks, itself takes two forms. The first is expressed through physical adaptation, and attains its highest expression in certain types of insects, for instance, ants and bees. In a community of harvester ants the worker caste and soldier caste are physically adapted to the performance of different tasks, and in consequence vary so much in structure and appearance that, unless one were aware of the facts, one would not think they belonged to the same species; moreover, among the workers themselves, there is a wide range of physical specialisation related to the tasks that each is called upon to perform. The second type of specialised socialisation, which is highly characteristic of modern man, is not expressed primarily through physical adaptation (although certain physical adaptations may occur), but through the capacity of the brain to acquire different skills by learning. This is a far more flexible arrangement than the first, and has a far higher survival potential. To precise the point, a worker ant cannot, by learning, acquire the functions of a soldier ant; a human office worker (specialised, say, for doing accounts) can, on the other hand, become a soldier if educated in the necessary skills. The reluctant transformation of accountants into soldiers is, in fact, an aspect of human life with which many of us have been familiar during two world wars.

It seems reasonable to assume that when our ancestors first descended from the trees they were mainly characterised by the first additive type of socialisation, based on 'safety in numbers'. This probably remained fairly stable until well into the Pleistocene, but was then gradually transformed in some lines into the second. This was based not on physical differentiation as in the insects, but on mental differentiation as expressed by the brain's capacity to acquire transmitted skills by learning. This flexible pattern of specialised socialisation, made possible by the sophisticated organisation of the higher primate brain, is unique to man. It not only gives him a survival potential superior to that of any community on earth, but a release of evolutionary energy which, in some members of his society, is expressed in forms of creative activity unparalleled in any other organism.

Limb specialisation, brain specialisation and socialisation; we have now dealt with certain aspects of three of the six characteristic attributes of man enumerated earlier in this chapter. What can be said of the remainder: speech, tool-making and conceptual thought? There is little reason to believe that any of these more advanced human characteristics had developed in early Pleistocene times, but this is nevertheless a convenient moment to make a few observations on each.

The importance of speech in the human story cannot be over-emphasised. Many types of animals communicate by display techniques in which sounds may play a part; only in man, however, has there evolved a complex system of communication where individual sounds and combinations of sounds stand for specific concrete, and even abstract, ideas. We may regret that these sophisticated methods of communication now vary from place to place on the earth's surface so that there is no universally intelligible system of communication; we may regret even more that many of us are still so handicapped by semantics that word symbols are sometimes regarded as more real than the ideas for which they stand; but these difficulties are temporary and essentially soluble by a new synthesis of the techniques of communication. What is important in the present context is that speech evolved at all, and became such a potent influence on man's development. Can anything be said about its biological origins?

As man is unique in the possession of speech it might be thought that the faculty depends on the special design of his vocal apparatus, but this is not entirely true. Every one of the living anthropoid apes possesses a jaw, tongue, larynx and associated musculature capable of producing articulate sounds. Moreover, even creatures as comparatively low in the evolutionary scale as parrots and mynahs can utter comprehensible sounds (although in this case, of course, we are not dealing with true speech, but with a special capacity for sound mimicry). The power of speech therefore does not primarily depend on physical adaptations in the vocal regions themselves (although these must also, of course, be present) but on the development of the higher intelligence which leads to conceptual thought.

In spite of this, we can point to several characteristics of the human skull which show that it is especially well adapted to the utterance of articulate sounds. For example, when the lower jaws of man are compared with those of an ape it will be found that there is in man a considerable broadening and opening out of the region between each half of the mandible, giving greater freedom of movement to the tongue. This freedom is increased by the absence in man of the ledge of bone, known as the 'simian shelf', which is found inside the front of the lower jaws of apes and monkeys. The function of the simian shelf is to strengthen the joint between the two sides of the lower mandible, but in our own species, in contrast to other primates, this bony brace is transferred from its internal position to the outside, where it helps to give man his characteristically prominent chin. A third modification associated with the mechanism of speech is the growth of backward-projecting spines of bone, known rather pleasingly as 'genial tubercles', in the interior of the chin region. These tubercles, which are unique to man, form useful points of attachment for the tongue muscles. Their size, or even their presence, is not in itself, however, an index of speech capacity, even at the purely mechanical level. As the late Professor Hooton drily pointed out, women have smaller genial tubercles than men.

We come next to the fifth item in our definition of man – his ability to make and use tools. For many years now this ability has been regarded as of decisive importance, and tool-making is certainly a highly characteristic attribute of our species. But if, as is sometimes claimed, it is to be regarded as an absolute criterion of human status then we are certainly stressing its significance too far. While it is true that all men are characterised by the ability to make and use tools, it is *not* true to say that all animals able to make and use tools are men. To prove the point we need only consider one other member of the primate group – the chimpanzee.

I have already referred to the ability of chimpanzees to fit two sticks together, or to build up a pile of boxes, to reach a coveted object. These activities were studied in a classic piece of research on the chimpanzee mind undertaken by Professor Wolfgang Köhler of Berlin in the early 1920s and are described in his book *The Mentality of Apes*, first published in English in 1925. Widely as this book has been read, the effect of its implications on the idea that tool-making is a diagnostic character of man does not seem to have been fully realised. It is most instructive to compare the using and making of tools by chimpanzees and men and see in what respects, if any, the process differs.

The most primitive form of tool manipulation practised

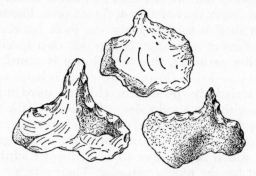

FIG. 5.   Three eoliths, or 'dawn stones', from Kent, England. *From Romer (1959)*, *p. 342*

by man's earliest ancestors was probably the use of naturally-shaped stones as weapons or simple implements. The remains of such stones, which are called eoliths, or 'dawn stones', are well known in Pleistocene deposits, and three examples are depicted on this page. These stones have not been deliberately fashioned into a particular shape by man, but have simply been selected for their natural suitability. The use of such ready-made objects is entirely comparable with the use of similar objects by chimpanzees. For example, in Köhler's experiments, the chimpanzee Sultan thought out without human assistance how a pole could be used as an aid to jumping, while other members of the group used straws as sucking implements, twigs as primitive spoons, and sticks as levers. It is difficult to see how the use by primitive man of an existing stone to break a skull and the use by a chimpanzee of an existing stick as a jumping-pole or lever can be said to differ in kind.

The next stage of tool manipulation among early men was the deliberate shaping of a stone or other object to assist in the performance of a particular and immediate task. Implements of this type made from wood and other perishable materials have not, of course, survived, but many examples of crude hand-axes and other stone implements are found even more frequently than recognisable eoliths on the Pleistocene sites. Still, however, the activity is not peculiar to man. The fitting together of two sticks to reach an otherwise unobtainable objective, as practised by Köhler's chimpanzees, is just as valid an example of tool-making, although at a rather lower level of sophistication, as the deliberate flaking of a flint.

Only in the third stage of tool manipulation can a valid distinction be drawn between the performance of men and chimpanzees. This stage is the deliberate manufacture of an implement, not for use in carrying out some immediate and visible task, but to meet the demands of some *future* situation which at the time can only be imagined, not seen. Köhler has shown quite conclusively that chimpanzees are capable of the former kind of tool-making, but man seems to be the only primate who is capable of the latter.

It is often overlooked that this distinction is not based on the act of tool-making itself, but on the *type of thought* that leads to the tool-making in two different sets of circumstances. In one case the thought is directed to the present – visible and immediate; in the other to the future – invisible and abstract. Man therefore cannot be defined simply as a 'tool-making primate', as is so often done; his only valid diagnostic character is his power of abstracting from particular past or present instances a general idea or principle which can be applied to a situation that has not yet come about. We thus arrive at last at the sixth item in our definition of man, and his unique distinguishing feature, the power of conceptual thought.

From its first evolution, conceptual thought enabled our ancestors to exercise a far more refined and effective control over their environment than had been achieved by any previous organism. Moreover, quite apart from the immense advantage it conferred in the purely physical field, it made possible the evolution of the higher faculties of man which he now utilises in all his most advanced endeavours. The values which we term beauty, truth and goodness are unknowable without the power of abstract thought; and science, art and religion, which are the means by which these values are pursued, could never have evolved if man's mind had remained tied to the objects of his immediate experience.

I shall return to these fascinating and complex aspects of man's nature later on. In the meantime there is a great deal to be said about his physical and social development. As the early part of this story will be largely reconstructed from the fossil bones of our earliest forbears and relations, we must look first at some features of the human skeleton, and particularly those which distinguish it from the skeletons of other primates. Although somewhat technical, this account will help us to see where the various fossils fit into the pattern of human development.

The chin is one of the most typical attributes of the human skeleton, and resulted, as we have seen, from the gradual evolutionary replacement of the internal bony brace known as the simian shelf by a brace of similar function but different structure on the outside of the lower jaw. In general, the more prominent the chin the more 'human' the skull, but there are many exceptions to this rule. Even among our own most intimate friends we may know people with receding chins, but it would be quite unfair to suggest that they are in consequence nearer to the apes than the lantern-jawed heroes of the popular strip cartoons. The chin is only one character among many enabling us to tell men from other primates.

Much more reliable evidence comes from the shape of the jaws and the nature of the teeth. I have already mentioned the broadening and opening out of the human lower mandible as compared with that of an ape in connection with speech. This condition is, of course, the same in the upper jaw, as the teeth surfaces fit directly one on another when the jaws are closed. The difference between the arrangements found in men and the higher apes will be made clear by the illustration on this page. In the gorilla jaw, which also closely resembles that of the chimpanzee, the two sides of the mandible are almost parallel, whereas in the human jaw the whole structure has the shape of a continuously curving arch. This is a most reliable guide in distinguishing the fossils of man and ape. The difference is emphasised by the tooth structure, which is also strongly contrasted. In man the teeth in both jaws form a continuous series without gaps, and the canines are the same height as their neighbours. In apes the canines are normally

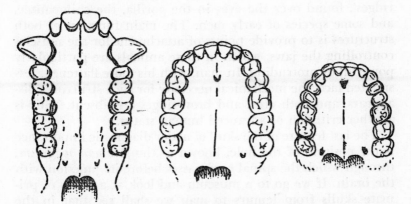

FIG. 6. Comparison between the palate and upper teeth of a male gorilla (left), *Australopithecus* (centre), and *Homo sapiens* (an Australian aboriginal). *From Clark (1960), Fig. 21, p. 68*

much longer, and a gap occurs in the series in front of the upper canines to make room for the lower canines when the jaw is closed. A similar gap occurs behind the lower canines to receive the upper canines, and there is also a sharp oblique ridge along the front of the two neighbouring cheek-teeth on each side due to their biting against the back of the upper canine crowns when the mouth is closed. These are just a few of the technical criteria used by students of fossils in distinguishing one primate jaw from another.

Several other differences between the human and ape skeletons are also very important. For instance, the greater size of the human brain naturally requires greater space in the cranium, or 'brain case', and this therefore has a greater cubic capacity in man than in apes of the same body size. The cranial capacity of an average western European male is about 1,400 c.c., whereas that of an average male gorilla is only about 550 c.c. Other cranial differences occur in the structures technically known as the 'sagittal crest' and the 'supra-orbital ridges'. The former, as its name suggests, is a crest of bone which runs fore and aft along the top of the cranium; it is particularly characteristic of the gorilla, although it sometimes occurs in the chimpanzee and orangutan in less prominent form. The latter are heavy ridges of bone, or 'brow-ridges', found over the eyes in the gorilla, the chimpanzee, and some species of early men. The main function of both structures is to provide points of attachment for the muscles controlling the jaws, which in these animals are particularly powerful or protruding. In man, with his more flattened, less snouted face, the mechanical necessity for such structures disappears, and both crest and brow-ridges are absent. This is another criterion of advanced human status.

The last feature of the skull of major diagnostic importance is the position of the hole, known as the *foramen magnum*, through which the spinal cord passes before its junction with the brain. If we go to a museum and look at a series of primate skulls from lemurs to man we shall see that in the skulls nearest to the line leading to man the position of this hole moves gradually forward from the back of the cranium until it is almost central to its base. This is due to the increasing tendency of these primates to adopt an upright stance. Clearly for an animal accustomed to going on all-fours the skull must be so attached to the vertebral column that a vertical section through the eyes will be roughly at right angles to the backbone. In upright animals such as man, where the vertebral column has swung through an angle of 90° relative to the ground, a vertical section through the eyes must be in the same plane as the backbone unless the animal is to be constantly looking at the sky. The inconvenience that would be suffered by a four-legged creature if it had the *foramen magnum* in the human position will be particularly well realised by any uncle who has played bears with the children at Christmas. Lumbering about the floor on hands and knees he must either tilt back his head in a most uncomfortable way, or else look constantly at the floor and risk banging his head on the wall.

The other bones of the primate skeleton are less often preserved as fossils than those of the skull, but can still be

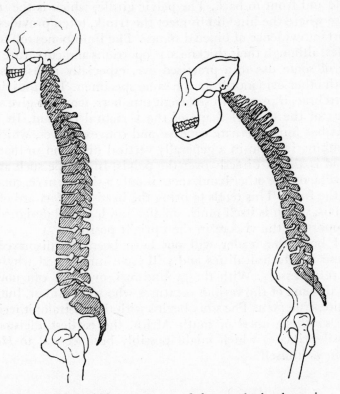

Fig. 7. The relative curvature of the vertebral column in *Homo sapiens* (left) and the gorilla is well shown in this illustration. Individual vertebrae, if present in sufficient numbers, give clues to the stance of their owner in life, and hence to his zoological status. *After Boule and Vallois (1957), Fig. 41, p. 74*

valuable aids to identification if they are present. Hands, feet, the bones of the structure known as the 'pelvic girdle', and, to a lesser extent, limb bones and vertebrae are the most useful. The hands may show by such characters as the proportions between the different finger joints whether their

71

owner was more human or ape-like. The feet are even more useful, and much of interest can be told from the length of the digits, the possession or otherwise of an opposable big toe, and by whether or not there is the characteristically human 'arching' of the whole structure both from side to side and front to back. The pelvic girdle, which is the structure where the hind-limbs meet the trunk, often provides important evidence of bipedal stance. The limb bones tell fewer tales, although their thickness, proportions and curvature may be of some use to a practised eye, especially in association with other evidence from the same specimen. The individual vertebrae, if present in sufficient numbers, may also give some idea of the general shape of the vertebral column. In man this has four alternate concave and convex curves, which in combination run in a generally vertical direction so that the head is almost directly over the pelvis. In an ape such as the gorilla, on the other hand, there is only a single curve, concave at the front. This tends to bring the head well forward of the pelvis, which is itself much smaller and less well designed for supporting the viscera in the upright position.

I hope the reader will not have been too dismayed by these few technicalities and will have understood why they were necessary. With the groundwork over, we can now go on to some of the various creatures who were almost, but not quite, true men. The story begins with the australopithecines, or 'southern apes' of south Africa, the earliest Pleistocene fossil primates which might possibly be ancestral to *Homo sapiens* himself.

Chapter Seven

THE AUSTRALOPITHECINES

AFTER THE tantalising Pliocene twilight the shape of human history reveals itself in the first half of the Pleistocene in far more distinct form. For the first time for many millions of years we have actual fossils to help us in our speculations. This always gives great relief to the serious student of evolution; at last he has some bones in his hand which he can measure and describe without fear of being regarded as a reckless theoriser or a crank.

These Pleistocene bones belong to a group of pre-human or near-human primates, known as the australopithecines (literally 'southern apes'), which seem to have been widely distributed in south and east Africa some 600,000 years ago. But the term 'southern ape', it is now suspected, may prove to be misleading. Many students are becoming convinced that the australopithecines were not apes at all, but hominids closely related to our own ancestry. (Plates 22 and 23.)

Although earliest in the evolutionary sequence, the fossil remains of the australopithecines were the latest to be discovered. The first find was made in 1924 at Taungs, a fossil locality some eighty miles north of Kimberley. Commercial quarrying had been going on in this region since 1910, and the remains of many different types of animals, particularly baboons, had from time to time turned up. Then in 1924, after the detonation of a blast charge, a quarryman discovered the cranium of an animal unlike any that had been discovered before. His find was submitted to Professor Raymond Dart of the Witwatersrand University in Johannesburg, who claimed that it belonged to a previously unknown species of primitive hominid, which he named *Australopithecus africanus*. His view turned out to be remarkably insighted, for the hominid

73

status of the fossil is now very largely accepted. But whatever view we may take about the classification of the animal a discovery had been made of the highest importance in tracing the course of human ancestry.

Since the discovery of the Taungs skull many other remains of australopithecines have been extracted from south African formations. These have generally been found in the rock-hard sand and limestone breccias which form the fillings of sink-holes and fissures in pre-Cambrian dolomites. Such rocks are notoriously subject to cave formation, and the filling is exposed by the weathering away of the original roof. As a result of these finds, of which the most important have been made in the region of Sterkfontein, Kromdrai, and Swartkrans near Johannesburg, we now have a sufficiently large collection of australopithecine remains to draw a remarkably clear picture of the creatures.

I do not intend to weary the non-specialist reader by describing the voluminous evidence fossil by fossil. But a few words must be said about the way the australopithecines are classified if we are to avoid a too superficial treatment of the subject. All the remains that have come to light since 1924 are now grouped together in a single family, the Australo-pithecinae, but opinions differ as to whether this family contains one genus or several. Anyone who is ever tempted to believe in the absolute authority of a scientific statement will be comforted to read of the wide divergence of expert views on this subject. Some authorities maintain that the likeness between the fossils is sufficiently great for them all to be lumped together in the genus *Australopithecus*. Others say that three genera must be recognised – *Australopithecus, Paranthropus,* and *Telanthropus.* Yet a third school of thought (although it has very few adherents) has sometimes maintained that the Australopithecines are not sufficiently different from man to warrant separate status at all, and should be grouped with ourselves in the genus *Homo.*

Recently the position has been still further complicated by the discovery of an east African australopithecine by Dr L. S. B. Leakey, the former curator of the Coryndon Museum in Nairobi. Always a sturdy individualist, Leakey has placed his fossil in a category of its own with the generic

74

name of *Zinjanthropus*. There is, however, little doubt that this form is so closely related to the others that for practical purposes we can regard it as a local or individual variation of the same basic stock.

We must now try to give an impression of what the australopithecines were like. As a general statement we can say that they were a race of erect-walking primates about the size of modern pygmies with moderately large brains, who may have made simple tools from wood, horn and bone and possibly also possessed the power of speech. If we look at a typical australopithecine skull we have to admit that in general appearance it is rather less reminiscent of modern man than of a man-like ape. The cranial vault is comparatively low, and the forehead slanting; the lower half of the face also protrudes as a fairly well-developed snout – a condition associated with apes rather than men – and the jaws are very large. But when we look at the skull more closely we begin to notice a number of significant characters suggesting its human affinities. For instance, the ridges or 'crests' for the attachment of muscles, so conspicuous in the skulls of modern apes such as the gorilla, are much reduced, and the forehead, although slanting backwards, is comparatively rounded and the brow-ridges are not pronounced. The design of the joint between the lower jaw and the base of the skull, the shape of the cheekbones, and the character of the bone sutures, or seams, are among other features more reminiscent of humans than apes.

One of the most striking likenesses is in the jaws and teeth. In man, as mentioned in the last chapter, there is a noticeable broadening out of the two sides of each jaw between front and back, whereas in the apes the sides are more or less parallel. In the australopithecines the condition is very man-like, the so-called 'dental arcade' being shaped in a continuous curve instead of being broken by angles on either side of the incisors. Another significant feature is the complete absence of a simian shelf.

Likenesses in the teeth themselves are equally remarkable. The incisors are small, as in man, and although the canines are more massively constructed than ours they scarcely project at all above the level of the other teeth. They are thus very different from the powerful projecting canines of the great apes. The premolars and molars are also extremely human, and the first lower premolars have twin prominences, or 'cusps', of human type instead of the single conical point possessed by all large apes, both fossil and recent. The upright stance of the creature is proved by the position of the *foramen magnum* which is much nearer to the middle point of the skull-base than in apes.

The average brain size of the australopithecines was some 600 c.c., with a maximum of 750 c.c., compared with 1,400 c.c. for an average western man. This does not at first suggest that the creatures were very intelligent, but when we remember that they were comparatively small and lightly-built, and that intelligence does not depend on absolute brain capacity but on the ratio between the size of brain and body, we can believe that their mental powers were probably considerable. In fact, in relation to their body size, they had a larger brain capacity than any animal that had previously appeared on the earth.

We come next to what scientists call the 'post-cranial' skeleton, but which most of us will be content to refer to as the body bones. Here we find that the shape of the pelvic girdle (see p. 72) is particularly revealing. Each side of this structure is mostly made up of a broad blade-like bone known as the 'ilium', which forms the point of attachment for several powerful muscles. Among these are the buttock, or 'gluteal', muscles which help to balance the trunk on the hind-limbs in standing and walking, and the muscles which enable a man to 'hold his tummy in' instead of letting it sag forward. The ilium also provides a natural bony platform for the support of the viscera.

Now the ilium of apes is shaped quite differently from ours. The broad, flattened appearance of man's ilium is a direct result of his upright stance; in apes, which are mainly arboreal or, if ground-dwelling, habitually go on all-fours, this adaptation is unnecessary, and the ilium is comparatively narrow and elongated. In the australopithecines we find, significantly, that the appearance of the ilium is much more like a man's than an ape's and therefore provides yet further evidence that the australopithecines may be cousins, or even ancestors, of *Homo sapiens* (see Fig 8, p. 77).

The possibility that *Australopithecus* was a tool-maker was naturally one of the first matters to be considered by those who studied the fossils. Professor Dart was particularly keen to prove this, and collected pebble-tools from near the various australopithecine sites, and also huge quantities of jaws, long bones and horn cores which he believed to be evidence of a pre-lithic industry. Unfortunately, however, there is no real

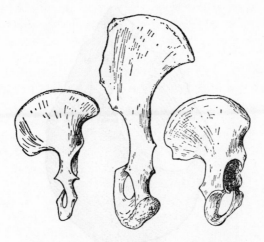

FIG. 8. Comparison between the iliac bones of an australopithecine (left), a chimpanzee (centre) and *Homo sapiens*. The australopithecine ilium much more closely resembles that of man than that of the chimpanzee. *After Boule and Vallois (1957), Fig. 57, p. 91*

proof that these objects, interesting as they are, were made by the south African australopithecines. Pebble-tools, which consist simply of stones with one end chipped into a rough cutting edge, are found over nearly the whole of Africa south of the Sahara, but most of them are of much more recent date than the early Pleistocene. It was also only at Sterkfontein that these shaped pebbles were definitely found in association with australopithecine bones. Yet although Dart's suggestion has not yet been supported by acceptable evidence in

south Africa itself, it has recently received spectacular con-
firmation from the discoveries of Dr L. S. B. Leakey in
Tanganyika.

Since 1931 Leakey has been working regularly on the fossiliferous deposits at Olduvai Gorge near the Ngorongoro
Crater in the Serengeti. Over the years he has built up a
picture of a pebble-tool culture which once existed in this

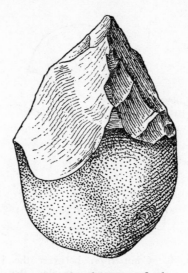

FIG. 9. A chopper of the
Oldowan culture from Olduvai
Gorge (half actual size). *From
Cole (1954), Fig. 9, p. 133*

region, and which has come to be known as 'Oldowan', after
the Gorge. This culture, which dates from at least half a
million years ago, is now generally regarded as the oldest
Stone Age culture yet discovered. Remains of tools of
Oldowan type have also been found in many other parts of
Africa, and even in Portugal, and although most of these are
more recent than those found at Olduvai itself, it is quite
possible that a far-ranging pebble-tool culture existed in
Africa and south-eastern Europe in the very earliest millennia of the Pleistocene epoch.

While exploring at Olduvai in the summer of 1959 Leakey

made a discovery even more remarkable than the tools themselves; he found the creature that probably made them. On
July 17th in that year his wife came across a tooth and a piece
of a temporal bone projecting from the rock. She immediately
called her husband, who was sick in camp, and after further
search an almost complete skull and a limb bone were also
discovered. In Leakey's view these bones belonged to the type
of primitive hominid which had made the pebble-tools, and it
was named by him *Zinjanthropus boisei*. Although he placed
it in the family Australopithecinae for convenience, he
claimed that it was probably a form still more closely related
to man. After examination by other experts, however, it was
felt that Leakey had perhaps been too hopeful. Most palaeontologists now believe that the Oldowan ape-man was simply
an east African variety of *Australopithecus*.

Now if the australopithecines made tools, is it also possible
that they possessed an articulate language? This question can
never, of course, be definitely answered, but there is certainly
nothing in their jaw structure that would have made speech
mechanically impossible. Even in animals much lower in the
evolutionary scale than the apes, particular sounds are associated with certain immediate emotions such as pain, fear,
anger, lust, etc., and the development of these symbols into a
coherent language is simply a question of abstracting from
the individual instance in each case the 'idea' of the emotion
which prompted it. The sound then comes to be understood
as representing the idea as well as the particular instance of
the idea, and it is possible for language as we know it, rather
than simple vocal reactions, to develop. The ability of the
australopithecines to make tools suggests that they were also
quite intelligent enough to have evolved some fairly elaborate method of sound symbolism as a means of communication.

Next we must inquire how the australopithecines lived
in that distant Pleistocene world of more than half a million
years ago. The climate would have played a great part in
determining this, and the geological evidence suggests, not
only in the regions occupied by the australopithecines but in
many different parts of Africa, that the continent underwent
a series of alternating wet ('pluvial') and dry ('arid') phases

which may have roughly corresponded to the glacial and inter-glacial phases of regions nearer the poles. (See also Chapter 5.) In the region where the earliest australopithecine remains were extracted the climate at the time was an arid one, a fact that was revealed by an interesting geological technique. The breccia in which the fossils were embedded consisted of grains of chert and quartz which had been carried into caves by wind action and there consolidated. The chert had originated in the local dolomites, but the quartz had come from some distance. Now by comparing the ratio between chert and quartz in the australopithecine breccias with that in formations of similar character but different date it is found that the proportion sometimes varies to a considerable extent. The cause, it seems, is related to climatic conditions. In dry conditions there is less rain to dissolve the dolomite, but the quartz is carried along more easily; in wet conditions the position is reversed. If we next compare the proportion of the two substances in the australopithecine deposits with the proportion found in modern Transvaal soils we find they are roughly equal. We can therefore deduce that the australopithecines probably lived in an arid climate very similar to that found in the region today.

These dry conditions would obviously have been reflected in the flora. There would have been no forests or jungles, and the vegetation would have consisted mainly of parched grasslands and perhaps a few scattered clumps of thorn. The location of the fossils suggests that the australopithecines made their homes in caves in low hills rising from the plain, where they probably lived by a mixture of hunting and food-gathering. Although nuts, berries and eggs must have formed an important part of their diet, it seems certain that their favourite food was meat. Bones of baboons, antelopes, tortoises, rodents, bats and birds have been found mixed with the fossil remains of the australopithecines themselves, and these creatures probably formed their main prey. Some of the baboon skulls show evidence of having been bashed in with a stone weapon, and there is little doubt that the australopithecines used material equipment of this kind to assist them in the hunt. Almost certainly they were social in habit, as are

II. Early man and his world

All reconstructions by Maurice Wilson

18 The Miocene ape *Proconsul*, which may have been ancestral to the living gorillas and chimpanzees and near the ancestry of man.

19 *Oreopithecus*, a human collateral of the Pliocene epoch.

20 The Pleistocene World (1): Inter-glacial Fauna of the Middle Pleistocene.

A spotted hyena watches two lions over a slaughtered wild pig. Beyond
the pool ancient elephants (*Palaeoloxodon antiquus*) are browsing.
Two Merck's rhinoceros (*Rhinoceros mercki*), three hippopotamus
(*Hippopotamus major*) and two cercopithecoid monkeys are seen to the right.

21 The Pleistocene World (2): Glacial Fauna of the Upper Pleistocene.

Reindeer (*Rangifer tarandus*) seek food in the snow-covered tundra.
Beyond are wild horses, a group of woolly mammoth (*Mammuthus primigenius*), and two woolly rhinoceros (*Rhinoceros tichorinus*).
A pair of arctic ptarmigan fly away to the left.

22, 23 The australopithecines, who were widespread in southern and eastern Africa between one million and 600,000 years ago, may have been the ancestors of modern man. They subsisted by food-gathering and by hunting baboons, gazelles and other small game.

24, 25 The ape-man *Pithecanthropus*, who lived in south-eastern Asia between 500,000 and 200,000 years ago, was almost certainly in the direct line of human descent. He made implements of quartz, was a skilful hunter, and had undoubtedly discovered the use of fire for heating, and also possibly for cooking.

23

4

5

26, 27 Neanderthal man, who flourished between 180,000 and 40,000 years ago, was probably a cousin, not an ancestor, of modern man. Above he is shown ejecting cave bears (*Ursus spelaeus*) from his home; and below treating skins.

baboons themselves, and we can easily believe that they devised co-operative techniques to win a coveted prize, such as a fleet-footed antelope which could not be captured in an open chase. Thus we can picture a hunting party of australopithecines advancing across the plain in open order, driving antelope and gazelle into some rocky cul-de-sac where they could be readily dispatched with throwing stones. Or we can imagine them cornering a baboon that had strayed away from its fellows, or perhaps even taking on a whole troop in open combat. The possibility that they used pit-traps or similar devices is rather less likely, as their brain-body ratio would scarcely suggest sufficient intelligence, but it cannot be entirely ruled out. When once the game was caught, implements would probably have been used to break up the bones and extract the marrow. The later australopithecines may even have known how to make fire and have grilled their baboon or antelope steaks on the embers.

One last, but exceptionally important, question remains. What position do the australopithecines occupy in the family tree of our own species? Are they directly ancestral to modern man, or are they an aberrant side branch lying somewhere between the main human stem and the line leading to the modern great apes? This is a much-disputed subject among physical anthropologists (who can be as jealous of their own pet theories as schoolgirls are of their dolls) and has led to several broken friendships. But the truth of the matter still is that we do not know. On balance the evidence seems to suggest that the australopithecines, although perhaps not directly ancestral to ourselves, were so close to the human line of descent that they certainly represent an evolutionary phase through which our species must have passed. A more precise statement must await the discovery of further fossils of intermediate forms. Meanwhile we must turn our attention to another group of hominids whose close connection with our own ancestry is much less in doubt – the pithecanthropoids of south-eastern Asia.

Chapter Eight

THE PITHECANTHROPOIDS

THE EARLIEST remains of hominids that are almost certainly in the direct line of descent of *Homo sapiens* were found in Java. The story begins in the eighties of the last century, when a young Dutch geologist and anatomist named Eugen Dubois was working as a lecturer in the University of Amsterdam. Like most people who have achieved any distinction in science (or in any other department of life for that matter) Dubois was an individualist with scant respect for the cautious and conventional attitudes of his seniors. More by insight than reason he had a passionate belief that the ancestor of modern man – the 'missing link', as it was then called – was an inhabitant either of Africa or the Indo-Malayan region of Asia. On the whole he felt that the latter was the more likely area and, with a praiseworthy determination to test his theories by experiment, he decided to make first-hand investigations on the spot.

At that time, however, this was more easily said than done. Dubois had no private means, and he therefore first tried to persuade the Dutch government to finance an expedition and place him at its head. But governments are hard nuts to crack, especially if asked to provide public money for the apparently hare-brained schemes of an eccentric young scientist, and the answer was a definite and uncompromising 'no'. Far from being disheartened by this reaction, Dubois tried new tactics. He resigned from the university and got himself a job in the Dutch colonial service as an army surgeon in the Netherlands East Indies. Within a short time he found himself in Java, where he at once set to work on his self-appointed task.

The East Indies are such an important region in the history of mankind that a few words must be said about their geological past. In Tertiary times Borneo and Sumatra were joined to the mainland of Asia, but it seems that Java was almost entirely submerged, with only a few volcanic peaks showing as scattered islands above the surface of the sea. In the first half of the Pleistocene, however, it emerged as a continuous stretch of land and for some time also became joined to Asia before later transgressions of the sea caused the region to assume its present pattern. In the modern island of Java there are two main series of Pleistocene strata, named respectively the 'Solo' and the 'Karst'. The latter have produced no human fossils, and of the former, which consists of three layers, only one need concern us here. This is the so-called 'Trinil' stratum, formed by river and volcanic action, on which Eugen Dubois first went to work.

The name Trinil is taken from a village near the town of Ngawi on the banks of the river Solo. The village lies near the foot of the great Lawu-Kukusan volcano, whose cone soars from a substratum of Tertiary marine deposits to a height of nearly 11,000 feet. Over the substratum are layers of sand, cinders and bolts of volcanic lava which have been rearranged by the fierce torrents rushing down the sides of the volcano. Mixed with these are river deposits consisting mainly of clay and compacted masses of the porous concretions known as 'tufa', which are often found in the vicinity of springs. Some of these mixed strata achieve in places the remarkable thickness of 1,500 feet.

In the autumn of 1891 Dubois' inspired guess that the remains of early man were to be found in the region was proved correct. He unearthed first a tooth, then more teeth, and finally a skull-cap, all apparently belonging to a creature intermediate in anatomical type between the living great apes and modern man. The following year a fossil femur was discovered within fifty feet of the original finds. Other bones found in the same stratum included those of hippopotamus, rhinoceros, deer, elephant and some tailed cercopithecoid monkeys.

Dubois was at first inclined to regard his skull-cap and teeth as belonging to a chimpanzee, in spite of the fact that

there is no known evidence that this ape or any of its ancestors ever lived in Asia. But on reflection, and after corresponding with the great Ernst Haeckel, Professor of Zoology
at the University of Jena, he declared them to belong to a
creature which seemed admirably suited for the role of the
'missing link'. This creature he called by the somewhat
tongue-twisting name of *Pithecanthropus erectus*, 'the erect
ape-man'.

After these early finds no other proto-human remains
turned up in the region for over forty years. But, then, beginning in the late thirties, a whole series of new fossils
was found by Dr G. H. R. von Koenigswald, including parts
of three more skulls and several jaws, some with a large number of the teeth in place. The discovery of the first of the new
skulls, which became known as *Pithecanthropus II*, exemplifies one of the more unexpected and entertaining hazards of
this kind of work. Von Koenigswald had offered a reward for
any fossil fragment of a human skeleton to be found by the
local natives and, naturally, when a piece of skull quickly
came in, he was delighted by the shrewdness of his plan, and
the finder was duly paid and congratulated. But then in the
next few days another fragment came in, and then another,
and yet another, each rather significantly fitting like a piece
of a jig-saw puzzle into the outline of its predecessor. What
had happened, of course, was that the natives had found the
skull intact and then broken it up to multiply the reward.
A change of policy swiftly followed and von Koenigswald
spent the next few days laboriously restoring his prize to its
original condition.

Before considering these Java fossils in greater detail we
must describe a parallel operation which was going forward
in China, near the town of Choukoutien, some forty miles
from Pekin. In the mid-twenties of this century there was
great enthusiasm in some scientific circles for the idea that
central Asia was the cradle of mankind. Expeditions were
sent out to the Gobi Desert and elsewhere, but although they
returned with a rich crop of eggs of the dinosaur *Protocera-
tops*, remains of the explorers' own ancestors proved to be
elusive. However, this ferment of interest did stimulate research in Asia, and played a part in encouraging Professor

Davidson Black of Pekin Union Medical College to intensify palaeontological investigations in the region of the capital. As a result of his labours a molar tooth was discovered at Choukoutien on which he based the identification of a new genus of hominid. He named it *Sinanthropus pekinensis,* or 'China-man of Pekin'.

Choukoutien lies on the west of the Chili plain, and the predominant geological formations consist of Ordovician limestone. During the Pleistocene, caves and fissures were formed by natural processes in these rocks and became filled with red clay, bones and fallen pieces of the cave roofs and fissure walls. These fillings became solidified and hardened by calcareous infiltrations so that they formed solid knots of rock in the softer limestone. Then, in recent times, large-scale quarrying began in the region. The cave and fissure fillings were gradually exposed, and were recognised by Black as being exceptionally worthy of investigation for Pleistocene fossils.

Between 1929 and the early thirties Black made an intensive study of the whole region. At his death in 1934 the work was carried on by his successor, Dr Franz Weidenreich, and by 1938 the fossil bones of nearly forty individual specimens of *Sinanthropus* had been brought to light. These were mainly represented by teeth, jaw fragments, and incomplete skulls, but of the latter six were sufficiently well preserved to show the capacity and some of the configuration of the braincase. Apart from the *Sinanthropus* remains the matrix also contained the bones of a large beaver, an early type of water buffalo, a deer with short, flattened antlers and a thick jaw, bears, rhinoceroses, hyenas, rodents and other mammals.

In recent years a comparison of the Choukoutien fossils with those of Java man have shown that in spite of the taxonomic distinction originally made by Black they almost certainly belong to the same genus of hominid. The two creatures are now almost invariably referred to by the generic name of *Pithecanthropus,* the Java ape-man retaining his specific name of *Pithecanthropus erectus,* his Chinese cousin being called *Pithecanthropus pekinensis.* Some authorities go even further than this and believe that the ape-men of both regions are entitled to inclusion in the genus *Homo.* In fact the time may be approaching when anatomists may regard both the australopithecines and the pithecanthropoids as deserving of this high status. (Plates 24 and 25.)

So much, then, for the discovery of this exceptionally important member of the human family. Let us now consider in more detail what the two eastern pithecanthropoids were like. In discussing them I shall not try the lay reader's patience by venturing into the deeper waters of anatomical argument concerning the significance of individual bones. All I shall attempt is a general picture of the whole group.

Pithecanthropus was rather short by modern standards, a typical full-grown male being little over five feet tall. The

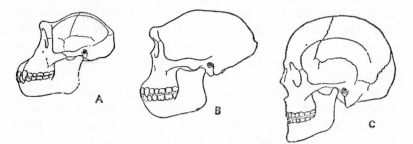

FIG. 10.   Side view of the skulls of (A) a chimpanzee, (B) *Pithecanthropus*, and (C) *Homo sapiens. From Clark (1960), Fig. 25, p. 78*

Java femur shows that he stood completely erect, and did not shamble along with arms hanging down in front of him like the conventional 'ape-man' of the strip cartoons. His erect carriage is likewise proved by the position of the *foramen magnum,* which is even more directly under the skull than in the australopithecines, and corresponds closely with that of *Homo sapiens.* The aspect of the pithecanthropoids was nevertheless very brutish compared with our own. Their skulls were exceptionally thick and heavy, and the prominent frontal ridges above the eyes met over the roof of the nose in a continuous projecting simian bar, or 'torus'. Both forehead and chin were receding, and the jaws, although containing a dental arcade of human rather than ape-like shape, correspondingly prognathous, or 'snouty'. The back of the skull was rather sharply pointed instead of having the even

86

curve found in modern man, and there was a large area for the attachment of exceptionally powerful neck muscles. The cranium was flattened from above so that, when viewed from behind, its width was greater than its height, with its greatest width at the base. This is in direct contrast to modern man, whose skull when similarly viewed is greater in height than in width, and has its widest dimension in the so-called 'parietal' region some way above the ears.

The brain itself varied greatly in size with different individuals. *Pithecanthropus pekinensis* seems to have had a considerably larger average brain size than his Javan cousin, which is only partly accounted for by the fact that his average bodily measurements were also somewhat greater. Five of the Chinese skulls were found to range in capacity from 850 c.c. to 1,300 c.c. with an average of 1,075 c.c., while the corresponding figures for three of the Javan skulls were 755 c.c. to 900 c.c. with an average of 860 c.c. Thus even after the brain-body ratio has been taken into account it seems that China man had by far the higher mental endowment, at least on the basis of the known specimens. It should be remembered, however, that the Java remains are comparatively few, and that any deduction based on the evidence of only three fossils may later prove to be extremely misleading.

Apart from the actual size of the brain-case an attempt has been made to investigate the character of the pithecanthropoid brain by a study of what are called endocranial casts. These are plaster casts taken of the interior of the skull which give some indication of the relative size of the various brain areas. It is sometimes also said that the casts provide evidence of this or that mental quality, but all such conclusions should be regarded with deep suspicion. So long as the casts are used for their legitimate purpose of indicating proportions, however, they are often of great interest and value. For instance, the illustration on page 88 shows quite dramatically the intermediate position occupied by the pithecanthropoid brain between that of a chimpanzee and modern man.

The anatomical primitiveness of the pithecanthropoid head as compared with the advanced development of the lower limbs, apparently so well adapted to an upright stance, illustrates an interesting principle of what is sometimes called

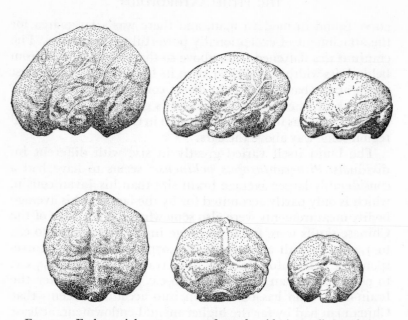

FIG. 11. Endocranial casts, as seen from the side (*upper line*) and the top (*lower line*), of *Homo sapiens* (*left*). *Pithecanthropus* (*centre*) and a chimpanzee. *After Clark (1960), Fig. 27, p. 80*

'mosaic' evolution. Our habits of thought might suggest that organisms normally evolve consistently in all their parts, so that change in one part is always correlated with change in another, the whole process being dictated by progressive adaptation to the environment conducted on a common front. The concept of mosaic evolution modifies this idea by showing that one particular feature of an organism may evolve at a faster rate than another or even that one may evolve while another temporarily stands still. This pattern, of course, depends on the genetic structure of the individual, and particularly on the occurrence of relevant mutations on which natural selection can act. If we consider the hominids and their ancestors in this light we can see that there is no reason why, say, brain development, speech, and upright posture should necessarily have evolved completely in step. All were, of course, interrelated, and the advance of one as the result of natural selection acting on a favourable mutation would

often have so altered the evolutionary tension that corresponding changes would have occurred in the others. But such
changes did not necessarily occur at exactly the same time,
and it is therefore by no means unexpected that one particular facet of an organism should at certain moments in
its biological history be temporarily out of phase with the
rest. This seems to have been the case with the skull/posture
relationship in the pithecanthropoids (and also, incidentally,
in the australopithecines).

The age of *Pithecanthropus* is now more or less universally
accepted as late Lower and Middle Pleistocene; that is to say,
between half a million and 200,000 years ago. This period is,
of course, a very long one, but it is extremely difficult to be
more precise. The geological evidence is interpreted in
different ways by different specialists, and even the most
modern techniques do not yet allow us to be dogmatic about
the absolute age of the Java and Choukoutien deposits in
terms of years. Relative dating is somewhat easier, however,
and we can say with reasonable certainty that the pithecanthropoids began to flourish at about the same time that the
australopithecines of Africa were beginning to decline. There
was thus probably a period when the two creatures existed
at the same time in their respective habitats, and this makes
it unlikely that the pithecanthropoids were direct descendants of the known australopithecines.

At the other end of the scale the division between *Pithecanthropus* and his possible neighbours in the line of hominid
descent is less distinct. It is quite possible that the later
pithecanthropoids may have had an ancestral relationship to
at least some of the divergent types of Neanderthal men to
be described in the next chapter, and also to modern man.
We can, in fact, argue that *Pithecanthropus* was the ancestor
of all the members of the genus *Homo* which later appeared
on the world's stage, although there is no certain evidence
for this and it would be quite wrong to dogmatise. To sum
up, we can best say that *Pithecanthropus* was a member of
the human family who represented a phase of evolution between the australopithecines on the one hand and Neanderthal man and modern man on the other, even though his
direct descent from the former is doubtful and his ancestral

connection with the latter cannot yet be proved. If we wish to give some approximate working date for the period of pithecanthropoid ascendancy we shall not be far wrong if we put it at 400,000 years ago plus or minus some hundred thousand years.

Outside Asia pithecanthropoid fossils have been found in both Africa and Europe, although the evidence in the different localities is not of equal value. One of the main finds occurred at Ternifine, near Mascara in Algeria, in 1954. In the summer of that year two French scientists, C. Arambourg and R. Hofstetter, discovered a complete mandible of primitive human type, with molars, premolars and two incisors in position, and also a half-mandible with the complement of teeth complete. Later finds included an exceptionally well-preserved mandible, a skull fragment from a fairly young subject, and numerous isolated teeth. The fossils were ascribed by their discoverers to a new genus of hominids to which they gave the name *Atlanthropus* ('Atlas man'), but they are so similar to the remains of the ape-man of Choukoutien that there is little doubt that they belong to a pithecanthropoid. The alternative name of *Pithecanthropus mauritanicus* has been proposed for this hominid, reflecting the view that it is a closer relation of the Asiatic ape-man than was originally supposed. Other African finds include some jaw fragments from a quarry near Casablanca in Morocco and a child's tooth from Olduvai Gorge in Tanganyika, but these fossils cannot be assigned to *Pithecanthropus* with the same certainty as the Ternifine jaws.

The only European pithecanthropoid fossil was found much earlier. It was unearthed in a sand pit at Mauer near Heidelberg in Germany in 1907 and first described by Dr Otto Schoetensack, who was then a lecturer in geology at Heidelberg University. For many years it was assigned to a distinct genus of primitive men, to which the name of *Homo heidelbergensis* was given; later it was believed to belong to a species of neanderthaloid type. But since the finds at Choukoutien more and more physical anthropologists have come to regard it as evidence of a European pithecanthropoid. We need not go into the arguments for this opinion here, but if they prove to be correct, *Pithecanthropus heidelbergensis* (as the fossil is already called by several authorities) would rank as the oldest fossil of this type of hominid which has yet come to light. The age of the bones is at least 400,000 years.

Enough has now been said about the various pithecanthropoid fossils to give some idea of the range, age and appearance of this primitive genus of men. We must next try to place them in their natural setting and see if we can discover anything about their way of life. Here we shall be particularly concerned to discover whether their cultural activities suggest advanced powers of conceptual thought.

To begin with Java man, there is unfortunately no evidence whatever of his cultural achievements, for not a single implement or hearth has been discovered in association with the Trinil fossils. This does not mean, of course, that Java man had no cultural tradition, for he almost certainly did, but simply that its nature is still unknown. With the Choukoutien fossils, however, the picture is very different. It is quite clear that Pekin man, as he is popularly called, not only made fire but also possessed a tool-making tradition far in advance of the pebble-tool culture of the australopithecines.

The layers in which the fossils of Pekin man were found include also large numbers of stone artifacts which most authorities regard as belonging to a basic flake-tool culture. Many of the implements have been intentionally fashioned, while others are natural flakes with signs of secondary trimming. It is obvious that Pekin man used to collect fragments of boulders and weathered pieces of rock from different localities and bring them back to his cave home to make into tools. He worked the fragments by resting them on a rocky anvil and then striking them with another stone. The main material used was quartz, but some crudely flaked pebbles of greenstone, quartzite and cherty rocks were also found in the deposits. Points, scrapers and choppers are all recognisable, and it is probable that some of the stones were also used as weapons, although none specifically fashioned for this purpose has been found.

Pekin man must have been a successful hunter, because large quantities of animal bones, especially those of deer, were found with his remains. Many of these had been split open to extract the marrow, and some of the fragments had

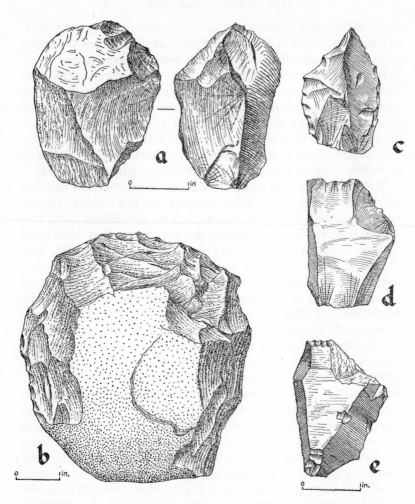

FIG. 12. Implements manufactured by Pekin man. *a*. A quartz chopper; *b*. A greenstone chopper; *c*. A pointed quartz flake; *d*. A bipolar quartz flake; *e*. A quartz crystal used as a tool. *From Oakley (1961) Fig. 31, p. 71*

been fashioned into primitive bone tools. Ashes found in the deposits are also clear evidence of hearths, and the charring of some of the bones suggests that Pekin man not only made fire for warmth and as a protection from wild animals but used it to cook his meals. There is some evidence also that he was a cannibal, for split and charred human bones are found among those of his animal prey. He was certainly quite as violent to his own kind as modern man is to his, for several of the Choukoutien skulls show that their owners had been killed by a hefty whack on the head. Moreover the skulls seem to have been broken open, presumably to allow the extraction of the contents. It may well be that the fried brains of Pekin man's weaker neighbours, garnished with nuts and berries from his food-gathering expeditions, formed the main course at many a primitive feast on the Chili plain.

Although definite proof is impossible, we can assume beyond any reasonable doubt that all the pithecanthropoids had speech. The degree of conceptual thought necessary for the manufacture of tools would certainly have been sufficient to create the sound symbolism of language. They also almost certainly had a well-developed social life in tribes or large family groups. This is not only suggested by their successful hunting activities, which must have required a considerable degree of co-operative effort, but by two very important developments which have not, in my view, been sufficiently stressed. The first of these is the evidence of the earliest reverence for the dead in human history. The fossils of seven of the Choukoutien individuals lay together under earth upon which red ochre or haematite had been scattered. It is difficult to escape the conclusion that this represented some kind of ritual burial. The second development is the evidence of the dawn of the decorative sense which is so characteristic of man. For the first time in the record of human evolution ornaments such as beads and perforated teeth and shells are found in association with the fossils. Both these developments are evidence of higher social activities than the basic co-operative interactions of a hunting group. We are at the dawn of the process which has led to the mind and society of twentieth-century man.

Outside China the evidence for pithecanthropoid culture is less conclusive. Broken bones similar to those found at Choukoutien, and also slabs of sandstone with flaked edges, were removed from the same deposits as the Heidelberg jaw, but it is very questionable whether these are deliberately fashioned artifacts. At Olduvai clots of red ochre which may

have been used for burials or physical adornment were found
in association with the child's tooth mentioned earlier in this
chapter, but as the tooth itself is only doubtfully pithecanthropoid it would be rash to draw any conclusions from this
fact. Only at Ternifine is there any definite evidence of association between bones and artifacts. It seems that *Atlanthropus* (or *Pithecanthropus mauritanicus* as we may prefer
to call him) fashioned hand-axes, choppers and flake-tools
from quartzite and sandstone. Even flint tools have been
found in the beds, but these are much more rare. The level
of workmanship, although still very primitive, is higher than
at Choukoutien, and these implements are assigned to the
so-called Abbevillian (or Chellean) culture which is characteristic of the early Middle Pleistocene.

To sum up, *Pithecanthropus* is of exceptional importance
as representing the second main phase through which human
evolution probably passed (the australopithecines being, of
course, the representatives of the first). The fossil and archaeological evidence shows that between quarter and half a
million years ago an erect-walking proto-human creature
existed on the earth with a tool-making tradition, almost certainly the power of speech, and a social organisation based on
food-gathering and co-operative hunting. We must now turn
to the third phase, as represented by the famous neanderthaloids, or Neanderthalers, who are the immediate fore-
runners of men of our own species.

Chapter Nine

THE NEANDERTHALERS

WE HAVE SEEN that although the australopithecines and the pithecanthropoids represent successive phases in the development of the hominids, the former were unlikely to have been the physical ancestors of the latter. With the Neanderthalers and *Homo sapiens,* however, who represent the two post-pithecanthropoid phases of human evolution, the position is somewhat different. It has been suggested (although there are alternative explanations to be dealt with later) that the Neanderthalers and modern man represent two divergent lines of descent from pithecanthropoid ancestors, the former having the earlier cultural flowering and then being superseded by the latter some 40,000 years ago. The present chapter will be devoted to the neanderthaloid phase, while an account of the development of our own species will be reserved for the third and fourth parts of this book.

Neanderthal man differs from both the australopithecines and the pithecanthropoids in being quite clearly a member of our own genus. Although living later than the African and Asiatic ape-men, his fossil remains were the earliest to be discovered, and the story of the various finds will make a convenient starting point for our description.

The name Neanderthal comes in the first place from a young seventeeth-century German theologian named Joachim Neander. He had nothing whatever to do with human palaeontology, being on the contrary a writer of hymns. His independent spirit was nevertheless apparent in his decision to abstain from Holy Communion, for which he was sacked from the rectorship of the Latin school at Düsseldorf. But his hymns were good ones as hymns go, and the pious citizens of Düsseldorf, showing more kindliness than the ecclesiastical authorities, commemorated him by naming a valley near their city the Neanderthal. In 1856 this valley was the scene of the discovery of the first bones of Neanderthal man to be recognised for what they were – the remains of a hominid closely related to our own species. The find was made by some workmen who were clearing out a limestone cave in a cliff face overlooking the Düssel river. It seems that a complete fossilised skeleton was dug up, but the workmen did not at first realise the value of their discovery and most of the bones were thrown away. However, a skull-cap, some limb bones, a few ribs, and part of the pelvis survived, and came into the hands of a Dr Fuhlrott of Elberfeld; he in turn passed them on to Professor D. Schaaffhausen of Bonn, who gave the first scientific description of them.

The discovery of the fossils antedated the publication of Darwin's *Origin of Species* by three years and at first attracted little attention. But the idea of evolution was in the air, and in 1863, at the instigation of the British geologist Sir Charles Lyell, the bones and the original description were studied by Thomas Henry Huxley. He reached the conclusion that they belonged to a primitive type of man, different but not wholly distinct anatomically from *Homo sapiens*. The following year (1864) Professor William King of Queen's College, Galway, recognised that the remains were definitely those of a new species of *Homo* and gave this the name by which it is still scientifically known, *Homo neanderthalensis*. (Plates 26 and 27.)

Since the time of Schaaffhausen, Huxley and King, numerous other finds of Neanderthal man have been described, and fossils discovered much earlier, but previously unrecognised for what they were, have been assigned to the same species. The fossil remains of over sixty individuals discovered between 1700 and the present day are now known. Of course, some of the fossils are much more fragmentary than others, and several individuals are represented by only one or two bones. But all can be regarded with a high degree of certainty as belonging to the Neanderthal species.

The range of this early cousin of ours seems to have been immense. Neanderthaloids apparently lived not only in western Europe, where the fossils are most common, but in the Middle East, north and south Africa, and central and south-eastern Asia. Some of their remains are so similar to those of *Homo sapiens* as to suggest that the two species were very closely related indeed; others seem to belong to a more brutish creature which in life may have closely resembled the shambling ape-man of popular imagination; others again seem to represent transitional phases between pithecanthropoids and Neanderthalers. To sort out the shades of difference between the various fossils would only be of interest to specialists, so I shall here limit my account to the two main types; the conservative or so-called 'classic' type, and the more progressive type with an anatomy approaching that of *Homo sapiens*.

The conservative Neanderthalers are represented by numerous fossils, of which some well-preserved remains discovered in a small cave at La Chapelle-aux-Saints in western France may be taken as typical. The find was made on August 3rd, 1908, by three French priests, the Abbés A. Bouyssonie, J. Bouyssonie and Bardon, and consisted of an almost complete skull, twenty-one vertebrae and fragments of vertebrae, an equal number of ribs or rib fragments, a collar-bone, and between twenty and thirty bones of the upper and lower limbs. The bones were submitted to the eminent French anthropologist Marcellin Boule in Paris who gave the first description of them. His paper *L'homme fossile de la Chapelle-aux-Saints* appeared in December of the same year and, although deformation of the skull led Boule into certain errors of interpretation, his description remains a classic of its kind.

The bones are those of an old man, and show signs that their owner was in an advanced stage of arthritis and senility. The skull is different from that of a modern man in many ways. It is exceptionally thick and large, with a low and retreating forehead, a much flattened brain-case, and heavy brow-ridges. However, the *foramen magnum,* which was formerly thought to be more to the rear than in *Homo sapiens,* is now recognised as being in approximately the same position. The limb bones are somewhat differently shaped and much shorter than our own, but the suggestion, still sometimes made, that the classic Neanderthalers walked with their knees bent is not really acceptable. In fact the evidence of both the *foramen magnum* and the lower limbs shows that they were most unlikely to have adopted the shambling ape-like gait shown in earlier reconstructions. Brutish in aspect they doubtless were, particularly in their prognathous faces, receding chins and coarse features, but in posture they probably differed little from ourselves. They were, however, much shorter, and very few specimens seem to have exceeded $5\frac{1}{2}$ feet in height. This reduction in height was mainly due to the shorter limbs, although the relative proportions of the different limb bones in the known fossils are identical with those of modern men. The trunk was about the same length as that of *Homo sapiens,* but much more thickset, and the neck muscles had to be particularly powerful to support and move the large, heavy head. In short, we can picture the classic Neanderthaler as a stocky, erect-walking creature, broad-shouldered and barrel-chested, with short, thickset legs, powerful arms, and a head with receding brow and chin which by our standards would appear considerably too large for the body.

In contrast to the rather unalluring physique of the old man of La Chapelle-aux-Saints and other classic types of Neanderthaler, the progressive members of the species are physically much more like ourselves. Their appearance can best be appreciated by considering the Ehringsdorf and Steinheim skulls from Germany, and the Mount Carmel and other skeletons from Israel.

The Ehringsdorf skull was found in a quarry near Weimar in 1925. It was not complete, but consisted of a brain-case broken into several fragments. Its owner, who was a young person of uncertain sex aged between 18 and 20, seems to have met a violent death. There is evidence of some five blows from a blunt instrument on the forehead and also several wounds inflicted with a sharper weapon such as a flint. Possibly, as in the *Pithecanthropus* remains at Choukoutien, someone had been feasting on brains.

Although it was rather difficult to reconstruct the skull, the fragments, when pieced together, showed that it was certainly of neanderthaloid type. There was, however, a notable difference. Instead of the 'squashed down' cranium of the conservative Neanderthaler the vault was high and gable-shaped.

Moreover, in spite of the presence of heavy brow-ridges, the forehead did not slope backwards at an acute angle but was inclined much more closely to the vertical. The unfortunate Ehringsdorf teenager can thus claim to be one of the first highbrows in human history.

The Steinheim skull shows similar evidence of refined neanderthaloid qualities. It was found in 1933 in the famous Steinheim gravel pits, which have also produced numerous remains of fossil mammals, including such warm-weather fauna as the ancient elephant and Merck's rhinoceros, as well as the woolly mammoth and other creatures of the snows. Part of the skull was missing, including the lower jaw, much of the left side of the face, and the area surrounding the *foramen magnum*; but the right side of the face and the whole of the cranium were beautifully preserved. The neanderthaloid features of the skull, which seems to have belonged to a young woman, were the massive brow-ridges and the heavily built upper jaw. On the other hand there were many features reminiscent of *Homo sapiens*. For instance, there was far less prognathism, or 'snoutiness', than in the conservative Neanderthalers, a brain-case more closely compressed from side to side, and 'wisdom teeth' reduced in size to almost human proportions. Although these differences are not comparable with those of the Ehringsdorf juvenile, we have here clear evidence of two Pleistocene Germans quite distinct in type both from their elderly French cousin of La Chapelle-aux-Saints and their compatriot from the Neanderthal valley.

The most graphic of all the evidence suggesting that there were two main Neanderthal types comes from Israel, where a whole series of neanderthaloid remains has been found. The earliest discoveries were made in some caves in Mount Carmel in the early thirties by a joint Anglo-American expedition directed by Miss Dorothy Garrod. Shortly afterwards a number of equally important fossils were discovered by a French expedition in caves in the Jebel Kafzeh near Nazareth. Altogether the remains of some twenty individuals were found, including several complete skeletons.

The remains showed a very wide range of differences. Some of the individuals had all the characteristics of the classic Neanderthalers of western Europe, others of modern man of the Cro-Magnon type to be discussed in the next chapter. Some of the most interesting material showed a mixture of characters in one individual, some conservative, some progressive. As an example we may take the skeleton of a woman found lying on her side, with legs slightly flexed, in the Tabūn cave at Mount Carmel. On the one hand she had the heavy brow-ridges, low forehead, snouted and chinless face, and powerful chest of the old man of La Chapelle-aux-Saints; on the other she had a more highly vaulted cranium and a more uniformly rounded occipital bone approaching the kind usually associated with *Homo sapiens*. The skeletons found in the neighbouring cave of Skhul likewise showed a mixture of characters, but tended much more towards the progressive type. The best-preserved specimen had much-reduced brow-ridges, a comparatively vertical forehead, a narrow chest, a well-marked chin, and an occipital bone as completely rounded as that of modern man. Moreover, this skeleton belonged to an individual some 5 ft. 10 in. tall, with far longer and slenderer limb bones than those possessed by the stocky conservatives.

We shall come to the possible significance of these finds in determining human lineage a little later on, but first we must consider two matters of great importance: the nature of the Neanderthal brain and the dating of the various fossils. We might think that creatures of such comparatively brutish type as the classic Neanderthalers would have had brains much smaller than our own, but this is not the case. In fact the average size of the Neanderthal brain was 1,450 c.c. whereas the average size of the modern human brain is only about 1,350 c.c. This does not mean, however, that the Neanderthalers were more intelligent than we are. Even though they were roughly comparable in bulk (although differently proportioned) to ourselves, so that the brain-body ratio does not affect the issue, brain size alone is still a very crude indication of brain quality. In two brains of comparable size the cortical region of one may still be largely concerned with the motor and sensory functions, while that of another may be specialised in the more advanced activities of memory, foresight and language. Natural selection works on the brain as it does on other structures and organs, and intelligence will depend particularly on which cortical areas it has caused to become enlarged. To clarify the point, let us consider two modern men with brains of equal cubic capacity. The first, although well developed in body, strong and physically efficient, may be intellectually quite dull; the second, who may have only a bare physical competence, may be much better equipped by his mental qualities to survive in the sophisticated human society of today. The reason why heavyweight champions are seldom the intellectual leaders of the modern world is also the reason why *Homo neanderthalensis* went down before the competition of *Homo sapiens*.

Turning now to the age of the Neanderthalers, the geological evidence suggests that they lived between some 160,000 and 40,000 years ago. Some of the fossils are found in association with the bones of a warm-weather fauna including the ancient elephant and Merck's rhinoceros, and it seems probable that these belong to the second part of the Third, or last, Interglacial Phase. But others are associated with such creatures as the woolly mammoth, woolly rhinoceros, reindeer, and cave hyena, and these can safely be dated to the last, or Würm, glaciation. Chronology is a difficult subject on which there are almost as many opinions as there are experts, but to sum up we can certainly say that the Neanderthalers were the dominant species of man on earth from the end of the Middle Pleistocene until they were superseded by our own species some 40,000 years ago.

The exact place of Neanderthal man in the lineage of mankind is still uncertain. It was stated earlier that he may have represented a line of evolution from pithecanthropoid ancestors parallel to that of our own species, but we can now see that there are a number of complicating factors. One of these, of course, is the existence of such a wide range of Neanderthal types; another is the evidence for mixed or transitional forms found in the Mount Carmel caves. Contrary to what one might expect, the progressive Neanderthal fossils can generally be dated to an earlier period than those of the classic or conservative type. This shows that they cannot be lineally transitional between the classic Neanderthalers and modern man, but probably represent a parallel line of neanderthaloid evolution with less extreme specialisations than the classic type. Another possibility is that the progressives are hybrids between the classic Neanderthalers and some variety of *Homo sapiens*. These and other matters connected with man's family tree will be developed in the next chapter.

Like the pithecanthropoids before them, the Neanderthalers knew the art of making fire and fashioning tools. Their characteristic industry is known as the Mousterian, the last of the seven main tool-making industries of the Lower and Middle Palaeolithic. The earlier industries are the Oldowan, the Choukoutienian, the Abbevillian (or Chellean), the Clactonian, the Acheulean, and the Levalloisian. Of these, as we have seen, the Oldowan comprises the pebble-tools of the australopithecines, and the Choukoutienian the quartzes of Pekin man. The remaining three will be omitted from our story, not because they are unimportant, for they provide fascinating evidence of man's increasing skill in tool-making during the pre-neanderthaloid period, but because they are of less importance to the main theme.

The Mousterian culture is named after the type site at Le Moustier, Dordogne. It evolved out of the Clactonian (itself possibly an offshoot of the Choukoutienian of Pekin), but was influenced by the Acheulean and Levalloisian traditions. The most characteristic Mousterian tools are of the so-called 'flake' type; that is to say, they are fashioned from fragments flaked off from larger pieces of stone, not from the residual core. Two main kinds of flakes are recognisable at Mousterian sites. The first are 'points', tools of roughly triangular shape with a heavy butt and two carefully trimmed convex edges meeting at a sharp, pointed tip. The second are 'side-scrapers', with a trimmed working edge, usually parallel with the long axis of the flake and opposite the butt. Tools fashioned from the core of the stone are also sometimes found.

By modern standards, and even by those of the Upper Palaeolithic, these tools are, of course, extremely primitive. They are, nevertheless, strictly comparable with some of the tools still used by the aborigines of Australia, where a typical Stone Age culture persists to this day. Although they do not represent a startling advance in inventiveness over earlier industries they are suited to a far wider range of uses than, say,

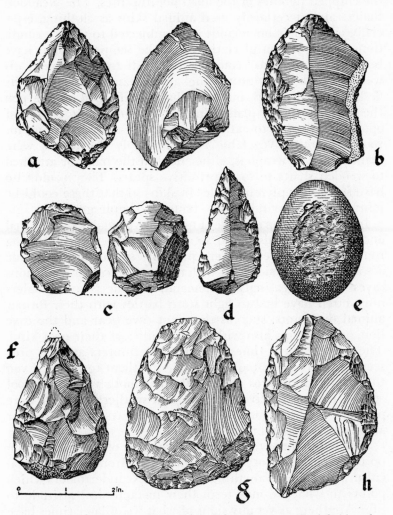

Fig. 13. Mousterian tools. *a* and *b*. Side-scrapers; *c*. Tool fashioned from the core of the stone; *d*. A point; *e*. A small anvil- or hammer-stone; *f*. A hand-axe from Le Moustier; *g*. A hand-axe of chert; *h*. A flint flake-tool from Kent's Cavern, Torquay, England. The figures *a* to *d* are the most typical examples of the Mousterian culture. *From Oakley (1961), Fig. 23, p. 55*

the chipped pebbles of the australopithecines. The Neanderthalers almost certainly used animal skins as clothing, especially when their homelands were subjected to the icy conditions of the Würm glaciation, and the scrapers would have
been well suited to removing the flesh from the pelts, as
well as actually skinning the animal and cutting up its
flesh for food. They may also have been used to sharpen
the wooden spikes placed in the bottom of pit traps, for
opening up bones to extract the marrow, and in digging for
roots and other vegetable food. Probably the points were
mainly used as weapons, either held in the hand or attached
to wooden shafts to form primitive spears. They could also
have served for piercing holes in skins so that these could be
joined to make wind-breaks, tents, or simple garments.

In the latter part of the Third Interglacial, Neanderthal
encampments consisting of a group of rough tents clustering
round a central hearth were probably spread far and wide
across the countryside. But with the onset of colder conditions
caves were increasingly in demand, and the Neanderthalers
must often have had to fight stern battles with their former
animal occupants, such as the giant cave bear and the cave
lion, and perhaps also with rival families of their own kind.
The men of these times were fearless hunters and no prey
seems to have been too formidable for them to tackle. Even
the woolly rhinoceros and woolly mammoth were not proof
against their primitive weapons, and smaller creatures were
probably run down with throwing stones, trapped in pits, or
ambushed by spearmen.

Finally we come to a question which is of the highest importance in the history of mankind. Apart from their material
culture, can we say anything about the Neanderthalers which
points to what we may term their metaphysical attitude to
life? Are there as yet any signs of what we of later times have
come to call spiritual consciousness, of the evolution of the
higher human attributes out of the purely practical pattern of
life in a primitive hunting community?

The evidence here is extremely fragmentary and inconclu-
sive. So far as we know, the Neanderthalers had no visual art,
nor is there even evidence that they had any patterned tools
or ritual objects. We can assume that they probably had

speech, but whether they had evolved the concept of song we can never know. In the harsh conditions of the time it seems unlikely, although the family groups round their camp fires may well have chanted and danced as a preliminary to the hunt, or as thanksgiving for the successful killing of a mammoth or some other highly prized quarry. The only real indication we have of the Neanderthalers' metaphysical beliefs is therefore based on evidence, admittedly of unequal value, that they practised hunting magic, animal worship, and ritual burials. This evidence must now be considered.

In a number of European caves of Mousterian times the skulls of cave bears are found arranged in a way that suggests they were placed there with ritual intent. For instance, in the Petershöhle, near Velden in the south German alps, there are huge accumulations of cave-bear bones, including a number of skulls set in niches in the cave walls. At one place in this cave, five bear skulls are neatly arranged in a niche nearly four feet above the cave floor, suggesting most strongly that they must have been placed there by man. Again, in a cave known as the Drachenloch in the eastern part of the Swiss alps, seven cave-bear skulls and a number of limb bones were found behind a low parapet of limestone slabs. The skulls were all orientated to face the cave exit, an arrangement that could hardly have occurred by chance. Another skull in the same cave had a femur thrust through the arch of the cheek-bone in such a way that it was only with difficulty removed. Similar discoveries have been made in France and elsewhere, notably at the Grotte des Furtins between Macon and Cluny in Saône-et-Loire, where seven cave-bear skulls were found arranged in a distinctive concentric pattern. There can be little doubt that at least some of these finds had a ritual significance.

We can interpret the finds in a number of ways, all speculative but at least reasonably based on comparisons with the animal magic of primitive hunting tribes of more recent times. Particularly significant in this respect are the customs of several primitive peoples in the outlying regions of northern Europe. The anthropologist Alfred I. Hallowell has in fact found evidence of a widespread bear cult among the hunting tribes of this area. The bear must not here be called by its real name, but is always referred to as 'grandfather', 'old father', 'fur father', or simply as 'he'. It is regarded as a mediator between man and the spirits of the mountain or forest, and is included as a kind of mythical 'first man' in the ceremonials of ancestor worship.

Several Siberian tribes also perform an elaborate ritual to honour the bear killed in the hunt. To propitiate its spirit the hunters first offer the carcase their profound apologies, and it is then carried into their camp in ceremonial procession, accompanied by dancing and swinging torches. When the bear has been skinned, one of the women wraps herself in its pelt and dances with its head carried above her own, exhorting the bear not to be angry or sad. The skin and head are then placed in the position of the honoured guest at the feast where the animal's flesh is eaten. It is offered the choicest dishes, and as a culminating point of the ritual the skull is given a ceremonial burial, or placed in some hallowed sanctuary.

Similar bear rituals occur among the Finns and other northern peoples. For instance, in the Finnish epic known as the *Kalevala* we can read how the bear is invited to surrender its valuable properties one by one, and how, when finally divested of these, its skull is placed in a tree where it can enjoy a splendid view of the surrounding landscape. The Lapps likewise treat the bear with great respect, burying its bones in a grave lined with birch twigs, with the vertebrae threaded on a rod and the genitalia and tail anatomically in place as in life. This ritual is intended to ensure that another bear will be sent to the hunters by the spirits of the forest, and equally successfully slain.

Of course, it would be rash to draw any definite conclusions about the hunting customs of the Neanderthalers from these modern instances, but when they are considered in conjunction with the cave-bear finds of the Mousterian period the likelihood surely is that some similar kind of magic rites must have been practised. Neanderthal man was a hunter and a savage, but like ourselves he was already quite capable of reflecting on his own nature and his situation in the world. He must certainly have been deeply conscious of his loneliness and apparent insignificance in a hostile or, at best, indifferent environment, where wit and cunning were his only weapons against the savage forces that sought to destroy him. To placate the wild beasts on which he preyed, and to help him overcome the panic that must often have assailed him when he contemplated his own precarious position, it is not surprising that he sought refuge in the supernatural. The cave-bear skulls, gazing sightlessly from their niches in the Palaeolithic caves, may well be the first material evidence we have of the dawn of the cosmic fear that lies at the heart of every religion.

A still more remarkable pointer to the Neanderthalers' metaphysical beliefs is that they apparently had a profound respect for the dead of their own kind. This is made clear by the evidence for ritual burials associated with a large number of Neanderthal sites. Although these were probably practised to some extent by the pithecanthropoids, it was not until Mousterian times that they became such a characteristic feature of human life.

The earliest examples of Neanderthal burials occur in the Crimea, at Mount Carmel, and in Uzbekistan, central Asia. All occur in caves, and date from the end of the Last Interglacial Phase. The Crimean cave contained the remains of a man and a child about one year old, the man being buried in a trench which seemed to have been shaped to fit the contours of the body. All the Mount Carmel skeletons showed signs of deliberate burial, being placed with the legs drawn tightly up beneath the buttocks. But the most conclusive evidence of deliberate burial at this time comes from the Teshik-Tash cave in Uzbekistan. A child's grave was discovered here just beneath a Mousterian layer, and around the skeleton was placed a circle of ibex horns in obvious ceremonial fashion. At a later stage the site had been ravaged by a wild animal – probably a cave hyena – which had considerably disarranged the skeleton but left the ring of ibex horns intact.

The Neanderthal burial sites of western Europe date from a somewhat later period than those just referred to. They belong to the first part of the Würm glaciation – that is to say, between 80,000 and 40,000 years ago – and are likewise always found in caves or under rock shelters. The first discovery was made in 1907 at Le Moustier, Dordogne, the type site of the Mousterian industry. Here the skeleton of a youth in his late teens was found lying on its right side with legs slightly bent, and the head pillowed on the right arm; this in turn lay across a pile of flint flakes. Later discoveries near La Ferrassie in the same region revealed what was virtually a family sepulchre containing a total of six skeletons. One of these, that of a man lying prone in a shallow depression, had the head and shoulders protected by stone slabs; the skeleton of a woman found nearby had the knees bent up close to the body in the characteristic attitude of Palaeolithic burials. Three other skeletons in the cave belonged to children, and there was also a formal arrangement of nine earth mounds running in three parallel rows of three mounds each from north to south. Under the most northerly mound of the central row were found the remains of a human foetus or very young infant, but nothing was found under any of the others. With the exception of the woman all the skeletons were facing the west, a fact which, as we shall suggest later, may have special significance.

The finds at La Ferrassie are perhaps the most spectacular evidence we have of the burial customs of Neanderthal man. There is, however, one further discovery of very special interest. In 1939 an Italian *restaurateur* named Guattari was quarrying to extend the terrace of his restaurant on Monte Circeo on the north side of the Gulf of Gaeta when his workmen came across a number of remains of fossil animals, and eventually discovered the entrance to a previously hidden limestone cave. By good fortune one of Signore Guattari's occasional customers was Professor A. C. Blanc of Rome University, who was told of the discoveries and kept informed of developments as the work proceeded. When the cave was fully opened it was found to contain the remains of a rich fauna of ox, a horse, deer and hyena, together with many coprolites, or fossilised droppings. But the most exciting find was a neanderthaloid skull, lying on its left side in a small pit surrounded by a ring of white stones. The jaw bone was absent, but beneath the cranium Blanc discovered two animal limb bones, one of a fallow deer, the other of an ox. The skull, of which the *foramen magnum* had been artificially enlarged, showed signs on the right temple of a blow of sufficient severity to cause death; the animal limb bones likewise seemed to have been intentionally fractured.

There are two main schools of thought about the significance of the Guattari skull. One maintains that the circle of stones was simply a hearth, and that the presence of the skull there is clear proof that the Neanderthalers, like their pithecanthropoid predecessors, sometimes ate their own kind. The other school believes that the ring of stones was a magic circle, that the cave was a sanctuary with the skull as its ceremonial centre-piece, and that the animal bones were the remains of ritual meals. The artificially enlarged *foramen magnum* can be used to support both views; either it had been cut away to enable the brain to be more easily extracted, or to receive one end of a pointed stake on which it was impaled as a ritual object.

Whatever the significance of the Guattari skull, the existence of magico-religious burial rituals among the Neanderthalers in other regions is too clear to be discounted. What may the meaning of such rituals have been? Again, as with hunting magic, the beliefs of people of recent times will help us in our attempt to understand the Neanderthal soul. Modern anthropological literature is full of instances of special veneration or fear of the dead among primitive peoples, while the records of ancient civilisations, such as that of ancient Egypt, show how deeply the dead were revered and how every effort was made to provide goods for their use in the after life. Even in the comparatively advanced civilisations of today the ritual of the funeral service, the burial of the dead and the erection of tombstones (or the ceremonial burning of the body and the scattering of its ashes) are evidence of a similar attitude.

There is no reason to doubt that the burials of the Neanderthalers were conducted in the same spirit. Even to modern man there is something awe-inspiring about the sight of a dead body. We are overcome by a strange mixture of feelings, dominated by pity, fear, or revulsion according to our natures, at the thought that the friend we were laughing and joking with only yesterday is now only a pallid mass of decaying matter. We long for his return and yet the more superstitious among us may fear this return almost more than we desire it. At night especially we find ourselves oppressed by a strange atmosphere of dread, and the thought of the ghostly presence of the departed person may cause us to see frightening visions or afflict us with strange dreams.

Primitive man must have felt such emotions with even greater intensity. No comforting edifice of religious belief had yet been erected by the human spirit to relieve its loneliness in the harsh environment of nature. The ghosts of enemies slain in battle might return to avenge themselves on their conquerors, just as the spirit of the dead cave bear, unless propitiated, would surely destroy the hunters who had robbed it of its life. To prevent such calamities, and to assuage the grief of those who had lost lovers, children or companions, it was inevitable that as soon as man achieved the powers of reflective thought he should have devised a primitive protective ritual to keep his fears at bay.

This ritual must have varied greatly in detail from region to region and age to age, but the general beliefs underlying it in the Neanderthalers' world can be reasonably assumed. The dead were buried, as at La Ferrassie, as a mark of reverence in which both genuine love, and also fear of the possible supernatural consequences of neglect, probably played a part. The fact that all the skeletons at La Ferrassie, except that of the woman, faced to the west suggests that the Neanderthalers may have conceived of a heaven, comparable to the ancient Egyptian 'land of the dead', which lay in the direction of the setting sun. The woman, we may assume, was either denied access to this heaven, or had one of her own in the opposite direction. The segregation of the sexes for certain purposes was commonly practised in early societies, and the concept may well have been thought to apply to the after life as well. The idea that the dead went to another world where their activities were carried on much as in life is also suggested by the association of what may be funerary equipment with some of the burials. But the evidence for this is somewhat dubious in Neanderthal times, and only becomes unequivocal when men of our own species appear on the scene.

Apart from the burials themselves it seems possible that the bones of ancestors, or of other specially powerful persons, who may either have died natural deaths or been sacrificed, were selected for ritual worship. The Guattari skull, with its circle of white stones, may be an example of this practice (that is, if we reject the more prosaic explanation that it was the remains of a cannibal feast). The idea underlying such worship may have been to secure the protection or advice of the departed person's spirit or, in the case of a sacrifice, to honour the god to whom the victim was offered.

Here, however, we are coming dangerously near to the borders of fantasy, and to conclude this chapter we must re-emphasise that no definite explanation of the magico-religious beliefs of the Neanderthalers can yet be given. Further archaeological evidence of their rituals and observances may yet, of course, come to light, although it is doubtful if this will differ greatly from the kind of evidence we already have. At present all we can say with certainty is that the Neanderthalers were by no means always brutal, soulless savages. The rigours of their life determined that they often had to be hard, tough and ruthless to survive at all; but alongside these qualities we see the dawn of that wonder at the world, and perhaps also even of that reverence for life, which was one day to produce the highest achievements of the human spirit.

Part 3

THE RISE OF HOMO SAPIENS

Chapter Ten

THE NEW SPECIES

SOME time between 40,000 and 35,000 years ago an entirely new type of hominid appears in the record of organic evolution. Although he shows some affinities with the advanced Neanderthalers described in the previous chapter he is recognisably a different kind of man. We are at last dealing with *Homo sapiens*, the species to which we all belong, and which has been responsible for all the material, mental and spiritual developments of the modern world. (Plates 42–44.)

Before we describe the early history of *Homo sapiens* we must first place the events of the human experiment in the perspective of time. Forty thousand years sounds on the face of it a respectable enough period for our existence, and even the seven or eight thousand years of civilisation are regarded by most people as taking us back to an extremely remote epoch. But, as anyone who has read this book so far will already appreciate, the period of our occupation of the earth has in fact been incredibly short. An illustration may help to bring this fact home to any reader who may still cherish illusions about his own significance in the cosmic scene.

Let us imagine that the 4,500 million years of earth history are represented by a distance of a hundred miles, and that we are walking from the time of the earth's origin towards the present. On the first half of our journey we should come across no life at all, and would have to continue for no less than eighty-eight miles before even such simple invertebrates as worms and jellyfish began to appear in any numbers. At ninety-three miles certain organisms would be leaving the water to invade the land, but our own parent group, the mammals, would not appear until we were already within two miles of our goal. The whole of man's physical evolution since the beginning of the Pleistocene epoch would occupy only the last twenty yards of our journey, and the age of written history, with all its panoply of civilisation, could be contained twice over in our very last stride.

The grandeur of our spatial and temporal perspective will seem depressing or exhilarating according to our individual temperaments. Whatever our reactions, however, we cannot but grow in wisdom by contemplating the history of our species. Only by learning the facts about our origins and understanding the way we have developed can we hope to speculate with any responsibility on the meaning of our individual lives and our relation to the universe around us. As a practical introduction to this immense task we must begin with our fossil remains.

The best-known find of true men of our own species occurred in the French village of Les Eyzies in the Dordogne in 1868. Here, in a rock shelter under an overhanging cliff, the French archaeologist Louis Lartet discovered the skull and some other bones of an old man, and parts of the skeletons of four other individuals. Associated with the bones were the hearths used by the shelter's occupants and a number of their flint implements. Earlier finds of true human skeletons had been made in other parts of Europe, but these had not been recognised for what they were. Lartet's discoveries at Les Eyzies less than a hundred years ago prompted man's first realisation of his own antiquity.

The rock shelter itself is called Cro-Magnon, and 'Cro-Magnon man' is the name still popularly given to this early physical type of *Homo sapiens*. The Cro-Magnon skeletons themselves probably date from some 30,000 years ago, but later discoveries at Combe-Capelle in Périgord and Lautsch in Czechoslovakia show that our ancestry goes back rather further than this. Men of our own kind have certainly occupied Europe for between 35,000 and 40,000 years.

Now what were the physical characteristics of this new type of man as contrasted with the Neanderthalers? They were in general rather taller, with long limbs, straight thigh bones, and a *foramen magnum* in the centre of the skull base, showing that they stood completely erect. The skull was lighter in structure than that of any previous hominid, and had the vertical sides and rounded back to the brain-case typical of modern man. The forehead was also high and domed, giving Cro-Magnon man an exceptionally 'intellectual' look, while the brow-ridges, found to some extent in all other species of men, were usually so reduced as to be almost indiscernible in most individuals. The capacity of the brain-case was exceptionally high. For example, the old man of Cro-Magnon had a brain volume of some 1,600 c.c., which is considerably greater than that of most modern adults. Although Neanderthal man often had a brain of comparable size, the shape of the Cro-Magnon head suggests that the brains of these men were developed in different areas. Probably the part controlling the motor activities was somewhat reduced and the cortex, which allows modern man to pursue his highest and most characteristic activities, was already developed almost or entirely to its present size. The chin had also become more prominent, and this, in conjunction with the increased doming of the forehead, caused the face to appear comparatively flat. The 'snoutiness' of more primitive types of men was absent, and only the outline of the nose had become more clearly defined by the recession of the parts around it.

This, then, is the basic Cro-Magnon type, but we must now briefly refer to another find of human bones which, over the past half-century and more, has been the cause of much learned argument among human palaeontologists. This find was made in 1900 near Menton on the French Riviera, just across the Italian frontier. At this time, under the patronage of the Prince of Monaco, French scientists were excavating a cave known as the Grotte des Enfants at Grimaldi. The name of the cave was derived from some earlier excavations in 1874 and 1875, when the remains of two children's skeletons were found there, but their skulls were so badly damaged that nothing could be said about their status. The new expedition had better luck, however, for the scientists found the well-preserved skeletons of an old woman and a youth of between fifteen and sixteen years of age. The old woman lay on her right side, her knees flexed up against her abdomen and her arms doubled under her chin. The boy lay beside her,

also on his right side, in a loosely flexed position with half-
bent arms and with his legs doubled up at right angles to the
axis of the vertebral column. His bones were stained with red
ochre, which suggests a ceremonial burial of the type often
practised by Old Stone Age man. Both skeletons were exceptionally short, the woman measuring 5 ft. $2\frac{3}{4}$ in. from head to
foot, the adolescent boy just over an inch less. (Plate 41.)

Now, the particularly interesting thing about these remains
is that although they definitely belong to members of our
own species they have been regarded by several eminent
authorities as being of Negroid type. The foreheads are upright and rather bulbous, the teeth are larger than the average, and the chins low and somewhat receding. At one time,
also, great store was set by the fact that the faces had the
somewhat 'squashed-in' appearance of Negroids, but this was
later discovered to be the result of breakage and faulty reconstruction by some nameless anthropologist. It has sometimes been suggested that the Grimaldi skeletons represent
early specimens of the black races of today. This is a tempting
theory, but it is so extremely unlikely that an isolated group
of Negroes existed in this region at the time that most authorities are now disposed to write off the skull traits as coinci-
dence. There is so much variation in the skulls of white races
that the Grimaldi fossils may quite easily represent atypical
examples of the Cro-Magnon stock which just happened to
show certain Negroid traits.

Another oddity, quite as intriguing as the Grimaldi
'Negroids', is the skeleton of a man of late Upper Palaeolithic
Age from the village of Chancelade near Périgeux in France.
This fossil was discovered in a rock shelter in 1888, and it
recalled to many anthropologists the physical traits of modern
Eskimoes. The skull is long and narrow, the face broad, and
the jaw particularly broad and strong. All these characters
are found in living Eskimoes, as are certain bony reinforce-
ments to the jaw, also found in the Chancelade skull, which
are assumed to be an adaptation to heavy chewing. It has
been customary for some time to think of this fossil as belonging to a distinct race of *Homo sapiens,* and this may well be
the case. On the other hand, as seems likely with the Grimaldi
skeletons, its peculiar physical attributes may simply be the

result of atypical variations of the Cro-Magnon stock in one individual.

Whatever the status of the men of Grimaldi and Chancelade, there is no doubt that the Cro-Magnons are the most important foundation stock of *Homo sapiens*. Between 40,000 and 35,000 years ago they were rising to complete ascendancy in Europe, and Neanderthal man dwindled in numbers and soon became extinct. The triumph of the new species is particularly significant in that, physically speaking, the Neanderthalers were by far the more powerful of the two. The Cro-Magnons succeeded mainly by the power of their brains. Their superior intelligence enabled them to devise more efficient methods of capturing game, and the Neanderthalers found themselves constantly losing in the battle for food. When, as seems likely, this competition led to warfare between the two species, the physically weaker Cro-Magnons nevertheless showed greater cunning, and annihilated their brawny rivals by the use of superior tactics and more efficient weapons. Superiority of brain, the legacy of arboreal life which nearly sixty million years previously had swept the primates to the top of the evolutionary ladder, was now beginning to play its part in the direct rivalries between man and man. This process has gone on through the whole of human history and is as apparent today as it was 35,000 years ago.

We must now deal with a twofold question which will certainly have already occurred to the reader. Where did the new species of man come from, and what are its relationships to the other species of the genus *Homo*? This is a most difficult problem, which is made worse by a serious lack of unambiguous evidence. The researches of physical anthropologists during the past hundred years have revealed that the Old World is peppered with the fossils of early man, but even now these are quite insufficient for us to make dogmatic statements about the pattern of human descent. The geographical place of origin of the tall men who advanced into Europe and replaced the Neanderthalers is almost equally obscure. The most we can do is to make a reasonable attempt at an interpretation which conflicts with none of the known evidence, bearing constantly in mind that new discoveries may cause many details of the picture to be changed.

The pattern of the lineal descent of groups of organisms is known as phylogeny, and many attempts have been made to produce a convincing phylogeny for man. We shall come to some of these shortly, but first we must consider a problem that is obviously of key importance. Did *Homo sapiens* spring from Neanderthal ancestors, or does he represent an entirely separate line of descent? In Europe in the Upper Palaeolithic, where Cro-Magnons and Neanderthalers were in direct competition, it is of course obvious that no such derivation of one stock from another could have occurred. Apart from the great differences of physical type between the two species at this time they had quite a different culture and way of life. But when we go somewhat further back – to the progressive neanderthaloids of the Israeli caves for example – there seem to be much greater affinities between the two species. This has led some authorities to suggest that the Israeli progressives are a transitional form between an early primitive Neanderthal stock and modern man. The Israeli conservatives, on the other hand, are a differentiation from this same stock along a line leading to the more specialised and 'brutish' Neanderthalers of western Europe.

Now, if this theory is to stand up there should obviously be no evidence of a particularly *sapiens*-like man before the time of the suggested divergence – i.e. 70,000–80,000 years ago. If anything before this time showed any marked suggestion of true human characters we should have to find an alternative explanation of the Israeli fossils. For instance, we should have to consider the possibility, or indeed the probability, that the Neanderthal and true human stocks had quite separate lines of descent and that the transitional forms in the Israeli caves were either freaks or the result of a later phase of interbreeding.

To follow up this theme I shall deal with only four representative fossils. These are: (1) the famous Swanscombe woman, from Galley Hill in the English county of Kent; (2) some fragments found in the Fontéchevade cave in central France; (3) the fragments of four skulls found by Dr L. S. B. Leakey at Kanjera in Kenya; and (4) the so-called Florisbad skull from near Bloemfontein in the Orange Free State. There is, of course, other equally relevant evidence – particularly, for example, the Ehringsdorf and Steinheim skulls discussed in the previous chapter – but if we are to reveal the broad sweep of the problem rather than its minutiae we must accept the limitations of a somewhat arbitrary selection.

Now, whatever their individual value, these four fossils do collectively suggest most strongly that the *sapiens* line was established for many thousands of years before the end of the main Neanderthal phase. To begin with the Swanscombe woman, we find that she is at least as reminiscent of our own species as of the Neanderthalers. She is known only from three bone fragments, found at different times between 1935 and 1955, but when fitted together these enabled the whole of the rear of the cranium to be reconstructed. In spite of the difficulty of making definite judgements without the bones of the forehead and at least some of the dentition, the flattened and moderately high sides of the cranium, and its estimated capacity of some 1,300 c.c., strongly suggest *sapiens* affinities. This woman pointed the way towards our own species, and yet lived many thousands of years before the dawn of the Cro-Magnon Age. At latest she comes from the end of the Second Interglacial Phase, and therefore antedates *Homo sapiens* by nearly 200,000 years.

More recent but even more spectacular evidence comes from the skull fragments of Fontéchevade. These date from the Third Interglacial Phase and are therefore not less than 80,000 years old. They were discovered in 1947, when the French archaeologist Mademoiselle Germaine Henri-Martin decided to open up the lower levels of the Fontéchevade cavern in Charente. Here, among bones of the warm-weather fauna preceding the Fourth and last Glacial Phase, she found the fragments of two skulls. They were small but extremely significant, for they showed by their shape, and particularly by the much reduced brow-ridges of the second specimen, that they were entirely comparable with the skulls of modern men. Here, then, is clear evidence that men of advanced type lived in Europe well before the Neanderthalers enjoyed their heyday in the second part of the Middle Palaeolithic.

Our two remaining fossils, both from Africa, give confirmatory evidence of the antiquity of the *sapiens* line. Kanjera man was discovered by Leakey in the early thirties. While exploring near Kanam on the eastern shore of Lake Victoria he came across fragments of four skulls which had been washed out of the ground by rain and subsequently damaged by the trampling of cattle. After some argument about their date these fragments are now generally regarded as belonging to the third African pluvial phase, which probably corresponds with the Third Glacial Phase in the north. They can thus be regarded as between 190,000 and 240,000 years old. The fossils, except for the greater thickness of the bones, are extremely reminiscent of those of modern man. They certainly have no resemblance whatever to those of the more specialised type of Neanderthal men of later times.

The remains of Florisbad man from the Orange Free State are much more complete than the fragments from Fontéchevade and Kanjera. He is, in fact, represented by the top and much of the front of a skull which was found in 1932 in a series of very complicated deposits round a lithium spring at Florisbad Spa. The sorting out of these deposits is extremely difficult, but modern dating techniques suggest that we are dealing with a fossil some 35,000 years old. Although the heavy brow-ridges of the Florisbad fossil give it a rather brutish appearance, their configuration is again quite different from those of the Neanderthalers. Florisbad man is certainly not on the main line of *sapiens* evolution, but could well stand on a side-branch derived from a more primitive *sapiens* stock. This in itself suggests that men of *sapiens* type were evolving along a different line from the Neanderthalers well before the Upper Palaeolithic dawned.

All the foregoing evidence makes it likely that the lines of evolution leading to *Homo neanderthalensis* on the one hand and *Homo sapiens* on the other have proceeded independently for much longer than one interpretation of the evidence of the Israeli caves seems to suggest. If this is so, the explanation of the various physical gradations found in the caves must probably be that interbreeding occurred between the two types of men at a comparatively advanced stage of their evolution. It is not an entirely satisfactory explanation, but seems the only way to combine the evidence from such a variety of sources into a unified picture. In any case, we must now abandon such theorising and recapitulate the pattern of events before the overwhelming success of our own species some 35,000 years ago.

The rise of the primates began, as we have seen, at the end of the Age of Reptiles. Its course through the Tertiary period was fairly obscure, but in the first half of the Pleistocene the race of advanced ground-dwelling hominids known as australopithecines was established in south Africa. Somewhat later the distinctly man-like pithecanthropoids appeared in south-east Asia and elsewhere, and showed the beginnings of such characteristic human activities as cooking, toolmaking, and killing each other for material gain. These were followed in turn by the Neanderthalers of Europe and the Middle East, and by a race of long-limbed, thin-skulled upright hominids essentially similar to ourselves. The last two types of man seem to have existed side by side in several regions, but whether they can both trace their origins on roughly parallel lines to a pithecanthropoid ancestor, or whether *Homo sapiens* diverged from a proto-Neanderthaler some 200,000 years ago is still unknown. All that seems certain is that the Neanderthal and *sapiens* lines split at a fairly remote period (even though some interbreeding may have occurred later) and that our own species eventually grew so much in intelligence that, in spite of physical inferiority, it swept the neanderthaloids from the face of the earth.

If we accept this concept of our origins we still have to ask in what geographical region the new species evolved. Once again, the only frank answer is that we do not know. If our species in fact represents an independent line of descent from the pithecanthropoids, then it certainly seems likely that our ancestors were cradled in the East. Perhaps descendants of Java man and Pekin man migrated northward into Tibet and other regions of central Asia where, over long millennia, they learnt to combat the harsh conditions of this wild and mountainous land. Certainly this interpretation would explain why they were so well equipped for success in the unsympathetic environment of Ice Age Europe when they later moved westward and drove the Neanderthalers from their caves. But it would be rash to do more than suggest this as a possible explanation of the course of events.

Whatever the true story of our origins, however, we have now arrived at the threshold of the human adventure. By the closing millennia of the Ice Age all material opposition to the triumph of our species had been removed. Our physical evolution was over, and the whole future course of human history was to be a record of what happened in men's minds and souls. It is this extraordinary story that will now mainly concern us, but first we must deal with one further aspect of our physical background: the nature of human races and the way mankind has spread and established itself in almost every corner of the earth.

Chapter Eleven

THE RACES OF MAN

WE HAVE NOW arrived, for better or for worse, at the triumph of *Homo sapiens*. By some 35,000 years ago our own species was firmly established on the earth, and since that time has known no rivals. But, as everyone knows, mankind does not consist of an homogeneous group. He is represented by a large number of physical types differing greatly in size, proportions, colour, smell, and even in the kind of blood that flows in their veins. These different 'races' of man sometimes occur in closely defined areas, but more generally overlap and intermingle, so that it is quite possible to see representatives of five different races in as many minutes walking down a crowded street. We must now inquire exactly what race is and how it arose, and see if we can sort out the major races of mankind into some kind of order. (Plates 28–40.)

Very broadly speaking a race is a population of individuals of similar physical type occupying the same area, habitually interbreeding and having historical continuity. Modern anthropologists recognise about thirty of such races, although the number could be made much higher or lower according to the criteria used. For instance, some authorities with a passion for 'splitting' rather than 'lumping' have increased the number to sixty or even more, while others tend to the wistful suggestion made by Professor Howells of Harvard that perhaps there are only two, the 'handsome' and the 'ugly'. Probably the best compromise is to regard the races of mankind, whatever their number, as belonging to six major divisions, or 'stocks': (1) the Negroids, (2) the Mongoloids, (3) the Whites (also sometimes called the Caucasoids or Europoids), (4) the Australoids, (5) the American Indians, and (6) the

Polynesians. This is inevitably an over-simplification, but it will be quite sufficient for our present purpose.

Race has so often been the subject of stupid, ill-informed, and even malicious talk among those who might be expected to know better, that it will be as well to establish straight away that there are no scientific grounds whatever for attributing some inborn 'superiority' to any one race or stock. Different races may, and often do, differ in the level of development they have reached in a particular direction, but this is due to the influence of the environment (in the broadest sense of that word) and not to some mysterious inborn characteristic. The concept of a 'master race' as put forward by certain French and German philosophers well before the time of Hitler, or indeed of any mystical significance in race, is as dated and out of step with the evidence as the idea, once held so fanatically, that the earth is flat. The full reasons for this statement will emerge later in this book, and in the present chapter we shall be mainly concerned with the application of basic biological principles to explaining the obvious physical differences between men.

Biologically speaking, races are simply the first stage of evolutionary divergence in a given species, and their differentiation in man has followed the same laws that have led to evolutionary change in general. As with other animals, the races of mankind have been formed by the workings of natural selection operating on the physical changes, known as mutations, which occur in the reproductive cells. The pressure of the environment sorts out the beneficial from the harmful mutations, encouraging the former and eliminating the latter. As a result, different strains are built up, each suited by its physical characteristics to a successful life in a given set of circumstances (see also Chapter 2).

There are several different theories as to when racial differentiation began in man. Some experts maintain that the process did not start until some 35,000 years ago, and that all existing races are descended from a single basic stock with strong Cro-Magnon affinities. Others believe that the divergence occurred somewhat earlier, and that several distinct races already existed when the Upper Palaeolithic dawned. This view is supported, although somewhat doubtfully as we have seen, by the fossil remains of Grimaldi man, with his Negroid characteristics, and the Chancelade skull, with its hints of Eskimo affinities. A still more extreme view, of which Professor Franz Weidenreich is the main exponent, is that racial divergence began so long ago that some existing races may be descended in a direct line from different pre-*sapiens* stocks. For instance, Weidenreich has suggested that Java man (*Pithecanthropus erectus*) may have led to the modern Australoids, China man (*Pithecanthropus pekinensis*) to the modern Mongoloids, and Cro-Magnon man to the modern Caucasoids. The great mass of the evidence makes it reasonably clear, however, that the modern races are probably a fairly recent development, and began to differentiate at the earliest during the first part of the Fourth Glacial Phase. The harsh conditions of that time may, indeed, have played a part in the process. Competition would have been intense, and there would have been a tendency for man to fan out into new environments and acquire different physical as well as mental adaptations in different regions.

Although we are reasonably certain, even if only within broad limits, of the time when races began to diverge, we are unfortunately much less sure about the exact stages of their individual history. If the reader were to ask exactly what was happening to, say, the ancestors of the Negroes 25,000 years ago, even the most learned expert would have to answer that he did not know. In spite of this we can be quite sure that racial differentiation is based on the need for special characteristics to be developed as an aid to life in different environments. This is proved by a study of modern racial types, many of which show a beautiful adaptation to the physical conditions found in their homelands. Before we go any further we must look at a few outstanding examples of the form such adaptations take.

One of the most striking ways in which men reflect the conditions of their environment is in the proportions of their bodies. As an example of this we can compare the shape of a Negro, such as a Dinka or a Nuer from the Nilotic Sudan, with that of an Eskimo from the frozen wastes of Greenland (see Plates 31 and 32). The typical Nilotic Negro is extremely tall with a straight narrow body and long thin limbs. The average height of a Dinka, for example, is well over six feet, and men of six foot seven or six foot eight are by no means uncommon. The Eskimo, by contrast, is extremely short and stocky, and his body is well covered with a layer of fat. One of the properties of these characteristic shapes is that the surface area of the Dinka's skin is very much greater in proportion to his body volume than that of the Eskimo. He is, in fact, designed like a highly efficient radiator which enables the heat of his body to be carried away swiftly and efficiently into the surrounding atmosphere. With the Eskimo exactly the reverse is the case. His more or less globular shape conserves his body heat to the fullest extent, as the radiating surface is proportionately much smaller. Without going into complicating factors, it is obvious that these two types of men show a basic and highly effective adaptation to the climates in which they live.

Other races have made equally spectacular adaptations. Mountain dwellers, for instance, show a strong tendency to be stocky and barrel-chested. The shape and size of the chest is a direct response to the need for bigger lungs, allowing for a less laborious intake of oxygen. The small stature of the pygmies of Africa is more of a mystery, but may well be an adaptation to the need to move swiftly and silently through the dense undergrowth of the rain forests. Most forest-dwelling races of animals tend to be smaller than races of the same species dwelling on the plains, and there is obviously an adaptive reason for this, even if we cannot yet be completely definite as to what it may be.

The different colours of men's skins, which generate such strong prejudices among ill-informed people, are simply another example – and a particularly good one – of racial adaptation. Our skins are not only the physical boundaries of our bodies, but are most useful to us in a variety of ways. They protect the softer tissues below from bacteria, and even assist in killing them; they are sensitive to touch, and are therefore one of our main sense organs; and they act as a heat regulator by allowing the passage of sweat which then evaporates and cools the surface of the body. One of the skin's main functions, which is directly associated with its colour, is to act as a filtering agent for light; its structure can be modified in

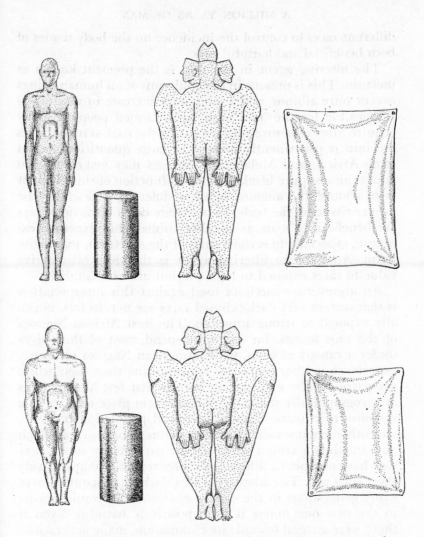

FIG. 14. This figure shows the ratio of skin surface area to body volume in two contrasted physical types. Although the two men, corresponding in bodily proportions to a Dinka (above) and an Eskimo (below), have the same weight and volume, the skin surface area of the Dinka is much greater in proportion to his body volume than that of the compact Eskimo. The structure of the two men represents a striking physical adaptation to the climates in which they live.

After Coon, Garn and Birdsell (1957), Fig. 1, pp. 38–9

different races to control the incidence on the body tissues of both beneficial and harmful rays.

The filtering agent in the skin is the pigment known as melanin. This is present in the epidermis of all human beings except pure albinos, and a temporary increase in melanin is responsible for the 'tan' even light-skinned people usually acquire after exposure to the sun. In the dark-skinned races melanin is permanently present in large quantities, and in some African and Melanesian Negroes may make the skin appear almost pure black. The main function of this pigment is to control the amount of ultra-violet light reaching the deeper tissues of the body. In moderate doses ultra-violet rays are beneficial to man, as to other animals, but excessive exposure, especially to certain parts of the spectrum, may cause harm. An effective filtering agent is therefore of adaptive value to races exposed to high concentrations of sunlight.

An argument sometimes used against this interpretation is that certain very dark-skinned races are not, in fact, normally exposed to strong sunshine. The west African Negroes of the rain forests, for example, spend most of their lives under a canopy of trees, while American Negroes obviously experience neither more nor less sunshine than their white compatriots. The explanation here is that few human races are geographically static. They move from place to place as a response to climatic change, increased population pressure, and other environmental factors. Thus a black race which now inhabits a region which is not particularly sunny may well have occupied a different sunnier region a comparatively short time ago. The adaptation of a dark skin, acquired over many generations in the earlier environment, would persist in the new one unless it were positively harmful. Even if there were a trend towards its elimination, many generations would have to elapse before the selection of appropriate mutations produced any appreciable change.

The white skins of northern races are not such a positive adaptation to environment as those of black races. We could argue that a white skin, with its much reduced melanin content, is a response to cloudy skies and diffuse sunlight, enabling its owner to take the maximum advantage from ultraviolet rays. But it would probably be truer to put the matter the other way round. The skins of northerners have remained pale simply because the need for additional protection has never arisen. Their colour is not so much a response to a problem, as an indication that the problem has never confronted them.

Another physical characteristic of human races that seems to be an adaptation to the varying incidence of ultra-violet light in different regions is the colour of the eyes. The migration of peoples has confused the problem of eye colour, but generally speaking the darker-skinned people living in intensely illuminated areas have dark eyes, while those of peoples living under grey and cloudy skies are lighter. Three major types of eye colour are recognised by anthropologists, brown, mixed and light, but two others should be mentioned for completeness. These are the almost black eyes found in racial types with the blackest skins, and the exceptionally pale eyes of albinos. Brown eyes are by far the commonest type, and are characteristic of all non-white races and some whites as well. Other whites have blue or grey eyes, while the 'mixed' type is represented by various shades of green.

To understand the possible adaptive qualities of these colours we must look a little more closely at the structure of the eye itself. This is essentially comparable to a camera, with a lens at the front and a screen at the back on which the visual image is projected. The lens consists in the eye of two main parts, the pupil and the iris. The pupil corresponds to the aperture of a camera lens, which actually throws the image on the film; the iris corresponds to the diaphragm which, in a camera, makes the aperture larger or smaller according to the intensity of the light. Now in the eye a pigment occurs both in the iris and the retina (the name of the screen on which the image is cast) which seems to have the property of filtering out excessive ultra-violet rays which might otherwise harm the sensitive layers and reduce the sharpness of the image. This pigment gives protection similar to that given by melanin in the skin. Dark eyes are thus highly protected by their pigments against excessive ultra-violet, while lighter eyes are less so. The extreme lightness found in albinos is a great disadvantage to efficient vision in bright light, and such people have to be particularly careful to avoid damage to their eyes.

These facts show how likely it is that the degrees of pigmentation found in the eyes of different races, which keep the incidence of ultra-violet light at a critical level, originated in adaptation to environment. Efficient eyesight is, of course, extremely valuable even in the sophisticated communities evolved by modern man where, apart from its use in such basic activities as reading and writing, it is essential to a variety of skilled activities from piloting an aeroplane to the construction of precision instruments. But in a primitive hunting community it is even more necessary, for keen eyes may actually mean the difference between survival and extinction. Such people must be able to recognise game at a great distance, even in the glaring conditions of a sandy desert or the arctic snows, and the resolving power of their eyes is thus one of the main advantages they possess in ensuring the continuance of their race.

Still further evidence for the adaptive principle comes from the hair. We find here, incidentally, that light hair is normally associated with light-skinned races and dark hair with their dark-skinned cousins, but this does not seem to be of particular adaptive importance and is probably only a side effect of the primary adaptation in the skin. The most striking adaptive features of hair are to be found in the way it grows, which is either straight, wavy, helical, or spiral in different types of men. Straight hair seems to have no particular significance and, like pale skin, is probably due to the absence rather than the presence of a particular environmental challenge. Wavy hair may be a factor in sexual selection – at least if we are to judge by the large sums spent by straight-haired women at the hairdressers – but this is its only obvious value. In helical and spiral hair, however, we find two exceptionally good examples of racial adaptation to environment.

Helical hair, which is found among Melanesians, Europeans, and people who resemble Europeans dwelling in other continents, consists of a number of repeated loops all of the same diameter. The springy quality of the hair causes it to bunch out on the head, thus forming a more efficient insulating layer either against heat or cold than straight or wavy hair. Spiral hair resembles helical hair except that the diameter of the loops decreases as they grow outward from the scalp. The main centre of races with spiral hair is Africa, and the so-called 'frizzy' heads of many Negroes are one of their most characteristic traits. It seems most probable that this particular kind of hair growth is based on the need to protect the head from intense sunlight like a kind of natural pith-helmet. Moreover, in its extreme form, known as 'peppercorn' hair, where the spirals are widely spaced out on the scalp, an additional adaptive advantage is conferred. Sweat can escape more easily from the spaces in between, and this leads to more efficient cooling of the head.

Turning now from the general to the particular, we may be intrigued to consider the Mongoloid face as an example of what Professor Carleton Coon and his co-authors in their book *Races* have aptly termed 'climatic engineering'. As long ago as 1775 Immanuel Kant suggested in his *Von den verscheidenen Rassen der Menschen* that Mongoloid structure was an adaptation to cold, and we have already explained how the body shape of such Mongoloids as the Eskimoes provides evidence for this. In the Mongoloid face we can see how such a general tendency was carried to quite remarkable lengths of refinement in a single structural feature. In spite of their body shape, Eskimoes, and such comparable Mongoloids as the Tungus, could never live in permanently frozen conditions if they lacked clothing and some form of shelter. But such artificial aids do nothing to protect their faces when they emerge from their homes to hunt, as these must still be exposed. It is therefore of great evolutionary advantage that this particular feature of their bodies should be as cold-resistant as possible. This end has been excellently achieved by adaptive modifications of the facial contours. In typical Mongoloids the protuberances are flattened out by a slight recession of the nose, and by a corresponding forward movement of the cheekbones, or 'malars', thus reducing the surface area to a minimum. The brow-ridges are reduced and the region round the eye has become well padded with fat. This fat gives protection to the vulnerable nasal sinuses and, banked up round the eye-balls, reduces the visible part of the eyes to the characteristic Mongoloid slits. This arrangement protects the eyeball from cold and the retina from excessive snow glare. The fatty pads round the nose also help to smooth out the facial contours, and provide additional insulation for the nasal passages so that the air can be warmed to the maxium extent on its way to the lungs. The characteristic 'flat face' of modern Mongoloids has thus entirely resulted from the harsh conditions in which their ancestors lived. Summing up the extreme efficiency of its structure the authors of *Races* go so far as to say: 'If an engineer were to sit down with pencil and paper and try to figure out how to make over the face of an undifferentiated human being to meet the world's greatest cold, he could only end up with a blue-print of existing Mongoloid features.'

Another important adaptation made by this race is connected with the growth of their hair. This is very sparsely distributed on the face of all Mongoloid men, and the beard of an Eskimo or Tungu grows only one-quarter as quickly as that of a white man. In extreme cold it is essential that the facial area of an organism should not be covered by excessive hair or the breath will freeze on the beard with disastrous results. Shaving or hair-plucking would be extremely difficult on the prolonged expeditions of an arctic hunter, and it seems that natural selection has provided a physiological mechanism which keeps the Mongoloid beard permanently reduced. Of course, many Mongoloids live in comparatively mild regions where such an adaptation is unnecessary. But this is the result of later migrations and does not weaken the explanation of how a reduction of facial hair occurred in the parent stock.

In spite of the importance of such basic physical influences as climate, it would be an over-simplification to say that these alone were responsible for the racial divergence of *Homo sapiens*. Other more subtle forces have also been at work. In the space at our disposal it would be impossible to discuss these at length, but three must be briefly referred to. These are the effect of social factors, the nature of the food supply, and the incidence of disease.

Social factors must have played an important part in selection as human society became more sophisticated. It seems that special skills and other personality traits may be as much the result of mutation as physical characteristics and, through educational development, can therefore produce individuals who are in some real way superior to their fellows. Thus in a random sample from a given community, certain individuals may show special abilities in hunting, leadership, and other qualities of social importance. These men will tend to acquire exceptional prestige in the eyes of their fellows, entitling them to special privileges in the acquisition of wives, the right to cohabit with the wives of others, and in other ways that will allow their qualities to be genetically transmitted to future generations. At the same time individuals less able to further the collective interests of the group may suffer penalties which prevent their innate personality traits being transmitted. Carleton Coon has quoted several reports from anthropologists to show that in such communities as the Eskimoes and the Australian aborigines of the Western Desert trouble-makers are killed by an edict of the tribal rulers. If, as seems probable, such mental qualities, both beneficial and adverse, are to some extent heritable mutations, then the social selection of desirable individuals will in time so alter the character of the community that the process can fairly be regarded as racial divergence at the psychological level.

Differentiation caused by the nature of the food supply is more basically physical than the above. To take only one example, many millions of people in the East subsist mainly on a rice diet. Europeans, and others with more sophisticated gastronomic demands, cannot do this, and contract a number of well-known deficiency diseases. Adaptation to diet is therefore one among many factors leading to the divergence of races.

Finally, there is the question of resistance to disease, and here again one example must suffice. In malarial areas of Africa and elsewhere large numbers of the population have acquired a critical level in their blood streams of a special cell, known as the 'sickle cell', which gives them a very high resistance to the disease. Such specialisation is essentially an adaptation to environment, and is an example of one of the less immediately obvious but still most important characteristics of physical differentiation in *Homo sapiens*. As most readers of this book will know, different men belong to different blood groups, and the blood from an individual belonging to one group cannot be used for transfusions to a member of another without harmful, and often fatal, results. Blood groups do not necessarily coincide with other racial characteristics any more than brown eyes always go with dark hair, but there is little doubt that the need to resist certain diseases in certain regions played a part in their differentiation.

Apart from natural selection, the only factor that seems to have any role to play in the making of race is the very obvious one of intermixture. At many periods during history, through conquest, infiltration, or mass movements of refugees, large numbers of people of different races have been brought into close contact with one another. The natural result of this is interbreeding, and if the admixture is strong enough the characters of both races will change to produce a new self-reproducing racial type. Except in a very few communities which have lived in prolonged geographical isolation, this process has affected the ancestors of every person now living on the earth. Whether we like it or not, all of us are mongrels, and the concept of 'racial purity' is as unscientific in its origins as it is degrading to those who accept it as true.

Although race is always in a state of flux as a result of interbreeding and of selective factors of the type already described, we have said that six main racial stocks can be distinguished in the modern world. It would be impossible to discuss all these in detail, but we must conclude by saying something about the characteristic traits of the three most important: the Negroids, Mongoloids and Caucasoids.

The Negroid stock is mainly centred in Africa, but is also represented in the Solomons, New Hebrides, New Guinea and other islands in the South Seas. When the slave trade was at its height between the seventeenth and early nineteenth centuries, many millions of Negroes were taken by force from Africa to the United States, where they are now among the most solid of American citizens. The classic Negro characteristics are heavy pigmentation; a broad, flat nose with a deeply depressed bridge; short black hair, coarse in texture and frizzy in form; and a marked projection of the middle

III. The living races of man

28 A Mangbettu girl from the Congo. The Mangbettu are lighter skinned than many African tribes but nevertheless well exemplify some of the more typical Negroid adaptations.

29

29 Pygmies from western Uganda.

30 Melanesian Negroid: a
Papuan warrior.

31 Nilotic Negroid from the Sudan.

30

31

32 This Eskimo woman, a typical Mongoloid, has features well adapted to life in a cold climate. The nose is flat and broad, and the fatty pads on the cheeks help to smooth out the facial contours and insulate the sinuses. The Mongoloid face is in general a remarkable example of what has been called 'climatic engineering' (see page 133).

33

35

33-35 On the left-hand page are shown the three main varieties of the Caucasoid race: Nordic (Plate 33), Mediterranean (Plate 34), and Alpine (the left-hand figure on Plate 35). All show striking physical adaptations to their environment (see Chapter 11).

36 This Pueblo Indian is a typical indigenous North American. Although his ancestors were of Mongoloid stock and probably migrated eastwards across the Bering Strait in the late Pleistocene, a temperate climate has reduced the need for the extreme adaptations found in the Eskimoes and other northern Mongoloids (see Plate 32).

36

37 This Peruvian Indian, from Ayacucho, south-east of Lima, although of Mongoloid origin, shows a still greater retreat from the typical Mongoloid features than the Pueblo Indian shown in Plate 36. There is a strong probability that some of his ancestors interbred with Caucasoid immigrants.

38 In contrast to the Peruvian Indian shown on Plate 37 this 'Colorado' Indian from Ecuador has preserved a typical Mongoloid structure.

39 (*facing page*) An Australoid from the interior of Australia. The Australian aborigines may be direct descendants of *Homo sapiens* at his most backward before large-scale racial divergence began.

40 This attractive Polynesian girl, probably with a mixed ancestry of Caucasoids, Melanesians, Negroids and Asiatic Mongoloids, well exemplifies the advantages of racial interbreeding.

face. But there are infinite variations on this basic formula. The long-limbed Nilotics of the Dinka and Shilluk tribes, the tiny pygmies of the rain forests, and the aristocratic Watussi of Ruanda-Urundi, are all basically of Negroid stock, but are very different in physical type. The picture is also complicated by the admixture of a white stock, especially along the east coast of Africa, which gives such peoples as the Ethiopians and Somalis a much less typically Negroid look than their cousins to the west. No one knows exactly how or when this occurred, but in the era before the development of modern communications it is obvious that Mediterranean merchants and adventurers would have found it far easier to voyage to east Africa by sea than to penetrate the dark interior. Sailors after a long sea passage having similar inclinations in all ages, it is not surprising that a considerable amount of cross-fertilisation took place.

The presence of Negroids in the South Seas is one of the major mysteries of anthropology. It is odd indeed that a stock so typically associated with Africa should be represented in isolated islands many thousands of miles away from their main homeland. The most probable explanation of the mystery is that the Negroids of Melanesia ('the black islands'), as the region is termed, have never had any connection at all with African Negroids. Either they are an example of parallel evolution of the same racial characteristics in a separate environment or, as some authorities suggest, they are a synthetic race including both Polynesian and Australoid elements. A similar problem arises in connection with the Negritos ('little Negroes') of the Andaman Islands, Malaya, and the Philippines, who closely resemble the well-known Negritos, or 'pygmies', of west Africa. The presence of these two pockets of Negritos at such a great distance from each other suggests either parallel evolution or, perhaps, the presence of a former forest belt running round the fringes of southern Asia from central Africa to New Guinea.

The Mongoloids are probably the most numerous racial stock living today, and people with Mongoloid characteristics the globe. The main centre of the group is central and eastern turn up in all sorts of unexpected places across the surface of Asia, and for many people the very word Mongol still conjures up a picture of slant-eyed Asiatic horsemen slashing off the heads of retreating enemies with broad-bladed swords. In fact a far greater variety of peoples belong to the Mongoloid stock than is suggested by such popular romantic images. The Eskimoes, as we have already seen, are Mongoloids; so, of course, are the vast numbers of people inhabiting China, Japan and many other lands of south-east Asia. The American Indians and Polynesians are certainly to some extent Mongoloid, and several anthropologists have even gone so far as to suggest (although this is very difficult to support) that the Bushmen of south Africa are Mongoloid in origin. What are the explanations of this wide distribution?

We have seen that the proportions of the Mongoloid body and the structure of the Mongoloid face are extremely effective adaptations to cold. In the harsh conditions which characterised central Asia in the Fourth Glacial Phase the building up of these features must have involved a rigid degree of selection in a comparatively small population. But when the climate began to get warmer upwards of ten thousand years ago, the reduced challenge of the environment would have allowed the Mongoloids to increase in numbers and spill over into new regions. This is, in fact, what seems to have occurred. Big migrations of Mongoloids took place, both to the south and south-east, where they mixed in varying proportions with the indigenous peoples of what are now China, Indo-China, Siam and Burma. Other contingents of the Mongol hordes moved eastwards into America across the present Bering Strait, and perhaps mingled with less specialised people who had preceded them. Less racial intermixture seems to have occurred with the Mongoloids who reached the regions now known as Korea and Japan, where some living Mongoloids are as classic in type as the Eskimoes. In the west a more limited expansion seems to have occurred, probably owing to resistance by men of the basic Cro-Magnon stock, but even today Mongoloid influence can be traced in many parts of south-eastern Europe and on the northern fringes of the Middle East. Mongoloid influence on the Bushmen of south Africa is much more unlikely, even though a few eminent authorities have favoured the idea in the past. It is almost inconceivable that the classic Mongoloids of the north should have travelled such a vast distance without leaving traces on the way. A much more likely explanation of Mongoloid features in Bushmen is that parallel evolution took place as an adaptation to the much colder climatic conditions that probably occurred in south Africa in the Fourth Glacial Phase. Even so the spread of the northern Mongoloids is impressive enough. In the words of Coon and his colleagues 'probably no other racial stock in the world has started with so few and grown to be so many, in such a short span of years'.

We come now to our third great racial stock, the Caucasoids, or 'whites'. These people, of basic Cro-Magnon type, have often been regarded as essentially superior in some way to members of other stocks. This view, as one might suspect, was itself of Caucasoid origin and has not been held with comparable enthusiasm by either Negroids or Mongoloids. In the fields of science and technology there have indeed been times when Caucasoids were well ahead of other peoples, but in the modern world, where better communications and a general raising of the educational level are constantly leading to a higher degree of racial convergence, the idea of Caucasoid supremacy has become a sad anachronism. We shall return to this subject in Chapter 20, but at present we are concerned only with the general appearance of the Caucasoids, and their distribution.

The Caucasoid stock is divided into three main types, the Alpine, the Mediterranean and the Nordic. The term 'Whites', loosely applied to this stock, is really very misleading, and is only justifiable on comparative grounds. The Alpine and Mediterranean peoples are both brunettes with olive skins, brown eyes, and brown or black hair, and only the Nordics can be regarded as approximately white. Even in these the skin is generally more pinkish than the pure white of Shakespeare's 'monumental alabaster', and has very little to commend it from the aesthetic point of view. That Nordics are conscious of this lack of allure is shown by the long hours they spend on sunny beaches trying to turn their skins to the attractive shade of brown which their cousins of other Caucasoid races have by nature.

Among the main physical characteristics of Caucasoids are medium to tall stature, an eye-colour varying from light blue to dark brown, and straight or wavy hair which may be any shade between ash blond and black. The chin is fairly prominent, the lips thin, and the face seldom prognathous. The hair grows more freely on the face, chest, arms and legs than it does in most other stocks. There is also a good growth of hair on the head, but in Nordics this tends to drop out rather early in adults – another factor which sometimes depresses this race of Caucasoids with their lack of aesthetic charm. Of the three component races, the Nordics are the tallest, usually with a somewhat narrow and angular face, light eyes and blond or light-brown hair. The body is generally slender, with a flat chest and small trunk, but exceptionally long legs. The olive-skinned Mediterraneans are comparatively slight of stature, with dark or black hair and brown eyes. Although the hair may be luxuriant and usually wavy on the head it is often scanty or sometimes almost absent on the body. The younger members of this race are normally thin in both sexes but run to fat in maturity – a tendency which in women is regarded as having powerful sexual attraction. The Alpines are also olive-skinned and dark with dark eyes, but are much more stocky than the Mediterraneans. The nose is less sharp than in either of the other two races, and is well padded with flesh. Like the Nordics, the Alpines usually have a well-developed growth of body hair, and the men are often characterised by their fine black beards.

As the names of the three races suggest, the Nordics make up most of the population of Scandinavia and the Baltic shores of Germany, the Alpines come from mountain regions in central and eastern Europe and Asia Minor, while the Mediterraneans occur especially in Spain, Italy, Egypt and other lands bordering the Mediterranean Sea. Their range is by no means limited to these areas, however. The Mediterraneans are found right through southern Asia to Indonesia, and Caucasoids in general have migrated to almost every region of the world. For instance, people of Alpine type are commonly found in western Europe, north Africa and North America, while the early development of the British Empire led to people of Nordic race establishing themselves in environments as diverse and distant from one another as the barren tundra of northern Canada, the fertile highlands of central and east Africa, and the arid interior of the Australian continent. Moreover in Europe a great intermingling of Caucasoids has taken place. The Welshman who serves you a drink in a Cardiff bar may well be of Mediterranean race, while in southern Europe, or even in north Africa, isolated groups of Nordics have been established for many generations.

As we have said, the Negroids, Mongoloids and Caucasoids represent the three most important racial stocks of mankind living today. For the other three stocks listed at the opening of this chapter, only a few words must suffice. The Australian aborigines, or Australoids, are probably representatives of *Homo sapiens* at his most backward, before the divergent specialisations of less isolated races began to occur. They probably originated in a primitive human stock in south-east Asia, which spread to Australia before the Mongoloid radiation and survived there undisturbed for many thousands of years. The American Indians are another great puzzle. Most of them have unmistakable Mongoloid features, but in other ways are much more generalised. Men certainly entered the continent by way of the Bering Strait at an unknown period in the late Pleistocene, but whether they had then already acquired an admixture of Mongoloid characteristics, or whether this came as a result of a later Mongoloid radiation, is quite unknown. Yet a third mystery is provided by the Polynesians of the South Pacific islands. This stock is obviously mongrelised to a great extent, and is probably made up of a mixture of Mediterranean Caucasoids, Melanesians, Negroids and the already much cross-bred Mongoloids of south-east Asia. The Polynesians, in fact, represent what our descendants may look like when racial prejudice has finally broken down and the interbreeding between peoples is regarded, as it must be, as the natural state of man. Even the most rabid supporter of *apartheid* should be able to take comfort from this in his losing struggle, for the Polynesians, with their brown skins, dark luxuriant hair, and aristocratic bearing are among the most physically attractive members of our species now living.

Every discussion of race is bedevilled by lack of definite evidence and the above synoptic account is no exception. But,

whatever the gaps in our knowledge, I would like to emphasise in conclusion that one point is abundantly clear to all
students of the subject. The physical divergence of races
among mankind as controlled by the blind forces of organic
evolution is now at an end. Whereas in other animals differentiation might have continued until new species were
created, cultural forces in man have halted the tide of divergence, and the trend is now once more towards an homogeneous stock. The growth of rapid communications in the
modern world, an increased understanding of biological principles, and an intelligent appreciation of the need for unity
rather than division among men, are now strongly counteracting the tendency to divergence. As I hope to make clear in
the last Part of this book, the survival of mankind depends
not on the forces that seem to separate one type of man from
another, but on those that bind them together.

Chapter Twelve

THE EXPLOSION OF MIND

WE HAVE NOW reached a critical point in our story. The previous chapter completes our account of man's physical development through the process of organic evolution. Race is the last example of physical divergence that was not consciously understood at the time by the species itself. We must turn now to the even more exciting story of man's mental evolution, which has led to his unique status among the animals. Although infinitely shorter than the long process of physical evolution that went before the story is extremely complex. In the remainder of this Part and in Part 4 we shall be concerned only with outlining some of its major aspects, leaving the possible interpretation of its significance for discussion in Part 5.

It will first be necessary to recapitulate some of the points already made about the human mind, and further define the concept of cultural progress. We have seen that the main distinguishing characteristic of man is his capacity for conceptual thought, reflected in his ability to make tools and other extra-corporeal devices which help him to adapt to his environment. Other organisms adapt mainly by physical specialisations in the body itself; for instance, the musk-ox has a long shaggy coat as a protection against the northern cold, badgers have strong claws as an aid to digging, and lions and tigers have developed sharp canine teeth as a means of killing their prey. Man has also made comparable physical adaptations to some extent (particularly, as we have seen, in his flexible fore-limbs and upright stance), but the main cause of his evolutionary success has been his ability to manufacture equipment that is not built into his body, but can be used or discarded at will. Thus instead of the shaggy coat of the musk-ox, the claws of the badger, and the canines of the lion and the tiger, man can put on clothes to keep warm, make spades to dig, or manufacture a wide range of specialised weapons to slaughter his prey or enemies. This is only made possible by the precocious development of his brain, and the objects manufactured form part of what is generally known as his 'material culture'.

The possession of extra-corporeal equipment is not, however, the only evidence of man's powers of conceptual thought. The development of the human brain has also led to an awareness of many aspects of the universe which are not part of the purely physical environment which offers the main challenge to the lower animals. Increased awareness brings with it additional problems based on more intangible pressures. For example, man must not only be able to adapt to the physical challenge of, say, an uncongenial climate or hostile organisms; he must also learn to conquer the alarming sense of his own loneliness in the vast universe around him, his feelings of despair at practical or emotional crises in business or love, and, perhaps above all, the fear of his own death. Such disturbing influences have become as much a part of the environment of a self-conscious being as its material features, and the frequent failure of man to deal with them is reflected in the growth of mental illness as human awareness has increased. The adaptations which man has attempted to make to these wider aspects of his environment are expressed in such characteristic human phenomena as art, religion and philosophy. These we may call his 'metaphysical culture', which is an extension of the material culture expressed in his technology.

This is not the place to develop these topics fully, although I shall return to them later, but an important point must be made concerning the means by which culture in all its forms is transmitted. Whereas the physical specialisations, and even certain instinctive behavioural traits, of lower organisms are passed on from generation to generation by the well-established principles of organic evolution (i.e., natural selection acting on mutations in the reproductive cells), culture, whether it be material or metaphysical, cannot be passed on in this way. The ability to play the piano, light a fire, or even to make a pebble-tool, is not inherited; it is the result of what we term education – the transmission from one generation to the next by word of mouth or written symbols of the accumulated knowledge of the species. Hence the exceptional importance to man of such techniques of communication as speech and writing, which allow his cultural tradition to be handed on. If we can imagine that by the intervention of some wicked fairy the transmission of culture was magically suspended for as short a period as a hundred years the whole of the human experiment would collapse. Man would no longer know how to talk or read or make a fire or even to shape a flint. He would once more be entirely at the mercy of the climate and his more powerful animal contemporaries, and even if for a second time he found answers to these challenges, he would have to begin his cultural development all over again.

With these somewhat disturbing thoughts in mind we will now return to the actual course of man's cultural development in the Upper Palaeolithic. We have seen that the rise of *Homo sapiens* to domination was finally completed between 40,000 and 35,000 years ago. By that time, and as a direct result of competition with the new species, Neanderthal man survived only in a few scattered outposts of the Old World and was soon completely extinct. The Negroid, Mongoloid and Caucasoid stocks may already have begun to diverge, and our species was certainly widely distributed in Europe, Asia and Africa. It is nevertheless in western Europe that the most significant evidence for the early development of human cultural processes is found and, without drawing any rash conclusions about inborn racial talent, it does therefore seem likely that the Caucasoids were the first *sapiens* stock to show an advanced degree of mental ability.

It is important to establish at this point that the Upper Palaeolithic, or late Old Stone Age, in which the events to be described occurred, is not a period in human history that can be defined by absolute dates. It is a name for a particular level of cultural achievement, identifiable by the type of artifacts and other archaeological evidence which it provides. It thus occurred at different times in different regions, and such primitive communities as the Australian aborigines are still today at the cultural level of the Upper Palaeolithic.

In western Europe the evidence for Upper Palaeolithic culture occurs between 40,000 and 10,000 years ago. Between these dates in this particular part of the world we are confronted with what can only be described as an explosion of mind. This was marked by an extraordinarily rapid cultural advance, both at the material and metaphysical level. Within the space of a few thousand years our Upper Palaeolithic ancestors not only invented a whole new range of material equipment but embarked on the sophisticated processes of abstract thought which were to lead to the religious and artistic experience of modern man.

To avoid confusing the main issue with unnecessary detail, the Upper Palaeolithic can be divided for practical purposes into five main cultural phases. These are distinguished by the archaeological evidence found at various levels in many different parts of Europe and the Middle East. Starting with the most ancient, the phases are named the Chatelperronian, the Aurignacian, the Gravettian, the Solutrean and the Magdalenian. A few notes about the material culture of each will also show how there was a growing tendency towards metaphysical culture as man's mental and spiritual horizons began to expand.

The Chatelperronian phase takes its name from the type site at Chatelperron in western France, and reached its full flowering over 30,000 years ago. The characteristic artifact of these people, who, like all Upper Palaeolithic men, were hunters and food-gatherers, was a flint knife with one straight, razor-sharp edge and the other blunted and curving over to the point. This method of fashioning flints probably originated in south-east Asia, but the tradition must have spread into Europe in Mousterian times, for tools showing a mingling of Mousterian and Chatelperronian characters occur in places as widely separated as Israel and France.

It seems that a second wave of peoples then moved westward from an unknown region in eastern Europe or western Asia, bringing with them a somewhat more varied toolmaking tradition. These men were the Aurignacians, named after a cave at Aurignac some forty miles south-west of Toulouse, which was one of the centres of their industry. They were physically of Cro-Magnon type, as we can tell from the association of their implements and skeletal remains on the same sites, and for a time they supplanted the makers of the earlier Chatelperronian tools. Although scrapers and blades of flint formed part of their industry, their great contribution to primitive technology was the introduction of bone as a substance for tool-making. Some of their polished bone pins and awls are very finely worked and their bone spearheads, which could be hafted to a wooden shaft, show a high level of technical achievement for the time.

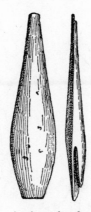

FIG. 15. Aurignacian bone points

The name of the next phase, the Gravettian, comes from the very sharp cutting and engraving tool known as a *gravette*, which is shaped rather like the blade of a penknife. The makers of this artifact flourished not only in western Europe, but on the steppes of southern Russia, where they hunted the herds of game inhabiting the grassy corridor between the northern ice-sheet and the frozen mountains to the south. Horses, bison and reindeer fell prey to these people, and even the mighty mammoth was trapped in artificial pitfalls. One of the uses of their *gravettes* was to decorate the ivory of the slaughtered mammoths to make bracelets and other articles of adornment.

The fourth cultural phase takes its name from the village of Solutré, near Macon in France, where there was a great camping ground of primitive man. The Solutreans may have

lived originally on the banks of the Danube, but some time
between 27,000 and 25,000 years ago they gradually radiated
westwards, and either supplanted the Gravettians or became
absorbed in their culture. They brought with them one of the

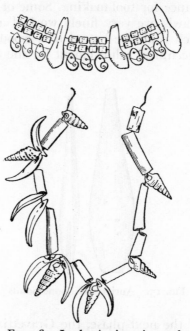

FIG. 16.   In the Aurignacian and
Gravettian cultural phases articles
of adornment begin to appear.
This figure shows (above) an
Aurignacian necklace made of stag
teeth, fish vertebrae and shells,
and (below) a Gravettian necklace
of shells and animals' teeth

most beautiful, as well as one of the most efficient, tool-making
traditions of the Upper Palaeolithic, characterised particularly by the finely fashioned willow-leaf and laurel-leaf points
known as 'foliates'. A significant feature of this industry is
that the Solutrean workmen often imparted to their products
a refinement and symmetry that went far beyond merely utilitarian needs. Their best artifacts clearly show the trend to-

wards the more metaphysical culture that added the embellishments of art to the need for basic technological efficiency.

Finally, some 20,000 years ago, we come to the Magdalenians, with whom the explosion of mind in the Upper Palaeolithic reached its apotheosis. Here, indeed, for the first time in human history we have clear evidence of a great flowering of creative energy which includes both aesthetic and religious

FIG. 17. A Solutrean 'laurel leaf' flint, so called from its shape and markings. Implements of this type were particularly characteristic of this phase of human technological development

elements as they are understood today. We shall return to these aspects of the Magdalenian mind shortly, but even in their material culture they showed an enormous advance over their predecessors. This was noticeable to some extent in their flint industry, which was exceptionally skilful; but here, of course, it was efficiency of function that was the main criterion and the intractability of the material left little scope for embellishment. In the working of bone, ivory and horn, however, the Magdalenians reached new levels of artistic expression. Although the primary motive of this industry was likewise utilitarian, the nature of the material allowed artistic concepts to be combined with basic functional needs to a much greater extent. Its products include exquisitely fashioned arrow-heads, harpoons, hammers, wedges, meat-adzes, and spear-throwers, some of which are engraved with pictures of animals and other designs. Objects of seemingly less practical use have also been found, including decorated bone pendants and carved batons that may be ritual maces. All these objects

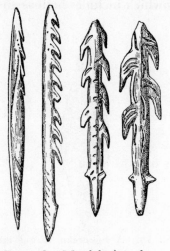

FIG. 18. Magdalenian harpoons. These and many other implements of the time were often elaborately decorated, and show artistic sensibility as well as manufacturing skill

show a much stronger trend towards a metaphysical culture than any produced by earlier members of our species.

Before discussing in more detail the artistic and religious developments of the Upper Palaeolithic we must say something about the way these people lived. When the period dawned, the Fourth Glacial Phase was still at its height, and the greater part of men's energies must have been devoted to the problem of sheer physical survival. They had to face life in a bleak world where snow and ice threatened to freeze the very blood in their veins, and where danger in the shape of a human rival or a fierce carnivorous animal lurked behind every bush. Even when the glaciers began to retreat some 15,000 years ago they still had to engage in a constant struggle to provide food and shelter for themselves and their families under conditions that would horrify the pampered city worker of today.

We have said that the basis of human economy throughout the Palaeolithic was hunting and food-gathering, and the extra mental ability which the early members of our own species brought to hunting techniques and the manfacture of hunting implements must have been one of the main reasons for their success. The new artifacts of flint and bone, becoming ever more efficient in design, would have enabled them to kill their prey with greater precision than their predecessors, while the invention of fish hooks and harpoons would have opened up a food supply in rivers, lakes and even the sea, which was only doubtfully accessible to earlier types of men. Equally important was the growing social sense of mankind which led to the combination of family groups into larger units, or tribes, able to exploit the advantages of co-operative hunting. In a large group there are opportunities for role specialisation which greatly increase the efficiency of the total effort. For instance, one man may be more skilled with the spear, another with the bow, and so on, and these can concentrate on the hunting of different kinds of game, which is then pooled by the whole group. Less proficient individuals earn their keep by digging pitfalls, acting as beaters, carrying the game back to camp, and fulfilling other more menial tasks. This kind of co-operative effort is obviously more efficient for the survival of the whole species than action by individual families which may include only two or three adult males without any specialised skills.

The main quarry of the hunters was the herbivorous game that roamed in great herds across the tundra and steppe to the south of the northern ice-sheet. In Magdalenian times this game existed in profusion, and the fact that, given reasonable skill, man could fill his belly without undue anxiety is one reason why he had energy to spare for his higher cultural activities. The game was of many kinds. Perhaps the most characteristic animal of the time was the reindeer, which occurred in vast numbers in tundra regions. This animal was much sought after by the Magdalenians for its flesh and antlers, which were used for making artifacts, and many prehistorians have given the last phase of the Upper Palaeolithic the popular name of the Reindeer Age. Mammoths were plentiful in the same region until some 12,000 years ago, and certain cave pictures suggest that they were caught in pitfalls and traps as well as hunted with spears. Horses abounded on the grassy plains, and the presence of their bones in huge numbers at

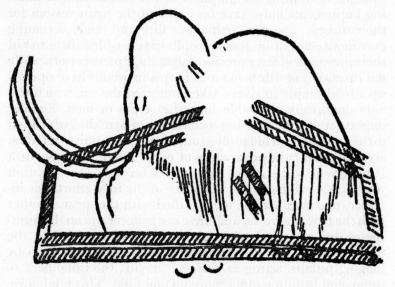

FIG. 19. Mammoth in trap, from a Stone Age design in the Font-de-Gaume cavern in France

some sites shows that they were much exploited as a source of food.

While the men went out hunting, the women remained in camp to cook, tend the children, or make local expeditions to gather berries and other vegetable foods. In this way they too fulfilled a specialised role in the economy. The value of the old people was probably at first sight less obvious to our ancestors, and it is indeed likely that in the earliest human communities they received short shrift. The struggle with nature leaves little room for sentimentality, and old people who became a burden to their fellows may often have been expelled from the group to die. But as society evolved, and the value of transmitted learning became consciously realised, the old people too would have been recognised, at least in some cases, as having positive value. The ageing chief with his council of elders is a feature of many primitive societies of today; these men are regarded as a source of wisdom and experience which, when transmitted to the younger and more vigorous members of the group, is a practical aid to its survival. There is no doubt that the more advanced Upper Palaeolithic communities likewise set store by the wisdom of the old, and turned it to good effect.

Although hunting and food-gathering were the foundation of the economy, other roles doubtless grew up within the tribes. The witch-doctor or medicine man, who had special skill in treating the victims of accidents or disease, or ministering to the injured in war, was certainly one of these. Another may have been the sorcerer, who through the magical relation he claimed with the spirits of the landscape or the game would foretell the success or failure of a hunt. It may even be that certain men and women had special skills in, say, physical adornment, cookery, sewing skins to make clothing, and thus have been, in a very primitive way, the forerunners of the beauty experts, chefs, and fashionable dressmakers of today.

The roots of science were also clearly apparent at the time, although many of these originated much earlier. The fashioning of stones, even as crudely practised by pre-*sapiens* man, required a knowledge of different rocks, and thus laid the foundations of geology. In the Upper Palaeolithic, flint of particularly suitable kinds was often transported long distances to provide the raw material for the various tool-making industries. Hunting, again, required an intelligent study of the habits of animals, and the modern zoologist can probably trace back his intellectual ancestry to the game scouts sent out by primitive hunting communities. Botany stems from the need to distinguish between harmless and edible plants, while the witch-doctor's use of herbs and other botanical remedies marks the beginning of medicine.

The application of fire to human needs of course dates back

far beyond the Upper Palaeolithic, but was now greatly extended. In his first use of fire man took brands from existing conflagrations such as forest fires and kept them ignited by feeding them with wood. But in the later part of the Old Stone Age fire-making, as distinct from fire-using, must certainly have been widely practised, and this involved an understanding of scientific principles. The techniques of fire-making were probably similar to those used by primitive peoples today, such as the striking of flints to cause a spark, or the use of friction by rubbing together two pieces of wood.

As a final example of the origins of science, astronomy doubtless had its beginnings in our ancestors' observations of the cyclical phases of the moon and the hours of sunrise and sunset. These would have been necessary in forecasting the seasons when edible plants produced their fruit or when the game was due to move from one region to another.

Most tribal groups at this time must have been at least partly nomadic, for they would have been compelled to follow the seasonal migrations of the herds. When thus on the move they probably lived in tents of skin supported by a central pole, which they carried with them and set up each night. Sometimes, however, a local concentration of game must have allowed them to settle for a fairly long period, and then they may have erected somewhat more elaborate shelters made from turves and the boughs of trees. Both for temporary and semi-permanent encampments caves were highly favoured, and in certain areas, such as western France, where game was reasonably plentiful all the year round, permanent cave stations were set up. There is even evidence of trade between such permanent settlements in Magdalenian times. For instance, the bones of marine fishes are so plentiful in Magdalenian refuse heaps in the Dordogne that it seems that sea-food must have been exchanged for mammoth and reindeer steaks between the inlanders and the fishermen of the coast. Other evidence for an early bartering of goods is provided by the shells of Mediterranean molluscs and crustaceans found at Palaeolithic sites many hundreds of miles from the southern coasts of Europe.

Fascinating as it is to speculate on the nature of life in these distant times we must be careful not to let our imaginations carry us too far. In most cases definite evidence is hard to come by, and is almost always open to several interpretations. There is, however, one aspect of the Upper Palaeolithic world where the existence of unequivocal data places us on comparatively firm ground. This concerns the role of the artist in the community, which we have strong reason to believe was an exceptionally important one. It is a topic which brings us back to the general place of art in prehistoric society as an

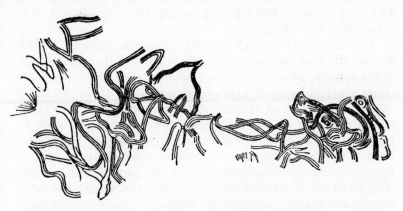

FIG. 20. Aurignacian 'macaroni' design from Altamira, including an animal's head. Total width of original 16½ feet. *From Maringer and Bandi (1953), Fig. 122, p. 96, after Breuil*

early manifestation of metaphysical culture, and also to its close relationship with primitive magic and religion.

The earliest evidence of Upper Palaeolithic visual art comes from the Aurignacian culture level. By modern standards it is extremely primitive, consisting either of profile outlines of animals roughly drawn in charcoal or with a pointed flint on the walls of caves, or simply of doodles (often known, from their appearance, as 'macaroni' designs) made with the tips of the fingers in mud, rather as a child draws random patterns on the sand at the seaside. Nevertheless, we should not underestimate the importance of these simple creations of the Aurignacian artists. In the modern world we have become used to seeing three-dimensional objects represented by visual symbols on a plane surface, but the technique by which this is done is by no means obvious, and must be laboriously learnt. Although the rough tracings made by the Aurignacians on the walls of their caves mean little in the eyes of a sophisticated person, they still represent the first steps in the evolutionary process which led to the paintings of Leonardo da Vinci and Rembrandt, and the ceiling of the Sistine Chapel. This is not, of course, to say that such creations had a primarily aesthetic object, for most Upper Palaeolithic art was, as we shall shortly see, strictly related to practical needs, but they are nevertheless the first stages in a technical tradition.

The Gravettians made considerable advances in artistic technique, and we have already mentioned their use of engraving-tools, or *gravettes,* to decorate their bone artifacts. They also fashioned objects which were more obviously works of art in the modern sense, although these, like all the art of this time, had a magico-religious character and cannot be regarded as a manifestation of pure joy in creation. Their best-known works are figurines of women carved from stone or mammoth ivory, or modelled from a mixture of clay and ash. The faces are absent, or only indicated, but the sexual parts are always highly emphasised. These objects were probably used in connection with fertility rites, symbolising perhaps the generation of strong sons and fertile daughters for the hunters, or the multiplication of game.

The artistic impulse of the Solutreans seems to have gone largely into their beautiful foliate flints, for little of significance in visual art has survived from this period. But when we come to the Magdalenians we find ourselves in the presence of a flowering of creative expression in visual art such as man had never before achieved, and which he was not to repeat until well after the establishment of civilisation. In the caves of western France and northern Spain the Magdalenian hunters engraved or painted pictures which every great artist of later times has regarded with the deepest respect. These range from rough but graphic outlines scratched on the cave walls with sharp-pointed flints to the great polychrome frescoes of Lascaux and Altamira, the supreme artistic creations of the prehistoric world. (Plates 45 and 46.)

Representations of the human figure are, however, rare at

this time and, when they occur, are so crude as to be almost unrecognisable. The main subjects are animals, particularly the animals of the chase, such as the mammoths, reindeer, bison, and horses which inhabited the bleak tundra fringing the ice-sheets or the grasslands further to the south. These are seen very much in the round, realistic and vital, so that one can easily imagine them as they were in life, roaming across the wild landscape outside the mouths of the caves. The simpler pictures are engraved or drawn mainly in profile silhouette, but in more advanced examples, particularly the painted frescoes, colour and shading is used to indicate the creature's form.

Beautiful as these pictures are, it seems that they were created mainly for material reasons. The practice of sympathetic magic is widespread in primitive societies, and the main purpose of Upper Palaeolithic cave art was to give the hunters a supposed power over the animals that formed their prey. By a seemingly magical act of creation the figure of a bison or mammoth appeared through the skill of the artist on the blank wall of a cave. By equally magical means could not a real animal appear outside to become the quarry of the hunters? Sometimes, though rarely, the artists even depicted the animal with a spear buried in its side, as they would wish to see it on their hunting expeditions. In other cases the pictures of the beasts are pitted with the marks of real spear thrusts, as if a ritual 'killing' of the image had taken place before the hunters set out in search of their living prey.

Another proof of the ritual nature of the paintings is provided by their situation in the caves. In most cases they occur deep in the hillside in remote chambers which could never have been habitually occupied by men. Moreover, they are often placed in the narrowest and most inaccessible crevices where the artist must have crouched in great discomfort to execute them, and where they can only be seen if a similar posture is adopted. If the main purpose of the pictures had been to give aesthetic pleasure to the occupants of the cave they would never have been placed in such unsuitable positions.

In spite of this we need not assume that some element of aesthetic pleasure, both to the artist and the beholder, was not associated with cave art. At Altamira, for example, the finest frescoes occur on the ceiling of a readily accessible chamber, which suggests by its atmosphere and contours that it may have been used as a kind of chapel. Although the main motive inspiring these grand creations may have been utilitarian, it is difficult to believe that on certain special occasions people did not enter the chamber simply to marvel at them as we might enter a beautifully decorated church today. Art, like science, may have had utilitarian beginnings, but as evolution has proceeded, its purely material functions have been transcended, and the work of art itself has become the key to a new level of awareness. The splendour of Magdalenian art suggests that this process of transition was already beginning in the painted caves of over two hundred centuries ago.

The artists themselves seem to have been specially trained for their task. This is suggested by the discovery of trial drawings on pebbles, which may be compared to the pencil sketches made by living artists before they begin a large composition in oils. Some of these 'roughs' have apparently been corrected by another hand, as if an experienced painter were showing a pupil how the design should be carried out. The ritual importance of art to the Upper Palaeolithic hunter was so great that the artist probably had special privileges. For instance, he may have been excused duties in the routine activities of the camp, and been given choice morsels from the quarry which his art had allegedly helped to slay. Of course, all this is very speculative, but the long hours the artists spent in the depths of the caves, often working in cramped positions by the guttering light of a moss-wicked stone lamp filled with foul-smelling animal fat, must surely have deserved some special recompense.

Apart from their great cave paintings, the artistic sense of the Magdalenians is expressed in many other forms. Engravings on implements of bone, ivory and horn are of a much higher standard than those of the Gravettians, and exciting work also occurs on pebbles, rock fragments, and lumps of amber and ochre which may have been used as charms. They must also have had a musical sense, for pipes and whistles of bone have been found in the caves. We cannot, of course, deduce from such evidence any of the special character of

Magdalenian music, but these primitive instruments were probably used to accompany ritual chants and also, we may hope, the joyful sing-songs which followed a successful hunt. The aesthetic awareness of these people comes out in a still more personal way in the adornment of their bodies. Animals' teeth and shells were used as necklaces, and bracelets made

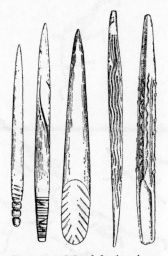

FIG. 21. Magdalenian implements. The two implements on the left are ivory points; in the centre is a light spearhead of bone; on the right are a point and spearhead, both of reindeer antler

from mammoth ivory, decorated with geometric designs, have also been found. Cowrie shells were particularly valued as aids to allure, and also as fertility symbols, perhaps because their shape suggests that of the human vulva.

The Magdalenian culture was not the only manifestation of artistic development in the Upper Palaeolithic. At the very end of the period in eastern Spain, Sicily and north Africa a quite different form of art was being practised, although this tradition also could probably trace back its ancestry to Aurignacian origins. It is much more impressionistic than that of the cave painters to the west, and although the pictures are less technically impressive, they are full of vivacity and acute observation. The figures are conventionalised to some extent, and are used rather as symbols to tell a story than as exact representations of the objects depicted. In this respect they

FIG. 22. An impressionistic rock drawing of fighting archers from the east coast of Spain, typical of the new artistic style being developed there, in Sicily, and in north Africa at the end of the Upper Palaeolithic.

foreshadow quite clearly the development of the modern stylised cartoon.

Between 12,000 and 10,000 years ago the dazzling aesthetic experiment of the Upper Palaeolithic came to an end. The ice-sheets were finally retreating, and the herds of reindeer and other gregarious game which provided so bountifully for the material needs of the Magdalenians withdrew northwards or died out. Tundra and steppe gave place to forest, and the challenge of a new environment caused men to seek new cultural adaptations to the problems of living. In this 'Mesolithic' phase of human history, as it is called, several different cultures are recognised, such as the Azilian, Tardenoisian, Maglemosian, Erteböllian, and Campignian, but the distinctions between these need not concern us here. What is important is that during the Mesolithic an entirely new pattern of

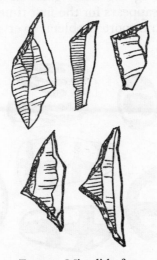

Fig. 23. Microliths from Star Carr, Yorkshire, England (actual size)

life evolved in western Europe. Men became concentrated in small groups in the forest clearings and along the banks of rivers, and the hunting of big game gave place to an economy based on fishing and the snaring of small forest animals and birds. The whole scale of life seemed to have become smaller, and even the implements of man's material culture were reduced to the pygmy microliths which characterise the period. This trend in man's cultural development can be studied at a large number of sites in western Europe including, in Britain, the famous Star Carr camp in Yorkshire. (Plate 47.)

There has been a tendency to regard the Mesolithic as a time of cultural retreat, and certainly it produced nothing in

the aesthetic field comparable to the cave paintings of the Magdalenians. Nevertheless, it would be a great mistake to mini-
mise the importance of this period in the story of man. It is
essentially an age of transition when new ideas were taking
shape and new inventions being made. In the field of material
equipment a whole range of carpentry tools was developed
from antler and flint, while the tiny microliths were perfectly
adapted for hunting the small game of the forest environment. The sledge appears for the first time in human history
as a solution to transport problems over snow and ice, and

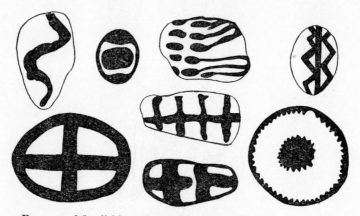

FIG. 24. Mesolithic painted pebbles (Azilian culture). *From
Maringer (1960), Fig. 37, p. 126*

the bones of dogs show that man had already domesticated
his traditional animal friend and hunting companion. Developments in art were visually unspectacular, but had immense significance in other directions. Mesolithic man did
not paint pictures, but daubed simple formalised patterns on
stones. Although not offering the incidental aesthetic rewards
of Magdalenian painting, these decorated stones fulfilled far
more efficiently the primary function of all prehistoric art,
which was to give a sense of magical control over the environment. They were created, we may be sure, for their ritual
significance, but could be produced with only a few simple
lines instead of the enormous effort that went into the creation of the Magdalenian frescoes. In consequence they opened

up new techniques of symbolic communication and, far more obviously than any previous art form, foreshadowed the invention of writing.

By Mesolithic times man had radiated from his primary evolutionary centres in Africa and Asia to the greater part of the earth. In Europe he had spread northwards to Britain and Scandinavia; from Asia he had broken the bounds of the Old World and fanned out over almost the whole of the American continent; in the Pacific he had occupied Australia and many of the remotest islands of the South Seas. Again, however, the spear-head of man's mental advance was to make its break-through in the Old World. In south-western Asia some time in the eighth millennium B.C. our ancestors were working out a technique of living more revolutionary than any that had gone before. We must next describe some of the vital aspects of this revolution, and see how it led to the most significant event so far to have occurred in human history: the birth of civilisation.

Chapter Thirteen

FROM PREHISTORY TO HISTORY

THE PLEISTOCENE epoch saw the gradual emergence of man from the intricate web of evolutionary development that had occupied the preceding 2,000 million years. Natural history led by gradual but logical stages into human prehistory and man rose to be the dominant animal on earth. Then, at the end of the Mesolithic some nine or ten thousand years ago, the tempo of the human adventure was dramatically speeded up. The Pleistocene gave place to the Holocene, the second of the two epochs which constitute the Psychozoic era of life on earth, the era of self-conscious mind. In this Holocene epoch, this very last stride of the hundred-mile journey of our time-scale (see page 115), the hunters and food-gatherers of Upper Palaeolithic and Mesolithic times adopted an entirely new mode of existence which was to have a profound effect on human development.

The basis of the new way of life was the establishment of agriculture and the domestication of animals. This revolutionary stage in human growth occurred in the so-called New Stone Age, or Neolithic period, and made possible the more sophisticated level of human culture found in the succeeding Bronze and Iron Ages, and also the establishment of the first settled civilisations in Mesopotamia and the Nile valley. With civilisation, the evolution of writing marked the end of human prehistory and the beginning of history proper, the stage where written documents first enable us to give a far more precise account of the course of events.

No more than the Palaeolithic can the Neolithic and Metal Ages be defined by exact dates. As the late Professor Gordon Childe delighted to point out, a trumpet did not sound in heaven between the different stages of human culture, causing men suddenly to drop one set of artifacts and pick up another. The new techniques and ways of life grew naturally out of the old as a response to the demands of changing environmental pressures. It was therefore only to be expected that their evolution should have had a different tempo and mode in different regions. For example, ancient Britain did not achieve a Neolithic level of culture until more than 4,000 years after this had been established in the Middle East, and the Neolithic phase in eastern Asia and America occurs much later than it does further west. Even today some inhabitants of Polynesia are only just emerging from the Neolithic culture level as a result of western influences.

Man's first experiments in a Neolithic economy probably occurred in south-western Asia between 8000 and 7000 B.C. This region, from the eastern Mediterranean littoral to the Zagros range between Iran and Iraq, was the home of wild grasses which were probably ancestral to our modern barley and wheat. The area was also occupied by wild oxen, goats, sheep and pigs, which formed the foundation stock of several strains of domesticated animals. Neolithic culture later spread along both shores of the Mediterranean, up the Danube valley to the lowlands of Germany, and reached the Atlantic and Britain between 4000 and 3000 B.C. It evolved independently in south-east Asia and among the Asiatic immigrants to the New World, and by 6000 B.C. was well established in India, China and Central America.

The transition from hunting and food-gathering to stock rearing and agriculture conferred enormous benefits on our species. Man was no longer dependent on the presence of game, nor had he constantly to go through the anxieties and dangers of the hunt; he had a goat or an ox to kill in the pen attached to his home. His women did not have to wander for miles through the wild countryside collecting roots and berries, but simply took what they needed from the nearby cultivated strip. As a result man made enormous economies in time and effort, and was relieved from many of his basic insecurities. The new economy enabled surpluses to be built up to support craftsmen who produced specialised goods, such as pottery, tools and clothing, in return for food. Although such specialisations probably did not occur to any great extent in Neolithic times, they are the essential basis of complex civilised communities. Without the economic discoveries of the Neolithic, civilisation would have been impossible.

The exact stages by which food-production came to be the basis of man's economy are not known, but the process must have been very gradual. Certainly hunting and food-gathering went on side by side with agriculture and stock rearing during the early part of the Neolithic. Perhaps one day a woman noticed that some of the wild seeds she had accidentally dropped a few weeks previously were beginning to sprout outside her hut. As the plants grew bigger she would eat them, and then it might occur to her that what could happen by accident could be made to happen by design. The idea would get around and soon experiments would be made in bringing in seeds to see if they would grow. Thoughtful individuals would study the conditions under which they flourished best, and these ancient agronomists, as we may fairly call them, would eventually discern some of the basic principles of cultivation. At first there would have been many disappointments. Soil exhaustion would often have led to crop failure, and the whole community would have been forced to move on to a new area. But gradually the inquiring agro-nomists would have found out the cause of the failure, and simple types of irrigation, manuring and crop-rotation would have been introduced. In some such way all the complicated techniques of modern agricultural science must have had their beginnings.

A similar process doubtless occurred with the domestica-tion of animals. A hunter may one day have killed a wild ox accompanied by a calf and brought the young animal back to camp alive. In times of plenty, when there was no need to slaughter it immediately for food, the calf might have become a kind of camp pet. Sheep and goats may likewise have been brought in, or wandered in of their own accord to raid the crops. Gradually it would have been seen that the presence of animals in and near the camp had valuable advantages. They could be placed in pens in times of plenty and kept un-til the game became scarce. From this it would have been only

a step to the deliberate breeding of the captives and the building up of herds.

The cultivation of the wild ancestors of wheat and barley
was certainly practised by the Natufians who lived on the
grassy uplands of the ancient Middle East nearly a hundred
centuries ago. These and other people did not take long to
learn the value of artificial selection to produce the best

Fig. 25. On the left is
the wild wheat *Triticum
boeoticum*. On the left is
its cultivated descend-
ant, known as dinkel or
einkorn. *After Cole (1959)*,
Fig. 5, p. 9

strains, and distinct varieties of cultivated grain were gradually established. One of these was dinkel, or einkorn, a wheat
descended from the wild species *Triticum boeoticum*; another
was emmer, descended from *Triticum dicocoides*.

In dry regions the grain was planted with the help of a
number of special implements, such as a weighted digging-
stick of the kind still used by the south African Bushmen, and
a rough hoe made from a forked branch. Where cultivation
was carried on in forest clearings, as in later times in Europe,
the seed may simply have been harrowed in among the ashes
of burnt timber. The most sophisticated piece of agricultural
equipment in Neolithic times was the ox-drawn wooden

plough, but this did not appear in the Middle East until about 3000 B.C., and no example is known from Europe until some 1,500 years later. Other crops were cultivated as the techniques were successively mastered, and orchard fruits, beans, peas and lentils were all known in Neolithic times in the Old World. Rice, then as now, was the standard crop in south-east Asia, and the basis of the Neolithic agricultural economy in America was maize.

Among animals, as we have seen (page 162), the dog was probably the earliest to be domesticated, but was a hunting

FIG. 26. This weighted digging-stick, used by the present-day Bushmen of southern Africa, closely resembles one of the first agricultural implements used by our Neolithic forbears

partner, and not itself a source of food. Remains of domesticated goats and sheep are known from archaeological levels dating back to 6000 B.C., and pigs and cattle appear slightly later. The donkey was the earliest pack animal, and had become a much valued servant of man in the Middle East more than 5,000 years ago. The domesticated horse does not appear until much later, and was probably introduced to Neolithic Europe from north-western Asia well after 2000 B.C.

One of the consequences of the new way of life was that

man in general became much more sedentary. His domesticated animals and plants provided him to some extent with
an artificial environment over which he had a good measure
of control. He was relieved of the necessity to follow the seasonal movements of the game, and only a fairly violent change
in climate could henceforward force him to make long migrations. Of course, in early times, before the principles of agriculture were fully understood, soil exhaustion in one region
might cause him to establish himself in another territory
some miles away. But these movements were essentially local,
and cannot be compared to the migrations that are often
imposed on hunting peoples by the habits of the game.

The more settled quality of Neolithic life had many important consequences. One of these was a tendency towards
a rapid increase in population. In a hunting community
small children are more of a hindrance than a help to the
adults, especially in times of food shortage or when long jour-
neys have to be made. Under more settled conditions, however, the children impose no strain on the community, as they
are fed from the crop surplus and can themselves be put to
work in the fields at an early age. A settled way of life is also
essential to the development of arts and crafts, as there is in
general greater leisure for these to be practised. In fact, some
of the highest forms of art, such as architecture and certain
kinds of sculpture, are not even physically possible unless
people are permanently settled in one place.

The first settled communities were not housed in villages
as we understand the term, but in permanent camps. These
probably consisted partly of skin tents and partly of more
solid structures of wood, turves and piled-up stones, but as
time went on, and the need for even limited movements was
removed, more elaborate centres began to be established.
Numerous Neolithic villages must have existed in the Middle
East well before 7000 B.C., and the remains of one of these at
Jarmo in Iraq gives us a very good picture of what they were
like. The houses were rectilinear and the main building
material was packed mud. Sometimes the foundations were
made of stone, and ovens and basins were often baked into
the floors.

As the population increased some of these villages grew

into townships, and a remarkable example of a Neolithic town
has been excavated at Jericho in Jordan. The site, which is
840 feet above sea level, is watered by a perennial spring, and
a Neolithic village may have existed there nearly 10,000 years
ago. By the beginning of the seventh millennium B.C. this
village had grown to the dimensions of a town of some 2,000
inhabitants, covering at least eight acres, and the super-
imposed rubble of buildings on the site shows that it must
have continued to be occupied by man for many thousands of
years. The earliest identifiable houses were of mud brick, and
seem to have been round with a domed roof made of branches
plastered with wattle. Next follows a stage when the houses
became rectilinear in plan, as at Jarmo, with plastered walls
and floors. At various phases the town was enclosed by five
successive walls of regularly arranged stones, and at least one
of these included a solid stone watch-tower some 40 feet in
diameter. The remains of this tower are still standing to a
height of 30 feet, and at the time it was built, perhaps as
early as 6800 B.C., it may have been upwards of 40 feet high –
the equivalent of a modern house of four storeys. (Plate 50.)

Although mud brick is a suitable building material for
desert lands where there is very little rain or humidity, its use
would be fatal in regions of unsettled climate. Even today
in Egypt, where it is still extensively used for poorer dwellings, one of the violent downpours that very occasionally occur
there may cause the buildings to collapse. When the Neolithic
reached Europe therefore, different building materials had to
be adopted to counter the weather conditions, and our Neolithic ancestors took advantage of the widespread forest in
the region to make many of their houses of wood. The most
elaborate examples are the famous Swiss lake dwellings, the
remains of which have in some cases been excellently preserved. It was once thought that these houses were built on
piles over the lakes, but recent research suggests that they
were more likely to have stood on a framework of beams on
the soft ground by the water's edge. Some may have been
raised a few feet on stakes at places where there was a danger
of seasonal flooding. The houses were tall structures with
steeply sloping roofs rising to a central ridge, and the floors
were often insulated with packed clay to keep out the damp.

Fully as interesting as the habitations of these first settled communities are their implements and utensils. As its name implies, the Neolithic was still mainly characterised by stone implements, but these were of a far higher standard of manufacture than those of the Palaeolithic hunters. The stones were elaborately smoothed and polished, and the people of the time went to much trouble to select the best materials. The need for forest clearance in western Europe meant that axe-heads were in great demand, and underground seams of flint were often exploited for the raw material. In England, the counties of Sussex and Norfolk were particularly important flint-mining localities, shafts being sunk in the chalk and the flint extracted from tunnels running off horizontally at different levels. Apart from axe-heads, finely worked flint arrow-heads and sickle blades are among the artifacts commonly found.

Some of the most attractive Neolithic objects are associated with the crafts that were growing up at the time. The more leisurely and secure way of life possible in a settled community encouraged the thoughtful design and embellishment of utilitarian objects. In fact the artistic sense of Neolithic peoples was mainly expressed in this way, for they have little to show in the so-called 'purer' art forms represented by Magdalenian painting and sculpture.

Pottery of a simple kind occurs in some stages of the Mesolithic in Africa and in Europe, but the Neolithic is the earliest period it came into general use. In Britain some particularly fine examples of Neolithic pottery have been found at a famous site at Windmill Hill in Wiltshire. The potter's wheel was not discovered at this time, and Neolithic pots were built up from rings of spiral coils of clay and then shaped with the hands. Even so they are examples of quite a sophisticated level of technical achievement. To make an efficient pot requires a sound knowledge of the qualities of different kinds of clay, and how they must be dried and baked before use. Much experiment was required, and early Neolithic pots are often coarse and excessively fragile due to incorrect mixing and firing. As time went on, however, their quality improved. Grit or vegetable matter was mixed with the clay to prevent it cracking, and ornamentation was added by making a border of pricked holes just below the rim, or by incising the pot with vertical lines. Some of the designs imitated the texture of other kinds of containers, such as baskets and leather bags.

Basketry itself was almost certainly an earlier invention than pottery. The simplest method used was to coil a twisted skein of grass round a central core and then to sew the coils together with fibre. The inner coils were sewn in a horizontal plane to make a flat bottom, and the outer ones then gradually raised at a progressively steeper angle to form the sides of the basket. In Neolithic times such basket-work containers were often lined with clay, and the accidental burning of one of these may have led to the discovery of pottery. Basket-making continued alongside pottery, however, and its basic techniques were gradually elaborated and applied to the manufacture of other articles. The fashionable basket-work lamps, hat stands, newspaper racks, and armchairs displayed in modern department stores can all trace back their origins to the simple utilitarian containers for fruit and grain made by our Neolithic ancestors.

A more advanced discovery made by Neolithic peoples was the art of weaving. The use of cotton, silk and wool, as well as cruder fibres obtained from the stems of vegetables, was already known at this stage, the spinning being done with the aid of a tapered stick weighted with a whorl. The thread was then woven on a simple loom, at first only in plain weave (which can be compared to the modern housewife's method of darning a sock), but later in more complicated ways. Remains of textiles found at one of the Swiss lakeside villages show that even the complicated art of brocading, in which a design is so woven as to be raised somewhat from the level of the background, was practised in Neolithic times. (Plate 49.)

As a final example of cultural progress we must mention the methods of Neolithic transport. Rivers have always provided man with convenient channels of communication, and devices for keeping afloat were probably some of his earliest inventions. Simple rafts made from logs or bundles of reeds must certainly have been in use in the Upper Palaeolithic, although the perishable nature of these materials means that no solid evidence has survived. But the polished stone axes of the Neolithic enabled more elaborate and durable vessels to be made, and examples of dugout canoes, mostly hollowed from the trunks of oaks, have been preserved at sites in Britain, Switzerland, Germany and Scandinavia. The fact that the bones of deep-sea fish are also found at some of these sites shows that the use of these craft was not restricted to the rivers, and that daring fishermen sometimes ventured for quite long distances out to sea.

Land vehicles probably developed a little later than waterborne craft although, as we have seen, the sledge already occurs in the Mesolithic. The first sledges were doubtless very primitive constructions made of hide or bark, which could be pulled by men or dogs over grass and damp ground as well as snow. In Neolithic times, however, more elaborate types of sledge were developed. These had proper runners of hard wood, and some may have been made from hollow tree-trunks like dugout canoes. Wheeled vehicles are almost unknown from this phase and, in times before a properly organised road system had been developed, would indeed have been of little use. Their first appearance in any numbers is associated with the higher level of cultural progress of the settled civilisations, and they were well established in Mesopotamia and India in the third millennium B.C. In Europe they are rare before classical times, the earliest evidence of their presence there being a wooden cart-wheel, dated about 1900 B.C. from a Neolithic trackway in Holland.

The progress of human culture as displayed in the Neolithic continued at an increasing pace in the succeeding Bronze and Iron Ages. These, however, coincided with the evolution of civilisation and will therefore be dealt with mainly in Part 4. Here we must limit ourselves to a few generalisations about the art of metal working itself and its significance in determining the course of man's cultural history.

The most important point about metallurgy is that it requires a far higher degree of specialisation than any of the crafts practised in Neolithic times. You can weave a basket for fun, and even make a pot as a side-line to other activities, but the complicated processes involved in the construction of metal objects demand full-time application. The introduction of metallurgy into the cultural scene was therefore deeply bound up with the nature of the general economy. Society had to be sufficiently provided with a surplus of such fundamental necessities as food, and also sufficiently advanced in its mental attitudes, to subsidise experts who made no direct contribution to food-production themselves, but whose role was to serve the community in other ways. While it is true that the Neolithic economy supported a certain number of expert craftsmen, such as potters and weavers, specialisation was not its essential characteristic. The advent of the metallurgist introduced an entirely new concept into human social organisation: the recognition that the full-time, highly skilled technologist was a key figure in achieving cultural progress.

Before the discovery of mixing copper and tin to form bronze, copper alone was used for the manufacture of vessels and other objects. This is only rarely found in its natural metallic state in the Middle East, but was nevertheless probably mined and carried around by itinerant craftsmen before the establishment of the first settled civilisations. They would go from village to village taking orders for different kinds of utensils which they would then beat into shape on the spot. This natural, or 'native', copper was probably regarded by early man as a superior kind of stone, and it was not until the art of extracting copper from its ores was discovered that the full potentialities of the material were realised. Although by no means a complicated process by modern standards, the extraction of copper must have presented great technological problems to the first metallurgists. In the first place a primitive kind of blast furnace would have been required before the copper could be melted, and in the later moulding stage elaborate precautions would have been necessary to ensure that the molten copper did not oxydise or stick to the mould. When we consider that these complicated techniques had to be laboriously worked out by a process of trial and error by men who only a few generations before had lived by hunting and primitive farming, the invention of metallurgy indeed seems an astonishing and admirable achievement.

A by-product of the newly developed crafts of the Neolithic and the first part of the Metal Age was a great increase in trade. As soon as there was a demand for specialised materials they often had to be imported, as there was no local source.

The need to pay for the imported goods caused the community to encourage the production of bigger and bigger surpluses of food and other basic necessities, which could be exchanged for the imports. Thus each community gradually established a central 'bank account' of food-stuffs, which was essentially a primitive forerunner of the national treasuries of today. At the same time an interchange of goods between different kinds of specialists began to occur. A village noted for its excellence in, say, weaving or pottery, would begin to barter its products with a neighbouring community which specialised in other types of goods. In this way began the complicated exchange system which forms the material basis of every civilised community.

These aspects of early metallurgy and the development of trade have been touched upon to show that they did not suddenly spring into being with the growth of large civilised communities but had their roots deep in the past. The development of such themes belongs essentially to the next part of this book, however, and we must now turn to some of the more abstract developments of the human mind which preceded the full flowering of civilisation. These are mainly connected with the growth of pure scientific observation, as opposed to its technical applications, and the evolution of religious beliefs.

All science has its roots in technology, which may be defined as the use of rational principles to achieve material ends. There is a tendency today among those who regard science as a kind of ivory tower of intellectual speculation to underestimate the role that technology has played in human history. It is often forgotten that the essentially technological use of external equipment by our primate ancestors was the key to the triumph of *Homo sapiens,* and itself made possible the development of 'pure' science. At the same time it is certainly true that technology has been transcended, although of course not superseded, as man's higher faculties have evolved. The principles which throughout human history have led to man's material welfare, and indeed been responsible for his very survival, are now rightly studied as ends in themselves. Can we see any trend towards this supra-utilitarian attitude to science in Neolithic times?

We must admit at once that any answer to this question, applied to a cultural phase before the invention of written symbols gives positive proof one way or the other, must be largely guesswork. It is, however, well known that pure scientific speculation was practised in the first settled civilisations, particularly in Egypt, and we may therefore fairly assume that it had its roots in the Neolithic. The more leisurely way of life made possible by a food-producing economy would have allowed a surplus of intellectual energy to be available for the disinterested contemplation of natural phenomena. And this, of course, with its attendant wonder at the beauty and complexity of the universe, has always been the motive that drives the 'pure' scientist forward.

While the first technologists were learning to polish stones and turn copper into bronze, men of a more abstract and poetic cast of mind must certainly have been opening up fields of inquiry less tied to the material needs of everyday life. We have no right to assume that, because the Neolithic mind was still largely concerned with physical survival, certain individuals were not already seeking answers to more fundamental questions, such as the laws underlying the mysterious cycle of life and death, and the dynamic principles controlling the motions of the stars. The types of minds that are interested, on the one hand, in the practical relevance of knowledge to human needs as expressed in technology and, on the other, in the pursuit of knowledge as an end in itself certainly had a common origin, and the two activities also certainly grade into each other at many points. But they must already have diverged to a considerable extent in Neolithic times or the distinction between them would not have been so readily apparent when the first large settled civilisations came into being.

This is not, of course, to say that certain Neolithic men would consciously have described themselves as pure astronomers or mathematicians. Such labels would have been quite untenable at the time. Even in ancient Egypt the pure sciences were often adulterated with magic and superstition, and only with the Greeks was their pursuit eventually recognised as respectable without a practical excuse. Nevertheless

7. From prehistory to history

Skeletons of an old woman and a youth from Grimaldi.

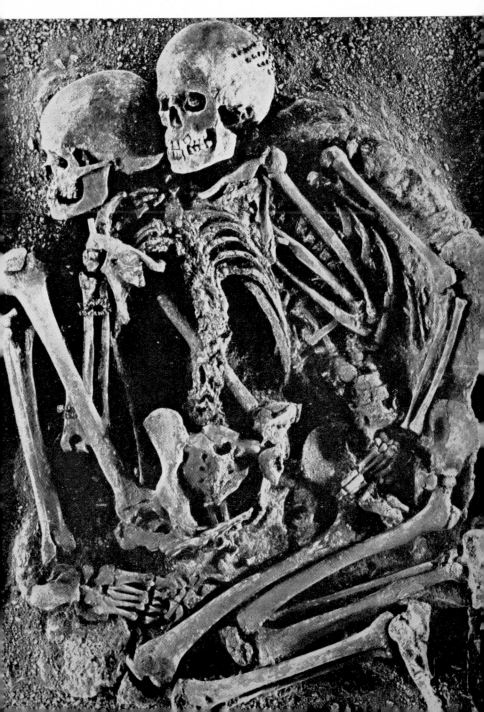

42 Upper Palaeolithic man driving wild horses over
a cliff edge in central France. The carcases were
later used as a source of skins and food.
Reconstruction by Maurice Wilson.

43 An old Stone Age sculptor at work
in a cave in western France.
*From a reconstruction
in the Chicago Natural History Museum.*

44 Like their predecessors the first true men
of the Upper Palaeolithic lived mainly in caves.
Reconstruction by Maurice Wilson.

42

44

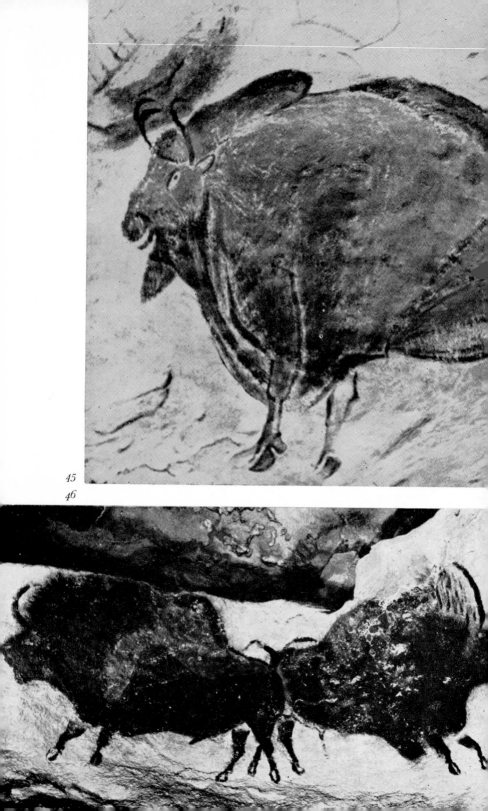

45
46

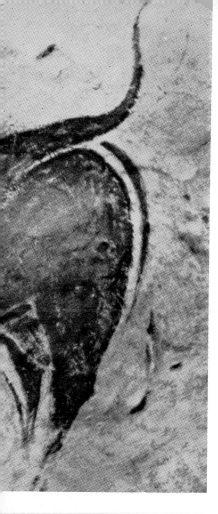

45 This polychrome fresco
of a bull bison from the
Altamira cave in Spain is one
of many fine animal paintings
made by Upper
Palaeolithic artists.

46 Painting of two bull
bison from the Lascaux caves
in south-western France.
The animals are even more
dynamically drawn than those at Altamira
(compare Plate 45 above).

47 Scene on a European river
bank in the Mesolithic period.
*Reconstruction by
Maurice Wilson.*

48

49

50

51

48 Danubian figurine of a naked female (Neolithic). **49** Reconstruction
of a linen textile from a Neolithic lake-side village
at Irgenhauser, Switzerland. Approximately one-eighth actual size.
Original in Landesmuseum, Zürich. **50** Excavated tower of the pre-pottery
period at Jericho, one of the world's most ancient buildings (*c.* 6800 B.C.).
51 An aerial view of the *alignements* at Carnac in Brittany, which
contain 2,935 megaliths.

52 (*left*) A Neolithic *menhir*, or long stone, in Cornwall, England. These megaliths were erected in many parts of Europe as tombstones, idols or monuments.

53 (*below*) The *dolmen* known as Spinster's Rock in Devon, England, a 'table-grave' of Neolithic man. The stones were originally covered by a mound of earth which has since been weathered away.

54 (*bottom*) Stonehenge in Wiltshire, England, is one of the most famous examples of a Neolithic *cromlech*, or 'stone circle'.

in Neolithic, and perhaps even in Palaeolithic times, fore-runners of this evolutionary tendency must have existed. They were the pioneers who paved the way to one of modern man's highest achievements: the disinterested pursuit of knowledge.

To conclude this chapter we must say something about Neolithic and early Metal Age religion. Here again we are on extremely speculative ground, for we have no written records to give an explicit statement of the religious beliefs of the time. We must therefore base our deductions entirely on archaeological evidence, carefully resisting the temptation to interpret this with any dogmatic finality. For reasons of space we must also restrict ourselves to only two aspects of this complex subject: the figurines and designs created by the Danubian farmers, and the so-called 'megalithic' culture of western Europe. (Plates 48–54.)

It must be made clear at the outset that neither of these manifestations of primitive religion is a pure Neolithic pro-duct. The religious beliefs of the people in the pre-civilised settlements of the Middle East are quite unknown, for they left no clear material evidence to show that they had any kind of organised worship. The Danubian figurines date from the close of the third millennium B.C. at the very earliest, and the most important megalithic remains are later still. There is no doubt that both developments were powerfully affected by influences from the first Middle Eastern civilisations, which were established much earlier. But even though they are in consequence hybridised products they do suggest the type of religious thinking that may have been practised by Neolithic communities before civilisation imposed its more rigid spiritual patterns on the human mind.

To begin with some generalities, we may say that the first manifestation of religion springs from a basic practical need just as surely as pure science evolves from the technological organisation of the environment. In Upper Palaeolithic times we have seen that the need to have power over game was the most vitally important factor in survival, and magic (which is, of course, religion in its most primitive form) was evoked in cave art and the activities of witch-doctors and sorcerers to attain this end. But in Neolithic times the basic factors making for survival had changed. Game animals were less important, and the emphasis was switched to the successful rearing of crops and the survival of the domesticated herds which formed the basis of Neolithic life. This led to a parallel change in religious concepts, and the animal magic of the Magdalenian hunters was superseded by the worship of gods of the elements, such as sun, wind, and rain, who might be thought to control the success or failure of crops and pasture. The principle of fecundity, which was so important to a hunting community in ensuring the multiplication of game, remained equally important in Neolithic times, but was now transferred from wild life to domesticated plants and animals. Coupled with these two concepts, and in a sense uniting them, came the idea of the earth itself, with all its natural forces, as a benevolent mother who, if suitably propitiated, would safeguard the interests of men. These three principles – control of the elements, fecundity, and the earth mother – run through the whole of Neolithic and early civilised religion and are embodied in their gods. It is particularly interesting to note in passing that the earth mother represents what was probably the first trend towards monotheism in human thought, combining the multitude of animal and elemental gods and goddesses in one all-powerful Person.

To come now to particular instances, innumerable figurines representing human beings and animals have been excavated from the sites of the Neolithic Danubian farmers of the third millennium B.C. Their artistic merit is slight (we have already said that the Neolithic is marked by a recession in pure artistic achievement), but they were of obvious symbolic significance in the rituals of some primitive cult. The human figurines are usually of nude females with the secondary sexual characteristics strongly emphasised. Animals occur not only as individual sculptures but as abstract engravings on small tablets of bone. The female figures very probably represent embodiments either of the principle of fecundity, or of the earth mother herself, while the animal sculptures and engravings, which are all of domestic forms, such as oxen, rams, goats and pigs, may have played a part in rituals concerned with the successful propagation of livestock. Nevertheless, in spite of the reasonableness of this interpretation, we must be cautious, and the more flippant interpretation that Neolithic peoples made at least some of their images of animals and girls because they liked them cannot be entirely ruled out.

One of the most interesting manifestations of the religious beliefs of Neolithic peoples in Europe was the cult of the bull. This animal, having the most magnificent and virile aspect of all the domesticated beasts, has always symbolised physical strength, sexual power, and a high degree of fertility. It doubtless played an important role in fertility cults in the very earliest stage of the Neolithic food-producing economy, but its use became formalised by ideas imported from the first eastern civilisations where, as we shall see in Part 4, it was firmly established.

The evidence for a bull cult in Neolithic Europe comes mainly from statuettes and engravings on various vessels. The bull itself may have represented the physical partner of the earth mother, who brought to her lands the indomitable masculine force that made them fruitful. The bull's head, or 'bucranium', seems to have been especially venerated, and appears as a stylised engraving on ceramics in outlying parts of Syria and Iran over 5,000 years ago. There is no direct evidence of the form of the rituals of the bull cult in the Danubian area, but we may fairly assume that they were based on the practices of the Middle Eastern civilisations. The only reservation here is that the ritual slaughter and burial of the animal was unlikely to have occurred. The bull must have been such a valuable creature to early farming communities that the luxury of sacrifice, even for the highest religious ends, could hardly have been afforded.

The megalithic ('huge stone') culture, which dates back in some regions to the third millennium B.C., is one of the most intriguing and mysterious aspects of religious development in prehistoric times. At the end of the Neolithic, and in the early part of the Metal Age in Spain, France, Britain and elsewhere in western Europe, our ancestors expressed their metaphysical beliefs through the erection of great structures of rough-hewn stone. The origin of the tradition is unknown, although the concept of the monuments is strikingly reminiscent of that which inspired the immense funerary structures of ancient Egypt. As the exact significance of the megalithic culture, and the nature of the rites associated with it, is also mysterious, we shall concentrate mainly on the monuments themselves without indulging ourselves at this stage in too much fruitless speculation.

Megalithic monuments are of four main kinds: (1) the so-called 'table grave' or *dolmen* (from the Breton *dol,* a table, and *men,* stone); (2) the long stone, or *menhir* (Breton *men,* stone, and *hir,* long); (3) the stone circle, or *cromlech* (Breton *crom,* circle, and *lech,* place), consisting of a circle of menhirs; and (4) the *alignement,* in which menhirs are arranged in long processional avenues. The remains of dolmens mainly occur along the Atlantic seaboard, although they are also occasionally found in coastal regions of the western Mediterranean. They consist of huge slabs of rough stone mounted on pillars of the same material, and are unmistakably the tombs of important individuals. Originally the stones were covered by mounds of earth, but this has often been weathered away, and the dolmens are starkly exposed for all to see (see Plate 53). A variant of this kind of tomb, lying under stone mounds, or *dysser,* is particularly common in Scandinavia. In both types the burial chamber was usually rectangular, and was either entered direct or was extended by a passage, also of giant stones, which ran some distance beneath the original mound before reaching the outer world. In the most elaborate structures the burial chamber had central stone supports for the roof as well as subsidiary chambers, while the entrance passage was divided into sections by rough doorways which could be sealed with stone slabs. The flat 'table-top' of the funerary chamber was sometimes modified into a high vaulted structure, and dolmens of this type can still be seen under gigantic earth mounds in Ireland and elsewhere.

The construction of dolmens must have involved a great deal of laborious work, for some of the stones weigh between twenty and thirty tons and may have been transported upwards of twenty miles to the site. This would have required the construction of a causeway and the use of large numbers of men to move the stones on rollers. The raising of the roofing stones was probably achieved by an approach ramp similar to that used in building the Egyptian pyramids.

The stones of the burial chambers and their approach passages are often engraved with geometrical designs and schematic figures of men and women (Fig. 27); traces of pigment show that originally some of these at least must have been coloured. The meaning of the figures is difficult to interpret, but they may have been a means of identifying the dead

FIG. 27. Schematic anthropomorphic figures, Soto dolmen. *From Maringer (1960), Fig. 47, p. 166*

person buried nearby. Thus the skeletons of a woman and child found at the Soto dolmen near Seville in Spain were associated with a design that seems to represent them in schematic form (Fig. 28). If this theory is true, some of the figures would be comparable to the inscriptions on modern tombstones, although in general a more likely explanation

FIG. 28. 'Mother and child', Soto dolmen. *From Maringer (1960), Fig. 48, p. 167*

is that they represent ancestor figures or magical symbols associated with the gods. Small idols, either flat or rounded and usually measuring only a few inches long, are also found in some of the graves. These are most commonly made of bone, although the more elaborate dolmens often contain idols of sculptured stone. The purpose of these idols is uncertain, but it seems most probable that they were either images of the dead themselves, intended to ensure their continued existence in the after life, or of ancestors and protective deities.

The similarity to Egyptian practice in all this evidence is quite remarkable. Prehistoric man in Europe undoubtedly had a cult of the dead quite as fundamental, if less elaborate in expression, as the dwellers on the Nile. As we have said, many elements of this may have been imported from further east, but wonder and fear at the nature of death and the desire to prolong the life of the dead person in another world must already have been deeply implanted in the human heart. The ritual burials of the Neanderthalers, the red-painted skeletons of the Upper Palaeolithic, and the idols and schematic designs of the Neolithic dolmens, are all evidence of a desire to preserve the body and ensure its immortality. These practices are part of a universal pattern of metaphysical evolution in the human mind which reached its most elaborate expression in the mummification of the actual body and the highly evolved funerary art of ancient Egypt.

Further comparisons with ancient Egypt are provided by the European menhirs and cromlechs. If the dolmens were the pyramids of Neolithic peoples, the menhirs and cromlechs were their obelisks and temples. Menhirs are single upright stones, either rough-hewn and undecorated, or quite elaborately carved. Some of them are of enormous size, and the now broken Men-er-Hroech in Brittany originally stood 66 feet high; many other examples varying from 10 to 35 feet are listed among the 6,000 known in France alone. Menhirs often occur in association with dolmens, and their function has been variously interpreted by scholars. Some believe that they may have been intended as perching places for the spirits of the dead when they emerged from their graves; others that they were simply landmarks enabling the returning spirit to find its own tomb; others again that they represent guardian deities or are simply elaborate tombstones. Such speculations are an entertaining imaginative exercise, but if we are honest we must again say, as so often in problems of prehistory, that we do not know their true significance. The quite frequent presence of menhirs unassociated with graves does, however, suggest that they may sometimes have been erected as idols, or simply as monuments to some particular event or achievement. If this is true, at least some of them could be compared to such later constructions as the Cenotaph and Monument in Britain and the Statue of Liberty in the United States.

When menhirs are grouped together in cromlechs and *alignements* their function is more obvious. Cromlechs, or stone circles, are clearly places where people gathered on solemn occasions to perform some kind of religious rite. The most famous example is Stonehenge in England, a religious sanctuary, or holy place, which is too well known to need detailed description. The present stones at the site belong to the Bronze Age, but the ancestry of the sanctuary goes back to the first half of the second millennium B.C., which lies in the English Neolithic. The sanctuary at that time consisted simply of a circular earth rampart surrounded by a ditch, and the menhirs were added in later phases. Like other English monuments of the same type, such as the stone circle at Avebury, the site is surrounded by earth barrows, and we may assume that the rites practised there were connected with interment. Their exact nature will probably never be known, but the orientation of Stonehenge towards the point where the sun rises at the winter solstice suggests that the sun god, who plays such an important role in all early religious beliefs, may have been the presiding deity.

The most famous example of menhirs arranged in the form of an *alignement* stands at Carnac in Brittany. This is one of the most awe-inspiring and evocative of all prehistoric sites. Nearly three thousand menhirs are arranged in a series of eleven parallel lines with broad grass avenues in between. Three different menhir complexes can be distinguished, each associated with evidence of at least one cromlech to which the avenues of the *alignement* form an approach. Once again the exact function of these impressive structures cannot be determined, but the labour that must have gone into their erection shows that they played a vital part in the religious rituals of the time.

This brief sketch of some of the outstanding aspects of life in the Neolithic and early Metal Age completes our account of man's prehistoric development. Every one of the topics we have dealt with has been the subject of profound scholarly investigation, and much of what I have said will necessarily seem superficial to the experts in each particular field. What I nevertheless hope to have conveyed is some sense of the extraordinary upsurge of life which swept man from his biological origins in the early Pleistocene to the complexities and splendours of civilisation. In less than a million years the grimacing erect-walking primate of the early Ice Age was transformed into self-conscious man. In only a fraction of that time the primitive hunter and food-gatherer of the Upper Palaeolithic had learnt to grow crops and domesticate animals, to build towns and villages and make simple machines, to create vessels of copper and bronze, and to erect gigantic monuments for the worship of his gods. That this swift and astonishing transformation was as much the result of natural processes as the gradual evolution of the whole of life from the primeval protoplasmic froth we can hardly doubt. But before we can even speculate on the possible significance of the human experiment, we must first look at some aspects of civilisation itself and describe how man has evolved in social organisation, mental perception and spiritual awareness over the last eight thousand years.

Part 4

CIVILISATION

Chapter Fourteen

THE ORIGIN AND NATURE OF
CIVILISATION

CIVILISATION is the most highly evolved technique so far discovered by any living organism to ensure the survival of the species, and at the same time to allow it to attain new levels of awareness. The word itself comes from the Latin *civilis,* meaning that which pertains to a citizen, but civilisation today implies much more than mere citizenship. It is a form of biological organisation where mind, which enabled *Homo sapiens* to achieve domination over all other life forms, itself embarks on a process of indefinite expansion. In achieving this expansion it is clear that the laws of mutation and natural selection have applied just as much as they did in the earlier organic phase of evolutionary development. To support this statement we must now consider the origins of civilisation and the major features of some of the great civilisations of the past.

We have already seen that the Neolithic stage of human development was characterised by a more static way of life and a considerable increase in the population. This compression of society also led to the beginnings of cultural specialisation, so that expert craftsmen who could provide valuable technological aids for the benefit of the community were subsidised out of a surplus of basic commodities. In the first civilisations the value of specialisation was still more clearly recognised, and an elaborate system of cultural interchange led to an increasingly complex organisation of society. Moreover, the recognised specialists were not only craftsmen making technological equipment, but others who were regarded as contributing to the common good in less material ways. Civilisation saw the growing influence of the artist, the priest and the philosopher as well as the skilled manufacturer of material goods.

The three most ancient civilisations grew up in three great river basins. Perhaps the oldest of all was that which evolved in what is now Mesopotamia along the banks of the Euphrates and the Tigris. But it may be equalled in antiquity by the civilisation of ancient Egypt, which was developing at the same time along the lower reaches of the Nile. The evolution of these civilisations from the Neolithic phase which preceded them occurred very slowly over many hundreds of years, so we can give no exact date for their origin; but both were well established by about 4000 B.C. A few centuries later, but still over five thousand years ago, yet a third civilisation was growing up along the valley of the Indus in India. All three of these civilisations seem to have had independent origins, and are thus examples of what a biologist would call parallel evolution. No large-scale interchange occurred between them until between 3000 and 2500 B.C.

The main characteristics of these first civilisations, and their successors in other parts of the world, will be described in the rest of this Part, and in this introductory chapter we shall be concerned with only two main questions. The first is to ask why the three earliest civilisations arose where they did, and in answering this I hope to show that civilisation grew up quite naturally, and in accordance with basic evolutionary principles, from the looser forms of human organisation which preceded it. The second is to ask what features of civilisation should be regarded as most typical and significant. By concentrating on these main features I hope to provide the reader with a rough and ready map which will help him to steer his way through the complex jungle of historical facts which I shall shortly have to enumerate.

The presence of water, either in the form of a river or a permanent spring, is of course necessary to the establishment of any settled community. Man must drink as well as eat, and bathing has always been one of his chief pleasures. But the location of the first civilisations in river valleys was not entirely dictated by this basic need. It was also due to the necessity of fertilising the soil for the propagation of crops.

We have seen that soil exhaustion was one of the main problems of the first cultivators, and often made it necessary for them to move to new areas where the land was fresh and unexploited. While it is true that they probably discovered quite early that the use of manure from domestic animals would help to put life back into the earth, this was not an adequate answer to the problem for a large and concentrated population. Now apart from their usefulness in supplying water as a basic necessity of life, rivers sometimes have an equally important use in rehabilitating the soil. A river such as the Nile, for example, carries a heavy load of silt which it spreads on either side of its course during periods of seasonal flood. This silt is a fine natural fertiliser and, when the flood subsides, vitality is restored to the land it has covered. It is not surprising, therefore, that the banks of rivers having a seasonal flood were much sought after as homes by the first farmers. They planted their crops after the flood, and when they were reaped the next flood conveniently refertilised the soil. This natural form of irrigation still plays an important part in the life of primitive agricultural communities.

In very early times it was gradually learnt that the natural bounty of rivers could be applied to cultivation in a more precise and disciplined way. Instead of relying on the vagaries of the flood, man discovered how to build dykes and canals to control the movement of the water. Artificial reservoirs were filled when the flood was at its height, and their contents carried by conduits to the appropriate place when the river fell. Smaller channels spread the water over the fields so that crops could be raised at times when, in the natural course of events, the soil would be cracked and parched by the sun. By the aid of this technique the farmers were often able to grow three or four times as much food as would have otherwise been possible.

Irrigation was one of the key discoveries leading to the growth of large settled communities. It was also extremely important in compelling the value of co-operative effort to be recognised more fully than at any previous stage in human history. The construction of the elaborate dams and canals which are essential to large-scale irrigation would have been far too onerous for a single farming family. The cultivators had to consult together and decide how the layout of the irrigation works could best be designed to meet their common needs. They then had to carry out the actual labour of construction in conjunction, and later to agree on the proportion of water to be allotted to each family in relation to the total amount available. This principle of co-operative effort for the good of the whole community instead of certain privileged individuals is fundamental to civilised society, and irrigation is one of its earliest manifestations.

Another way in which rivers were of vital importance to the first civilised men was as highways of commerce. We have seen that in the wild forest lands of Mesolithic Europe they must already have been the main arteries of communication, but with the growth of specialised crafts, and the need to interchange the craftsmen's products between widely separated regions, rivers became more vital still. Gordon Childe has aptly called them 'moving roads' which enabled cargoes to be transported from one place to another with a minimum of effort. This aspect of rivers, as well as their basic use in providing water for men and their crops, is another reason why the world's first civilisations were established on their banks.

These facts make it quite clear that civilisation did not arise fortuitously in the regions of its origin, but occurred in accordance with the same laws which govern every kind of evolutionary change. Man, like other organisms, is engaged in a constant process of adjustment to his environment. The break-through to the new level of biological organisation represented by civilisation occurred in the river valleys of Mesopotamia, Egypt and India, simply because these offered the most suitable physical conditions for such an advance to take place.

We must now turn to our second question, and define civilisation's most typical and significant qualities. Co-operative effort, as we have said, is one of its fundamental attributes, but this is also a characteristic of many prehistoric, and even non-human, animal societies. The special character of civilisation is more readily appreciated by an analysis of the various means by which such co-operative effort is expressed and controlled, and I now propose to consider these under three main heads: (1) social order; (2) material culture; and (3) metaphysical culture. Each of these aspects of human life has already been mentioned in connection with the earlier development of *Homo sapiens,* but it was not until the evolution of civilisation that they reached their most significant forms of expression.

A social order is found in many different kinds of animal groups, but in civilised man it has reached a very high degree of complexity. A large settled community is a delicately poised biological unit which relies for its stability on the efficient interchange both of commodities and ideas. In the early development of civilisation this interchange was greatly simplified by two major discoveries: the invention of money and the invention of writing.

Money, according to a popular song of the last few decades, is the root of all evil. The misuse of money to achieve personal power is certainly an evil thing, for it deflects human energies from the highest and noblest responsibilities of manhood. But, when its nature and use are properly understood it is seen to be a most useful and necessary means of regulating the exchange of goods. In early pre-civilised societies trade had to be carried on by the simple process of bartering one commodity for another, and is still so practised by uncivilised communities today. Thus so many pottery vessels may be traded in by a craftsman for a single sheep or goat; so many goats or sheep will be regarded as equivalent to one cow; and so many cows will enable a man in need of sexual gratification and domestic service to purchase a wife. But this is a very crude and inflexible system. As man grew in experience it became clear that to endow commodities with a certain abstract quality known as their 'value', and to represent this value by durable and easily portable material symbols such as coins, would make the process of exchange much simpler. Thus a cow could be exchanged for, say, twenty pieces of bronze, silver or gold, which the vendor could retain and exchange for other commodities as the need for these arose. He might, over a fairly extended period, exchange two for a basket, three for a pot, and six for a sheep, or, if he needed none of these things, he might retain the whole twenty as 'capital'. The security and temporal power which a primitive chief possessed by owning, say, two hundred cattle, was thus gradually transferred to a man who had the coins which represented the 'value' of the cattle.

The position was complicated (and still is, as anyone who has examined the workings of the Stock Exchange well knows) by the fact that 'value' is related to laws of supply and demand, and to the intelligence and folly of individuals. Thus a man who exchanges a cow (or a diamond ring, or a holding of stocks or shares for that matter) into coinage or its equivalent symbols, such as paper money or a credit in a current account, may gain or lose according to whether the 'value' of the original possession is going up or down. But such complicating factors do not affect the use of money as a fairly stable measure of exchange values in the growth of complex societies.

Writing was an even more important invention in the transition from barbarism to civilisation. We have already seen how language evolved as a coherent system of sound symbolism, enabling experience and culture to be transmitted from one individual to another without the wastefulness of a constant process of trial and error. But even language itself is a somewhat unsatisfactory means of transmitting an acquired tradition. As thoughts are passed on from one generation to the next they may become falsified by the mental limitations of individuals so that the hard-won knowledge is gradually lost. Writing is simply a means of turning sound symbolism into visual symbolism of a comparatively permanent kind. Before its invention a specially intelligent or insighted individual could only pass on his accumulated experience by telling his descendants what he knew, and this legacy might then easily be lost by a failure in comprehension in his hearers. But when he was able to write it down it could survive for many generations, and be picked up again in its original form after an interval of perhaps many hundreds of years. The visual symbolism of writing has thus played an immensely important part in the development of civilisation.

Although money and writing are two basic techniques associated with civilisation they are not, of course, its main features. Valuable as they are as aids in stabilising the social order, they do not themselves determine its pattern. This is mainly done by the influence of two other still more abstract concepts: government and law.

For a community to survive it has to regulate its behaviour, both internally and externally, according to certain principles. Moreover these principles are constantly changing with the physical and psychological environment. A civilisation must thus be in a state of constant development similar to that of a biological organism, or it will likewise become extinct by a failure to adapt. The 'brain' determining the pattern of behaviour and the way it must be modified to fit changing circumstances is known as government. This may take many forms, including the dictatorship of a single individual, the government of a group of experienced and, it is hoped, intelligent men, or the complex government achieved with greater or less success, 'of the people, by the people, and for the people' as expressed in parliamentary democracy. Each has its advantages and disadvantages, and lends itself to greater or lesser abuses, but all systems have the same end; to ensure the survival of the social order.

Associated with governments, of whatever kind, there has to be 'law'. This is a code of behaviour, based on experience and precedent, which seems to have made for stability in the past and which, it is hoped, will therefore make for stability in the future. Usually it is written down in a number of formalised edicts, but these are reinforced in all societies by a more primitive kind of law, based on 'taboo', or what is and is not 'done'. The use of law by government, and the readiness of most members of a society to conform to it, is again based on the need for the social organism to survive. But again, if survival is to be assured, law, like government, must be flexible and take account of changes in the physical and psychological environments. The successful survival of a civilisation has always been based on the readiness of its members to modify its system of government and the application of its laws as evolution progresses to new levels. To sum up the concept of social stability as a characteristic of civilisation, we may say that it is basically achieved by government and law, acting through the interchange of commodities and ideas (in which money and writing play a vital part), but that the stability is only ephemeral unless it is constantly adapting to changing environmental pressures.

We come next to the role of material culture in the development of civilisation. Both this and metaphysical culture are entirely dependent on the stability of the social order for their highest expression, but once this is achieved they quickly flower. The material culture of a civilisation is an extension of that of primitive man, but under the stable conditions of a settled and well-ordered society it is enabled, if the trend of human energy lies mainly in that direction, to express itself in a progressively more complex technology. Material aids to the problems of physical survival become increasingly refined and efficient so that the basic struggle for mere existence is transcended, and the act of living becomes pleasurable in itself. The process is accompanied by a higher and higher degree of specialisation, leading to the construction of ever more complex machines. Whereas the Stone Age specialist was essentially a man with a high degree of individual skill in the manufacture of a comparatively simple weapon or tool, the specialists of the bronze, iron and atomic ages have relied more and more on team work. Compare, for example, the technological processes leading to the manufacture of even the finest flint axe-head with those needed to produce such a complex article of material equipment as a wireless set. One specialist alone could produce the former, and at very most there might be three – one to locate a suitable stratum of flint, another to chip the axe-head into shape, and a third to give it its final polished gloss. To make a radio set hundreds of specialists are required. There must be the man who understands the basic principles of wireless telegraphy which causes the set to function at all, and there must be craftsmen who know how to make all the complicated component parts such as valves, condensers, resistances, speakers, and so on. There must be other men who can supply the materials from which such components are made, and those who understand how to design and make the machines that help in their construction. And there must be a vast range of specialists in related activities, such as marketing, advertising, servicing and so on, so that this particular type of set shall be sold in preference to another, and so become an 'economic' proposition. All these specialised roles are characteristic of the material culture of a civilised society. The combination of many specialists to achieve the desired result is a remarkable example of the co-operative effort which plays such a vital role in man's advance.

Although social order and the material culture expressed in technology are fundamental parts of the character of civilisation, they are not its highest achievements. If we regard the most desirable state of mankind as happiness, and I think few would dissent from this view, then it is clear that neither order nor material culture can themselves provide it except at a very primitive level. A man who is less likely to be robbed or murdered because of the protection of a legal system, or to starve because the technical advances made in a state of civilisation ensure that he has a secure supply of food, is certainly more 'happy' than one who lacks these advantages. But the very growth of intelligence and awareness that has made such developments possible brings new problems in its train. The mind need no longer concentrate all its efforts on ensuring basic physical survival, and time and energy are left over for different kinds of problems. The question 'how?' begins to be replaced by the question 'why?' As men become less preoccupied with how to get enough food to live, they begin to speculate on why they are alive at all. From concentrating on how to control the external world to permit their physical survival, they begin to consider the nature of the universe itself, and their own significance in the general scheme of nature. Not surprisingly such questions are often extremely disquieting, and the absence of answers to them can lead to consequences quite as disastrous at the psychological level as the absence of food and water would be at the physical level. To deal with such complex problems, which for want of a better word are usually called 'spiritual' problems, new techniques have to be devised. And this brings us to that most vital and important characteristic of a civilisation which is expressed in its 'metaphysical culture'.

The word metaphysical in this context should not be misunderstood. I do not wish to imply that these higher manifestations of evolution are in any way supernatural. Certainly

many expressions of metaphysical culture – particularly religion, for example – have had magical trappings; but these
are the result of the transition, which may or may not be consciously appreciated by advanced exponents of the particular
cultural activity, from the more primitive phase of thought
that went before. Properly conceived, metaphysical culture
has evolved as logically and, in the broadest sense of the word,
'scientifically' from material culture, as the latter evolved
from the purely physical stages of evolution preceding it.

Man's metaphysical culture is manifested in an exceptionally important way in the various forms of artistic expression.
Visual art, as we have seen, already formed an important part
of man's culture in the Upper Palaeolithic, but was at that
time mainly a utilitarian adjunct of hunting magic. With the
growth and spread of civilisation, however, its manifestations
became increasingly diverse under the influence of different
social environments and it began to fill many different roles.
In some fields its value remained primarily utilitarian, and
this function of art is still apparent in advertising and other
aspects of commerce where what we now term 'visual aids' are
used. It also became associated with other art forms to produce a composite manifestation of metaphysical culture: in
opera and drama for instance, where décor forms an important part of the total effect, and even more fundamentally in
ballet where a balanced combination of visual art, music and
dancing are essential to the result. Religion and art have
likewise often been closely associated, particularly in medieval
Europe, and here again we have an example of two aspects of
metaphysical culture working in collaboration to produce a
total effect. In its purest manifestations, however, art has
become a culture form in its own right, and the work of such
painters as, say, Cézanne and Picasso, or such sculptors as
Rodin and Epstein, owes little to other means of cultural
expression.

Music has followed a similar type of evolution to visual art,
although again the social environment has determined its
form in different regions. Originating in the rhythmic sounds
made by primitive peoples, either as signals or accompani-
ments to dancing, it grew progressively more abstract, until it

became a most subtle and flexible means of expressing the composer's vision of the universe. Far more exactly than words, music can provide a commentary on man's metaphysical awareness of his environment, and in its highest forms may offer an illumination of the world much more valid and direct than any offered by formalised religion. But like visual art, it also often retains the functions it possessed at an earlier stage of evolution; for instance, man enjoys dancing to music as much as his primitive ancestors, and, until the invention of radio, the bugle was still a vital and essential means of communication on the battlefield.

We have already seen how Palaeolithic religion partly grew from the terror and dread that afflicted man when he first became conscious of his lonely situation in the universe. This first impulse of the individual to protect himself from the appalling thought of his own insignificance behind a comforting screen of supernatural beliefs was greatly developed in civilised societies. Religious systems increased in complexity, and assumed many divergent forms in different communities. Religion is therefore as characteristic a manifestation of the metaphysical culture of a civilisation as art. In the long run, however, it has proved to be of lesser evolutionary significance, largely owing to the reluctance of religiously minded people to abandon supernatural beliefs. Whereas in many of its aspects art continues to make a valid and illuminating contribution to the study of the psychological and spiritual environment, the supernatural elements enshrined in so many religious systems have caused its influence to diminish as man's capacity for critical analysis has increased. Nevertheless we shall need to look closely at the manifestations of religion in the various civilisations, for although its main function has been to provide a kind of rough and ready first aid to man's evolving mind, it has had an enormous influence on the general pattern of human development, particularly in encouraging the moral attitudes which tend to stabilise rather than disrupt the social order.

As a last example of man's metaphysical culture we must refer to his faculty for disinterested philosophical speculation. This is itself closely related to his readiness to conduct pure scientific inquiry regardless of the result in terms of wish-fulfilment. Perhaps even more than art and religion, philosophical and scientific speculations play a vital part in the development of the highest type of civilisation, and their manifestations must therefore be considered with special attention in our study of the civilisations of the past.

Much thought has been devoted by historians, and particularly in recent years by Professor Arnold Toynbee, to what may be called the taxonomy of civilisation. How many civilisations can be recognised in the human story, and how many of these have played a significant role in the emergence of modern society? The answer to this question will depend on the point of view adopted, which is itself conditioned by the type of mind of the individual student. If human history is looked at in close-up, and therefore divorced from its biological context, a determined analyst can make a case for recognising at least a score of different societies, each with a characteristic type of civilisation. Fortunately in the wider perspective of nature as a whole such refinements are not only unnecessary but out of place. The major trends of man's psychosocial evolution can be better understood by dealing in turn with comparatively large segments of the forest rather than individual trees. For this reason I propose to consider in this Part only the five major manifestations of human civilisation which can be said to typify different stages in the development of man's evolving mind. These are, firstly, the two major civilisations of the ancient Middle East; secondly, the civilisation of ancient Greece as modified and consolidated by that of ancient Rome; thirdly, the two major civilisations of the ancient Far East; fourthly, the abortive but fascinating civilisations of pre-Columbian America; and fifthly, the civilisation of the western world as it emerged after the so-called Dark Ages and, by its remarkable development of scientific and economic ideas, became the dominant civilisation on earth.

In discussing these civilisations I shall be concerned partly with the record of actual physical events which marked their growth, but much more with the general cultural concepts which controlled their transformations. In this way I hope the reader may begin to discern some of the main evolutionary lines which our species has followed in the brief but significant period of its civilised development. I begin in the next chapter with Egypt and Mesopotamia, the two main geographical regions where civilisation achieved its earliest expression.

Chapter Fifteen

THE ANCIENT MIDDLE EAST

OF THE THREE earliest civilisations established by our species those of Egypt and Mesopotamia are by far the best known. They seem to have evolved quite independently in their two geographical centres, and it was not for many centuries after they had arisen that they began to interact on a large scale. Their lines of development were parallel, however, and although their culture was expressed in different forms the broad trend in the two regions was very much the same.

Both the initial independence of the two civilisations and their likenesses were mainly due to geographical factors. Then, as now, the Nile valley and Mesopotamia were separated by broad deserts, which would have made communication difficult. At the same time, the physical conditions in the two centres were very largely comparable: both were almost rainless areas entirely dependent on river water for their fertility. It is common in biological evolution to find organisms in separated regions reacting to similar environmental pressures in very similar ways, and this has likewise happened with human societies. The marked parallelism between the evolution of Egyptian and Mesopotamian civilisations was therefore the result of well-established biological principles. To emphasise the point we must now briefly summarise the historical events and the nature of the cultural development which took place in the two regions.

The archaeological record of Egypt is exceptionally rich, and extends in a largely unbroken sequence from the Upper Palaeolithic to the present day. In early prehistoric times the climate of the Nile valley was less arid than it is now, but the desert gradually encroached on either side, and the transition from Palaeolithic hunting to Neolithic farming took place within a few yards of the banks of the river. By the fourth millennium B.C., or even earlier, the first Egyptians were smelting copper for ornaments and weapons, and were already beginning to master many of the most important techniques that make a high degree of civilisation possible.

The first farmers of the Nile valley would have needed to fight a twofold battle with their environment. Trapped between the thick growth of papyrus and jungle that proliferated along the river banks and the encroaching sands which threatened them, sometimes only a few hundred yards away on either hand, they had to learn how to dominate both. It was necessary both to clear and tame the vegetation to provide space for their cultivation, and at the same time to channel water as far from the river banks as possible to keep the desert at bay. This was an arduous task, and there was naturally a strong tendency for men to combine into fairly elaborate social groups to overcome the challenge of nature. At the dawn of the historic period we find that, up and down the banks of the Nile, a number of centralised communities had been established which enabled such co-operative techniques to be more efficiently organised and thus assist in the survival of the species. These communities were the fundamental social and political units of Egyptian civilisation, and may be compared in some ways with the city states of Greece and early Mesopotamia. However, their common reliance on the Nile discouraged the policies of individual aggrandisement and self-interest which states having a less specialised geographical environment are often tempted to pursue. At first autonomous, the Egyptian city states gradually abandoned all but certain local administrative powers and combined into larger units based on co-operative effort. In the earliest historic times, known in Egypt as the Pre-dynastic Period, two such major agglomerations of local communities were already established. These were the kingdoms of Upper and Lower Egypt, which eventually became unified into a single unit under the half-legendary king Mena some time before 3000 B.C. With Mena began the long sequence of dynasties, which lasted until the Persian conquest in 525 B.C. This is the time which saw the great flowering of Egyptian civilisation.

Throughout the greater part of her history, Egypt was ruled by a succession of god-kings known as Pharaohs. The name Pharaoh itself means 'Great House', for it was regarded as blasphemous to refer to the king by name. The Pharaoh not only had supreme temporal power, but claimed to be an actual son of one of the gods of Egyptian religion, although usually by an earthly mother. One of many other expressions of this idea is found in primitive Christianity, where the Virgin Mary is supposed to have been fertilised by the Deity Himself without the assistance of any merely human personage.

The record of actual events in Egyptian history is too long and complex to be told here, and anyway lies outside the scope of our story. It must suffice to say that in spite of periods of empire building, which extended Egypt's boundaries far into the Middle East, and of conquest by such invaders as the Hyksos, or 'shepherd kings', of Arabia and Palestine, the geographical isolation of the Nile valley, bordered as it was by deserts on either side, caused its civilisation to develop without great influence from neighbouring regions. We shall now be mainly concerned with the particular nature of its social order and with the course of its cultural progress in the major departments defined in the previous chapter.

The governmental system of Egypt was centred on the person of the Pharaoh, who required obedience both as a temporal ruler and as a god. He was surrounded by an entourage of wealthy nobles and backed by a privileged priesthood. With the exception of an enormous civil service of secular officials the rest of the population consisted of merchants, craftsmen and serfs. Little is known of the Egyptian legal system, but it seems that social behaviour was regulated more by moral precept than statute. Control over the lives and property of all members of the state was ultimately vested in the Pharaoh, who governed according to the edicts of the gods as interpreted by himself and his priests. Although such a system was open to obvious abuses, these do not seem to have occurred to any great extent. One of the most remarkable features of ancient Egyptian civilisation was its stability over such a long period, and this could never have been achieved unless the governmental system had been acceptable to most of the Pharaoh's subjects.

Evidence for the moral basis of Egyptian life is found in the 125th chapter of the group of texts collectively known as the Book of the Dead. Here is written the so-called Negative Confession or, as it is more appropriately termed, the Declaration of Innocence. This bears a striking resemblance to Job's protestations in the Old Testament, and also to the Ten Commandments, although expressed in the form of statement rather than exhortation: 'I have not robbed', 'I have not killed', 'I have not borne false witness', 'I have not committed adultery', and so on. A morality which provides a just and reasonable basis for relations between man and man has always in the long run made for greater permanence in a society than a system of laws imposed by dictatorial power. The moral basis of Egyptian life was certainly one of the main reasons for its strength.

The transmission of ideas throughout the great length of the Nile valley was greatly assisted by the invention of the hieroglyphic script. This consisted of a number of pictorial symbols, some standing for syllables, some for individual letters, and others marking the ends of words or determining special meanings. These signs were often in the form of men, animals, or familiar household objects, but sometimes purely geometrical shapes were used; the words were built up by placing the individual signs in a right-to-left series. The hieroglyphic system of word-making can be likened to the rebus, or 'picture pun', so much enjoyed by children. In this a drawing of a group of tents round a fire followed by a bicycle bell indicates the name 'Campbell', while a bee and a leaf is the picturegram for the word 'belief'. Parallel with this beautiful but rather primitive development of picture symbols there evolved the so-called 'hieratic' script in which the hieroglyphs were simplified into more rounded and abbreviated signs suited to rapid writing. The hieratic script stands in much the same relationship to the hieroglyphs as handwriting does to printing today, and it was used mainly for business and other practical purposes, such as doing school exercises and writing letters. Much later yet a third type of writing developed – the so-called 'demotic' script – which was

Fig. 29. Ancient Egyptian writing. The lower line is the equivalent in hieratic script of the hieroglyphic script in the upper line. A comparison between the two scripts well shows how the formal hieroglyphic picturegrams became simplified into a form more suited to rapid writing

based on colloquial speech and largely replaced its two predecessors for all everyday purposes. Thus in ancient Egypt man's evolving mind made three distinct answers to the problems of symbolic visual communication – answers which have been paralleled in one form or another by every community which has recognised the value of 'freezing' speech into the more permanent form of writing.

In contrast with their progress in writing techniques, the ancient Egyptians were slow to grasp the uses of money as a means of exchange. In fact, throughout the whole of Pharaonic times they had no coinage, and barter was the basis of their economic life. Bills were paid in corn and other vegetable produce or livestock, and the rich landowners, and even the Pharaoh himself, counted their wealth in precious objects rather than cash. Money in Egypt was an importation of the foreigner, and even today foreign coinage remains the basis of the country's economic life. In the villages barter still persists, and even the revolution has not yet completely changed the system whereby tenants pay for their land by surrendering a portion of their crop rather than a monetary rent.

One of the most important contributions made by the Egyptians to the ordering of life was the invention of the calendar. The Egyptian calendar was the direct ancestor of the calendar we use today, which it very closely resembles. The Neolithic predecessors of the civilised Egyptians probably dated events by the intervals between two corresponding points in successive phases of the moon, but these occupy only twenty-nine days, and are therefore inconveniently short for measuring long periods. Moreover, the thirteen annual cycles of the moon do not coincide exactly with the grand procession of the seasons as determined by the earth's rotation round the sun, and this caused confusion. To avoid such difficulties the Egyptians chose as their measurement of time the period of roughly 365 days between the arrival of successive Nile floods. They then divided this into twelve months of thirty days each, devoting the five days left over to prayerful observances of the birthdays of the gods. This arrangement, with the newer corrections introduced in Roman times and by Pope Gregory XIII in the sixteenth century A.D., is the basis of time measurement still in everyday use.

In material culture Egyptian civilisation was characterised by spectacular developments in applied science and technology. All the crafts associated with man's mental development grew and flourished, receiving a special impetus from the demands made by the Pharaoh and his nobles for objects of supreme luxury and refinement. Apart from the traditional crafts of pottery, weaving and basket-making, metallurgy reached a particularly high level of sophistication. Goldsmiths used small furnaces to make jewellery and fine gold leaf and, in a more practical vein, elaborate tools such as drills and rip-saws were made from bronze, and later from iron. Wheeled vehicles were introduced in the second millennium B.C., but much more important were the large ships, propelled by sail and oar, which transported agricultural produce and the manufactures of the craftsmen up and down the Nile from the first cataract to the delta. Although the Egyptians were never daring navigators, they sometimes took these ships onto the open sea to bring cargoes of cedar wood from the Lebanon and to carry on trade on the north-east coast of Africa.

One of the most useful and important inventions of ancient Egyptian civilisation was a writing material made from the papyrus reed that then flourished along the banks of the lower

Nile. The pith from the stems of this plant was cut into strips of equal length, which were then flattened, dried, and laid side by side. A further layer of stems was next laid on top and at right angles to the first. Finally the two layers were pressed together with an adhesive substance between them to produce a flat writing surface. The numerous records left on papyrus, written with a reed pen and a dye made from the sap of plants, provide us with much of our information concerning early Egyptian history.

Perhaps the most spectacular achievements of ancient Egyptian technology were in irrigation and building. The practice of extensive and efficient irrigation was made necessary by the environment, and the waters of the Nile were controlled by an elaborate system of dams and canals. Building was not prompted mainly by domestic needs, for in the warm and congenial climate of the region the peasant was satisfied with the same kind of simple house of sun-baked mud brick which his descendants still live in today. The great monuments of stone which are such a characteristic feature of Egyptian civilisation were inspired rather by the people's religious beliefs, which must now be briefly described.

The basis of Egyptian religion was polytheism. The chief gods and goddesses of the country were associated with natural forces such as the sun, the moon and the Nile, and in this way they are the logical successors of the gods of primitive peoples at a pre-civilised level of development. Other deities symbolised more abstract concepts such as joy and fertility, while different towns and crafts each had a god or goddess of their own. The various gods were often represented in the form of human beings with the faces of different animals. For instance, Anubis, the god of the embalmers, had the head of a jackal, and Sobek was given the form of the Nile crocodile. Among the chief of the gods was Ra, the god of the sun, and the mighty Osiris, the stern but compassionate judge of the dead. Supreme among female deities was Isis, the wife of Osiris and goddess of the moon.

The Egyptians loved and respected their gods rather than feared them, and the concept of a God of Wrath, as represented in the Old Testament, would have been quite foreign to their nature. The animals in whose form the gods were so

FIG. 30. Six deities of the ancient Egyptian pantheon. *Upper line (left to right)*: the jackal-headed Anubis, the god of the embalmers and the guardian of tombs; Sobek, the crocodile god; and Ra, the great hawk-headed god of the mid-day sun. *Lower line (left to right)*: Osiris, the stern but compassionate judge of the dead; Isis, wife of Osiris, goddess of the moon and the Nile; and Ptah, the god of Memphis, patron deity of Egypt and the guardian of artists

often conceived were themselves worshipped, and elaborate animal cults played a large part in Egyptian religion. Representatives of the sacred species were specially protected in their lifetime, and after death were embalmed and buried with the reverence nowadays reserved only for human beings. Whole cemeteries were devoted to cats, ibises and crocodiles, and the bull was particularly revered as the living incarnation of Osiris. The Egyptian bull cult was centred on Memphis, just south of the modern Cairo, where a bull with a black coat and a white triangle on its forehead was kept in the temple in great splendour and luxury. When the animal died it was given a ritual entombment in the famous bulls' mausoleum, now known as the Serapeum, at Sakkara, and the whole of Egypt went into mourning until a successor was found.

Like all reflective men, the Egyptians were deeply preoccupied with the mystery of death, and their religious system was very largely devoted to providing an answer to its terrors. They had the same passionate need as ourselves to believe in personal immortality, and the existence of the dead person was supposed to continue in the other world very much as it had in life. The Land of the Dead lay towards the setting sun, and the dead themselves were known as 'Westerners'. For the individual to survive it was believed that his actual body must be preserved as a habitation for his soul, or *ka*. This was achieved by the practice of embalming, which was already being employed in the third millennium B.C. At first embalming was reserved for the Pharaohs and leading nobles, but it was later extended to the great mass of the population. The cult of the dead was also expressed in the elaborate tombs constructed to receive the mummies of rich and powerful persons. The most remarkable of these are, of course, the pyramids, especially the Great Pyramid of Cheops, but a great variety of mastabas, rock tombs and other funerary sites are still to be seen along the left bank of the Nile from Giza to Upper Egypt. The tombs were richly decorated, and filled with useful and splendid objects which their occupants might need in the Land of the Dead.

The great emphasis placed on funerary architecture, and also on the construction of temples for the worship of the

·gods, led to a tremendous development of building techniques. The energy, organisation and skill needed to erect
such a massive structure as the Great Pyramid of Cheops is
deeply impressive, even by the standards of the modern age.
Occupying an area of about 13 acres and rising to a height of
450 feet, this vast edifice contains over five million tons of
stone. This would be sufficient to build a wall ten feet high
and one foot thick around the whole of France. The individual blocks weigh some two and a half tons, and each had
to be raised individually by the combined use of ramps,
rollers and levers. The technical knowledge required for
building some of the great temples of Upper Egypt was no
less remarkable, and would have required an almost equally
vast deployment of labour. The sheer scale of the concepts
which originated in the cult of the dead is one of the most
typical features of Egyptian civilisation.

The art of the Egyptians is particularly expressive of the
character of their society. It is grand and simple rather than
subtle or romantically appealing. The greater part of it is
based on religious beliefs, and sculpture particularly is mainly
dominated by the grave and imposing effigies of the gods and
Pharaohs. In the tombs, however, more homely scenes are
often painted on the walls. These give us a very good idea of
the day-to-day existence of an ordinary Egyptian. We see a
farmer in his fields supervising the work of his serfs, or a
citizen at a night club or some other place of entertainment
sipping his wine as he watches the sensuous movements of the
dancing girls.

In pure scientific inquiry the Egyptians did not excel. A
civilisation so dominated by irrational religious beliefs was
not an environment in which disinterested philosophical
speculation could flower. The scientific achievements of the
Egyptians were by-products of their practical or religious
needs, and suffered from the limitations of this utilitarian
approach. An appreciation of scientific principles was nevertheless achieved in some departments of knowledge, even
though they were not the main object of research. For instance, the need to forecast the movements of stars and
planets, which were regarded as influencing men's lives for
good or evil, led to a considerable knowledge of astronomy,

and advances in building techniques and hydrology were necessarily accompanied by a growing understanding of the principles of mathematics. The study of abstract principles as ends in themselves was not, however, practised to any extent in ancient Egypt, nor in fact in any other part of the world before the time of the Greeks.

We must turn now to the other great civilisation of the ancient Middle East, which grew up along the banks of the Euphrates and the Tigris. This became established at the eastern end of the so-called 'fertile crescent' where man first entered the Neolithic culture phase, and thus counterbalances the Egyptian civilisation, which is an extension of the crescent's other horn. Scholarly argument still goes on as to whether Egypt or Mesopotamia was the earlier of the two civilisations to be established, but in fact the question is of little interest. Much more important is the fact that each almost certainly represents a separate emergence of civilisation from the Neolithic level, and that neither can be said to derive from the other.

Differences in the geography of Mesopotamia and the Nile valley certainly had an effect on their respective histories. Whereas the Nile formed a comparatively isolated environment, protected by deserts and the sea, Mesopotamia was vulnerable to attack by the nomadic tribes that roamed across the arid plains to the west and south, and to invasion by Asiatic peoples coming through the mountain passes to the north and east. Civilisation in the region was therefore subjected to different stresses from that of Egypt. The environment made for a lesser degree of stability, but for this very reason encouraged greater flexibility to meet the challenge. In spite of this, as we have already said, a marked parallelism existed between the two civilisations, and enables us to consider them as different currents in the same cultural stream.

The first Mesopotamian peoples to achieve a civilised level of development were a group of round-headed Caucasoids known as the Sumerians. Their place of origin is unknown, but they were probably a mountain people who had come down into the fertile lower reaches of the Euphrates and Tigris from the northern plateau of Persia. Here they established themselves in a number of independent city states centred on townships built along the banks of the two rivers. Larsa, Lagash, Ur and Erech are but a few of the famous towns associated with this early civilisation. Each state was organised on a quasi-feudal pattern with a king or dictator ruling over a hierarchy of nobles, land-owning citizens and serfs. This was a logical development of the more primitive communities of Neolithic times. Somewhat later a second group of people, who became known as the Akkadians after their principal settlement at Akkad, was moving into Mesopotamia from the west. These people were likewise Caucasoids, but of a Semitic-speaking Mediterranean group which had formerly lived a nomadic existence in the arid semidesert lowlands of Syria and northern Arabia. They established themselves on the upper reaches of the two rivers in city states very like those already founded by the Sumerians in the region lying nearer to the head of the Persian Gulf.

A comparatively small region peppered with vest-pocket states was obviously not destined to remain long in tranquillity. As certain states increased in population and strength they began to look, as states will, for opportunities of expansion. Local wars were common, and the more powerful states tended to absorb their weaker neighbours. At length, about 2350 B.C., an exceptionally forceful Semitic leader named Sargon arose who not only succeeded in bringing the Akkadians under one rule, but also invaded Sumer and united all the inhabitants of the Euphrates and Tigris valleys in a single Sumerian-Akkadian Empire. Even then, however, stability was not assured, and during the two millennia before the birth of Christ successive invasions of peoples from Arabia and the west, north and east imposed their will on the land. The Amorites, Kassites, Assyrians, Chaldaeans, Persians and Greeks successively overran the two river valleys, bringing with them new ideas and acquiring in their turn many of the ideas of the peoples they had conquered. In the eighth century B.C. even the isolation of Egypt was disturbed, for the Assyrians extended their rule to well beyond the modern Luxor on the Nile. The full story of these complex events does not concern us here, for it would throw little light on the principles of human development as a part of nature. More relevant to our theme are the major cultural aspects of Mesopotamian civilisation as they existed in the early years of its growth in Sumer and Akkad, and as they developed at the end of the third millennium B.C. when Babylon had become the country's main centre.

Of the two peoples originally occupying the Euphrates and Tigris valleys, the Sumerians had by far the higher level of civilisation. Life in the Sumerian city state was centred on

FIG. 31. The ziggurat of Nabonidus at Ur. These storeyed towers, dominating the temple enclosure, were a feature of many Mesopotamian cities. *Reconstruction by Sir Leonard Woolley.*

the temple enclosure, dominated by the *ziggurat*, a storeyed tower made of sun-baked mud brick. The temple itself was the headquarters of a divine ruler, or priest-king, and was surrounded by workshops, store-houses for grain, the town school and library, and the dwellings of high officials. Beyond these were the rough houses of the poorer citizens, and then a rampart of earth or brick which protected the town from human enemies and the floods that often inundated the river basins.

Such communities were well established by the fourth millennium B.C., when they already possessed a metal culture based first on copper and later on bronze. Agriculture was the basis of the economy, and extensive irrigation allowed two or even three crops of grain to be raised each year. Wheat, barley and millet were mainly cultivated, and goats, sheep, cattle and donkeys were the chief domestic animals. Considerable advances had been made in material culture, and the traction plough and wheeled vehicles were widely used in the fields. Even at the earliest sites archaeologists have found evidence of a highly sophisticated development of arts and crafts. The Sumerians were famous for their carvings on hard stone surfaces such as cylinder seals, their gold and silver work, and their painted pottery. The great hoards of furniture, jewellery and other funerary objects which were found in the royal tombs at Ur, and date from at least 2500 B.C., surpass in craftsmanship and artistry anything found at the same period in Egypt. Yet perhaps the most important of all the cultural achievements of the Sumerians was the invention of the cuneiform script, a form of writing in which wedge-shaped symbols were impressed on clay tablets. Vast collections of inscribed tablets have been found, and are our main source of information about Sumerian life.

War in these times was accepted as a law of nature, and much energy was devoted to its successful prosecution. As we have already said, the city states fought against each other constantly, and the more powerful states gradually brought their weaker neighbours under their sway. Larger and larger units were thus gradually formed, which in turn fought with other conglomerations of states which had achieved unity in the same primitive and wasteful way. In the process of conquest the victors and vanquished influenced each other in roughly equal degrees, and culture thus became increasingly homogeneous over a larger and larger area. This growing tendency to social aggregation, although often temporarily interrupted by periods of social breakdown and disintegration, has been a universal characteristic of our species in its civilised phase. As will become clear in Part 5, the behaviour of civilised man in this respect is a logical extension of the biological processes that have operated for the past 2,000 million years.

Government in ancient Mesopotamia, both in the original

phase of independent city states, and also after the unifying conquests of Sargon I and his successors, was entirely despotic. The priest-kings of Sumer and Akkad had dictatorial powers based on their personal interpretation of the will of the gods. The leaders who ruled over the larger social units created by conquest and assimilation followed the same principles. Sometimes they were benevolent, and society advanced as well as could be expected under such a primitive form of government. At other times the abuse of personal power and similar manifestations of human stupidity led them into rash adventures, both civil and military, which undermined the tenuous stability that society had already achieved.

One of the wiser leaders of the Mesopotamian world was the king Hammurabi, who rightly described himself as 'a real father to his people'. He belonged to the Amorites, a Semitic-speaking people from Syria, who established their rule over the ancient land of Sumer and Akkad towards the close of the third millennium B.C. These people established their capital at Babylon, and Hammurabi, who was the sixth in line of their kings, ruled over the whole of the Euphrates-Tigris basin some 4,000 years ago.

The greatest achievement of Hammurabi was to formalise a large number of existing customs into a comprehensive legal code to regulate the relations between man and man. This code had a moral basis similar to that which we have already described as lying at the root of Egyptian society, but had the great advantage of being written down. A permanent statement of the disciplines that should control social behaviour in a given society helps to diminish abuses by unscrupulous men who wish to invoke custom and tradition to serve their personal ends. The ordinary man, even in the twentieth century A.D., is largely governed by his emotions and desires, and is thus easily led by the nose, at least for a time, into the channels thought most desirable by the leaders of his society. If these leaders are intelligent, disinterested and wise the results may be good. But unfortunately intelligence, disinterestedness and wisdom are qualities rarely associated with those who possess power, and even if initially present are often quickly corrupted. When this occurs destructive policies often prevail. The great advantage of a written code of law is that it tends to embody the collective wisdom of several generations and, once it acquires authority, is difficult to overthrow by purely individual action. Hammurabi's achievement was that, for the first time in human history, he made a code of this sort available to a comparatively large and advanced society.

The edicts of ancient Babylonian law are often reminiscent in spirit, if not in their exact application, of the kind of laws which still condition the behaviour of modern societies. Many sections dealt with the regulation of personal relationships, such as marriage and divorce, and the adoption and care of children. Thus a Babylonian was expected to have only one wife, and although he had the right to repudiate her he had to make provision for her maintenance if she had not been guilty of obvious misconduct. Concubines could be selected from among slaves, but had to be financially supported, and adultery (at least on the part of women) was punishable by death. In less personal matters, severe penalties were imposed on those who attempted to bribe a judge or witness in a legal action, to misappropriate public funds, or to indulge in other misdemeanours still commonly practised today. Such extreme crimes as stealing from the temple, or kidnapping for personal gain, were punishable by death. Many of the laws may strike the modern mind as rather more savage than intelligent. For instance, a son who struck his father could have his fingers cut off, and a man who blinded another would have his own eyes plucked out. But when we remember that English law imposed the death penalty for sheep-stealing only a little over a century ago, and that a man who is mentally ill can still today be hanged for murder, or electrocuted for rape, we shall not feel that the gap between ancient Babylon and ourselves is particularly wide. The application of any law is limited by the collective mental awareness of the society in which it operates, but this does not diminish the value of the legal principle as such. The laws of ancient Babylon, as set out in Hammurabi's code, were the first attempt by a civilised society to regulate social order by statute and precedent rather than personal whim. As such they are of extreme importance in the history of our species.

We have dealt so far mainly with the material culture of

Mesopotamian civilisation and some of the ways in which it sought to achieve social order. We must turn now to the main aspects of its metaphysical culture as reflected in its religion, art and science.

The gods of the first inhabitants of the Euphrates-Tigris valley closely resembled the nature gods of pre-civilised times, The most important were personifications of natural phenomena, and included Enlil, the god of the atmosphere, Enki, the god of water, and the great earth-mother Ninhursag. Other less powerful gods personified the crafts and domestic activities of men, such as pottery or farming, while even everyday implements such as the pick and the plough each had their own deities.

Unlike the exotic animal gods of the Egyptians, the gods of ancient Mesopotamia were all believed to have human form. Their behaviour was also regarded as being in many ways more human than divine, and scandalous exploits were often attributed to them. In fact the amorous adventures of some of the Sumerian gods are reminiscent of those later practised by the deities of the Greek pantheon.

The beliefs associated with Mesopotamian religion were often cheerless and sombre. They gave no hope of a happy future life such as is promised by Christianity and other more optimistic religions. Man, it was believed, had been created solely to amuse and work for the gods. After death the individual descended to Aralu, 'the land of no return', where he spent eternity in a dark and gloomy world with only dust and clay for sustenance. This depressing outlook was in strong contrast to the Egyptian faith in the continuance of a joyful bodily existence in the Land of the Dead.

The gloomy nature of Mesopotamian religion was also expressed in a strong belief in demons and evil spirits. These, it was held, had been deliberately created by the gods to be a scourge for mankind. They were often represented in the terrifying form of dragons and serpents, and had to be regularly propitiated by sacrifice. The priests were also constantly reading omens and divining the future by casting lots, interpreting dreams, and peering at the entrails of sacrificial animals. A mystical importance was attached to certain numbers, especially seven, which was regarded as specially significant

THE ANCIENT MIDDLE EAST

for either good or evil. In fact a Babylonian calendar has survived which sets aside every seventh day as evil or unlucky. This anticipated (although obviously with a different interpretation) the special importance of the Hebrew sabbath.

Much of the art of Mesopotamian civilisation suffers from the same lack of gaiety and optimism as its religion. The statues that have come down to us are for the most part rigidly executed and somewhat lacking in life; even the occasional masterpiece of portrait sculpture impresses us more by its strength and austerity than by any positive expression of joy. The bas-reliefs are usually more lively, but are still the products of an essentially pessimistic imagination. Their keynote is too often one of violence, horror, or cruelty to inspire much sympathy in the eye of a modern observer. Egyptian art was frequently solemn and imposing and sometimes savage, but its creators were equally capable of relaxing into the lively and often joyous pictures found on the walls of the tombs. There is no evidence that any stage of civilisation in Mesopotamia could produce an art of comparable vividness and appeal.

In pure science, as distinct from technology, progress was as slow in the valleys of the Euphrates and the Tigris as it was on the Nile. In neither region, it seems, had man gained sufficient experience in the art of deducing general principles from particular instances to deal in abstractions at the level demanded by science in its most advanced form. Speculation on the nature of the universe was still based on magical beliefs rather than reason, and personal preoccupations continued to limit the disinterested pursuit of truth as an end in itself. It seems that the human mind was still reluctant to venture beyond the practical applications of scientific thought required by technological progress. It was not until the height of Greek civilisation that a few individual minds began to achieve emancipation from the tyranny of fear and self-interest which was the legacy of man's biological past.

Nevertheless, in the middle and later stages of Mesopotamian civilisation, developments in the capacity for abstract intellectual speculation were to some extent foreshadowed by an increasing interest in astronomy and mathematics. While it is true that the heavenly bodies were studied by the priests primarily as magical aids in foretelling the future (and curious students of the popular Press will not need to be reminded that the pseudo-science of astrology is with us yet), it is at least possible that some of them may have asked more searching questions about the phenomena they observed. Similarly it seems possible that at least a handful of those who studied numbers for their magical significance may have been moved to wonder at the mathematical order of the universe, and the complicated system of abstract relationships which mathematics symbolically describes. In Mesopotamia, as in Egypt, mental evolution was already driving man forward, however reluctantly, to face the challenge of a new world of abstract experience.

To conclude this chapter, how can we best sum up the significance of developments in the ancient Middle East? We can see there how two roughly parallel lines of social evolution expressed themselves in a double emergence from an intricate web of biological tensions. The pressure of change led to the establishment of two highly complex psychosocial communities, both moving laboriously but inexorably to new levels of awareness. Material needs and spiritual fears were still the main motivating forces determining evolutionary change, but already out of these were beginning to emerge a few of the thought processes that have led to the modern world. Our knowledge of these processes is still pathetically limited, and the study of them will doubtless never lead to definitive knowledge. We can, however, say with certainty that Middle Eastern civilisation saw the earliest movement by two highly organised societies towards an awareness of the nature of the universe and of man himself. The fact that this movement was often slow, tentative and confused must not cause us to underestimate the immense importance of the episode in the story of human evolution.

Chapter Sixteen

THE ANCIENT FAR EAST

PARALLEL with the development of Middle Eastern civilisation a similar emergence of human culture was taking place in the regions now known as India and China. The early stages of this story are less well known than in Egypt or Mesopotamia because the intensive archaeological investigation of the region did not begin until comparatively recent times. However, the broad pattern of man's cultural evolution in the Far East is reasonably clear, and enough can be deduced by comparison and analogy to suggest explanations for its particular character.

Indian and Chinese civilisation owes much to the geographical isolation of south-east Asia. A vast wall of mountains cuts off the Indian sub-continent from all land communication with the outside world except through one or two isolated passes, and China is likewise hemmed in by the Tibetan tableland in the west and the Gobi Desert in the north. To the south and east the whole region occupied by the ancient Asiatic civilisations is protected by the sea. Outside influences did, of course, occur, but these were nothing like so violent or so frequently repeated as those which operated in the comparatively open and accessible environment of the Middle East. As a result of this lack of external stimulus the tempo of evolutionary development in the Far East was much slower than in the eastern Mediterranean. The phrase 'the unchanging East' is therefore not entirely a journalistic cliché, but to some extent a description of civilisation in the region before new methods of transport rendered its physical bulwarks ineffective.

The centres of the Asiatic civilisations, like those of the Middle East, were river valleys. Since the earliest times the most favoured and populous regions were the banks of the Indus, Ganges and Brahmaputra in India and of the Hwang-Ho, Yangtze and Si in China. To arrive at a true picture of how the first human societies became organised in these areas is quite impossible owing to lack of reliable evidence, but we may assume that the pattern was very similar to that found in the valleys of the Euphrates, the Tigris and the Nile. The rivers were a perennial source of water in the dry season, a convenient means of transport, and were bordered by fertile land especially suitable for the raising of crops. Their banks were thus naturally sought after as places of habitation, giving comparative security from hunger and thirst, and thereby releasing men's energies for fairly advanced forms of cultural expression.

We will begin our summary of events in the Far East with India. Here everything that happened before about 500 B.C. is still largely speculative. However, excavations at a number of sites in the Indus valley show that perhaps as early as 3000 B.C. man was already emerging from an advanced Neolithic culture into a state of civilisation. For example, at Harappa in the Punjab and Mohenjo-Daro in Sind two large cities were established, with dwellings of many rooms, public baths, shops, temples and well-engineered public drainage systems. The buildings were made of burnt brick and stood in streets of regular width arranged in a uniform pattern. Apart from the traditional crafts of pottery and weaving, a high level of copper and bronze culture had been attained. Wheeled vehicles were used for transport, and the buffalo and even the elephant had already been domesticated. A form of picture-writing, the use of weights and measures, and creations of high artistic excellence in sculpture and metalwork show that the level of civilisation was fully comparable with that of the Middle Eastern centres. This culture was moreover, of independent origin, for we have already seen that little or no communication took place between the Indus and Mesopotamia until the end of the second millennium B.C.

The absence of walls round the ancient cities of the Indus suggests that the region was a peaceful one. At least for a time the bounty of the river provided enough for all, and the land was not ravaged by constant warfare. However, some time after 2000 B.C. the tranquillity of the region was shattered by the arrival of a new people from the north-west. These were men of Mediterranean race, probably with lighter skins than the original occupants of the valley, and speaking an Indo-European language closely resembling that of Persia. The newcomers were generally known as Aryans, and they not only imposed their rule on the inhabitants of the Indus valley, but spread over the whole of India except the extreme south and south-eastern parts of the peninsula. These regions are still occupied today by a distinct type of people, the Dravidians, who have a different language and literature from the men of the north. Some students hold that the Dravidians are the remnants of the earliest pre-Aryan inhabitants of the country, but as there is no certain evidence for or against this view the question must remain open.

The Indus valley, being geographically the most accessible region, was naturally the first to be occupied by the advancing Aryans. Our main knowledge of life there at the time comes from the famous Indian literary work known as the *Rig-Veda*. The word Veda is the Sanskrit for 'knowledge' or 'wisdom', and the *Rig-Veda,* which consists of more than a thousand hymns used as prayers and spells, means literally 'Veda of Praises'. It was composed at some period in the second millennium B.C., although it was not written down until about the eighth century B.C. From a careful study of the *Rig-Veda* many interesting facts can be discovered about early Indo-Ayran life. For instance, we learn that, although agriculture still formed the basis of the economy, wealth was now largely reckoned in cattle. Chariot racing and hunting were popular sports, and gambling was widely practised. The land was not unified under one king but was divided into tribal states ruled by an elected chief. A powerful priesthood led the worship of nature gods whose human and attractive qualities remind us of the heroes of classical mythology. Among the most powerful gods was Indra, who personified thunder, lightning and rain, and was regarded as a powerful source of inspiration in battle; Agni, the god of fire, who had to assist at all sacrifices; Ushas, the god of the dawn; and, above all, Dyaus Pitar, the supreme being in the sky, whose heroic and omnipotent qualities anticipate those ascribed to the Greek Zeus.

As time went on, and the Indo-Aryans spread to the Ganges valley and the plateau of the Deccan, this polytheistic nature worship went through a number of important transformations which finally led to the basic concepts of the Hindu faith. By the eighth century the priests, who now styled themselves Brahmins (from the sacred power, known as Brahman, of which they claimed to be the sole custodians), had established a unique authority. They formed the chief of the four primary orders of society which at this time were already hardening into the castes which are such a distasteful but important aspect of Hinduism. The other three orders were to become the castes of the Kshatriyas, or nobles and warriors, the Vaisyas, or herdsmen, farmers and traders; and the Sudras, the manual workers, labourers and slaves. These eventually split into a large number of subsidiary castes, so that today at least three thousand caste divisions are recognised by orthodox Hindus. The castes were rigidly maintained, and anyone who had contact, even by eating and drinking, with a person of a supposedly inferior caste had to purify himself by performing various penances. In addition large numbers of people were regarded as so base and vile as not to merit a place even in the most humble caste. These formed the tragic group of the Untouchables, who by the simple fact of being part of a line of, say, butchers, road-sweepers or tramps, were condemned to live for ever apart from other members of society, and to perform only the most menial tasks.

The caste system was one of the most shameful concepts in the whole history of human thought, and only in recent years has a more enlightened attitude in India suggested that it may be gradually eliminated. Even if we leave its moral implications aside, it has proved quite disastrous to India's economy by purely practical standards. Although the argument, so often put forward by its defenders, that it made for social stability, is certainly true, this stability was based on such stubborn and inflexible principles that the progress of the country was fatally retarded. A person's occupation, and in fact his every action, was limited by his caste from birth to death quite regardless of his talents or aspirations. Largely as a result of these prejudices, Indian society became almost entirely static, a kind of gigantic octopus slowly strangling itself with its own tentacles of ignorance and superstition. The tragic results of this uneconomic and intellectually unsound system are now only too apparent among the undernourished and often hopeless millions who still make up so much of the country's population.

To return to the development of ancient Indian religion, we find that, with the transformation of early Vedic nature worship into Hinduism, the gods themselves acquired a different character and new deities began to emerge. The three great gods of the Hindus are Brahma, the Creator, Vishnu, the Preserver, and Siva, the Destroyer. These may be said to symbolise respectively the three great events of birth, life and death which have always been of paramount importance to men. Brahma was additionally regarded as a Supreme Being whose spirit permeated the universe, and in this respect he represents the closest approach of Hindu religion to the monotheism of such later religious systems as Christianity. In their abstract form the Hindu gods would have been incomprehensible to the great majority of the people, and were therefore often represented in human and animal form. A great body of legend grew up around the exploits of these incarnate gods, or 'avatars', and they inspired the two great epic poems of the time: the *Ramayana* and the *Mahabharata*.

The romantic adventures of the Hindu deities are often reminiscent of those of the gods of Greek mythology transferred to a more exotic and romantic setting. But although these were attractive as tales, the religion they were supposed to illuminate suffered greatly from the reduction of the gods to material form. There was a general growth of idolatry, and the life of the temples became characterised by increasingly rigid rituals and an insistence on formal sacrifice. Eventually certain Brahmins began to react from this growing materialism, and adapted a more abstract approach to religious questions. They felt the need to worship a power which controlled the whole of the seen and the unseen world, and believed that the road to awareness of this power lay in mystical contemplation. Accordingly they retired as hermits to the jungle, where they meditated on the nature of the universe and life, and compiled a body of writings known as the *Upanishads* (meaning literally 'sitting near a teacher') in which the core of their philosophy is expressed. In the *Upanishads* anthropomorphism is completely eliminated, and the Universal Spirit, Atman, is regarded as the essence of the universe, controlling all objects, all movement and all thought. The divine element in living things, it was thought, came from Atman, but needed to pass through a number of incarnations on earth before final absorption in the Absolute. Thus the transmigration of souls, which might reside in successive phases in the body of a man, an animal, a plant, or even in an inanimate object, was an important feature of the Upanishad teaching. Release from the cycle came when, by right living in a sufficient number of incarnations, the divine element in the individual became finally absorbed in the Universal Spirit.

This mystical doctrine played an important part in the genesis of Buddhism, a facet of man's mental and spiritual evolution destined to have very considerable influence on the thought of later ages in the East. The fuse that led to the explosion of this particular episode in the psychical advance of our species was an Indian prince from a small clan in the foothills of the Himalayas some hundred miles north of Benares. His name was Gautama, and he must certainly have had the extrovert upbringing of other members of his class. As an aristocrat his early life was one of easy luxury, and his diversions those pursued by the leisured classes of all ages – hunting, banqueting, playing games, and enjoying the society of beautiful women. At the same time, however, he was an exceptionally thoughtful person who, like the authors of the *Upanishads,* rebelled against the empty formalism of orthodox Hinduism, and became almost obsessively interested in the profounder aspects of human destiny. Abandoning his luxurious background, he at first became an ascetic, but soon realised that excessive self-denial was as foolish and negative as excessive self-indulgence. He based his thought on right action and right thinking without distinction of caste or any other kind of social status. His philosophy was founded on four basic tenets which are in some respects significantly reminiscent of other sophisticated religions, including

V. Some works of civilised man

55 Ancient Egypt. The coronation of a Pharaoh as ruler
of Upper and Lower Egypt. *From a relief
at the Temple of Edfu between Luxor and Aswan.*

56 Head of the Pharaoh Amenhotep IV from the Temple of Amon at Karnak.
Egyptian Museum, Cairo. **57** The Pharaoh Seti I teaching his son,
later to become Ramses II, to hunt bulls. *From a relief at Abydos.*
58 The step pyramid at Sakkara, built as a tomb for the Third Dynasty
Pharaoh Zoser (*c.* 2800 B.C.).

59 A Sumerian statuette from Lagash, *c.* 2500 B.C.

60 Impressions from Sumerian cylinder seals, third millennium B.C.

61 Terra-cotta head of a Babylonian demon, sixth to seventh centuries B.C.

The objects illustrated on this page are in the British Museum.

62 India. Queen Ahalya Bai's temple at Ellora, Hyderabad,
late eighteenth century A.D.

63 India. Relief depicting the Hindu god
Siva and his consort Parvati from a temple at
Khajraho, central India, *c.* tenth century A.D.

64 China. Group of glazed pottery figures
playing a game. Han Dynasty
(206 B.C.–A.D. 221). *British Museum.*

65 China. Tiger, by Mu Ch'i, thirteenth century A.D. *British Museum.*

66 Ancient Greece.
Two sections of the frieze
of the Parthenon in Athens
(the Elgin marbles) depicting
horsemen in the Panathenaic
procession. *British Museum.*

67 Model of the original
Parthenon, which was built
in the fifth century B.C.
and partially destroyed
in the Venetian bombardment
of the Acropolis
in A.D. 1687.

Four examples of Greek art. **68** Attic amphora depicting Achilles slaying
Penthesilea, Queen of the Amazons, *c.* 540 B.C. **69** Cycladic jug, *c.* 675 B.C.
70 Bronze of a mounted warrior, *c.* 550 B.C. **71** Bronze of a running girl,
probably Spartan, *c.* 500 B.C. *These objects are displayed at the British Museum.*

72 Ancient Rome. The aqueduct
known as the Pont du Gard,
built in the first century B.C. across the river Gard in
southern France, is one of the finest surviving examples of
Roman civil engineering.

Two examples of Roman portrait sculpture. **73** Bronze head of the Emperor Augustus (27 B.C.–A.D. 14); **74** Marble bust of the Emperor Trajan (A.D. 98–117). *Both in the British Museum.* **75** The Roman theatre at Gerasa (the modern Jerash) built in the early years of the Christian era.

76 Ruins of the Temple of the Sun
at Palenque, Mexico. Maya, seventh or eighth century A.D.

77

78

79   80

77 A lintel showing two gods or priests at Yaxchilan, Guatemala.
Maya, seventh or eighth century A.D.
78 Aztec stone mask representing Xipe Totec, the deity of growing maize.
79 Gold necklace from Eten, northern Peru. Inca, *c.* twelfth century A.D.
British Museum.
80 Golden llama. Inca. *British Museum.*
81 Tampau Colorado, an Inca site on the Peruvian coast.

82 An extract from the Koran in Kufic script, tenth century A.D.
From Arabic MS Or. 1397, f, 13a in the British Museum.
83 The Creation of Adam by Michelangelo (A.D. 1475–1564), from the roof
of the Sistine Chapel in the Vatican City.

Christianity. These tenets were (1) that the life of the individual is transitory and full of suffering, or *dukka;* (2) that the cause of this suffering is intense desire, or *tanha,* based on the needs of the individual personality; (3) that suffering will be abolished by relinquishing all personal cravings and entering into a state of universal passionless peace, known as *nirvana;* and (4) that entry to *nirvana* can only be achieved by following the so-called Eightfold Path of right orientation in understanding, aspiration, speech, livelihood, ethical behaviour, action, thought, and contemplation.

This philosophy has many limitations, especially in its neglect of reason and the constructive uses of a passionate and disinterested curiosity, but was nevertheless a great advance on Hinduism. Perhaps its greatest contribution to man's mental evolution was its rejection of the caste system and the emphasis it placed on the role of abstract thought instead of formalised rituals in trying to arrive at an understanding of the universe. On the other hand it failed to legislate for a social order which would replace the narrow and limiting stability which caste admittedly imposed. Buddhism was a reaction from a materialistic faith, but as a philosophy it was essentially unpractical. By concentrating on man's spiritual hopes it neglected to deal with his immediate biological condition in a logical way. Its influence was therefore destined to diminish when science gradually began to reveal that earthly pleasures are as much within the reach of a rational society as spiritual joys. The gradual replacement of both Hinduism and Buddhism by the values of scientific humanism is already under way in the Far East, and may well be completed within the next hundred years.

The art of the Indian sub-continent received much of its inspiration from religious ideas, but at the same time preserved an element of joyous sensuality which gives it great vitality. Alongside statues and reliefs of the Buddha seated in serene contemplation on his lotus throne we find pictures of naked dancing girls with lithe figures and alluring eyes. The often grotesque and enigmatic figures of the gods are accompanied by uninhibited reliefs showing men and women and even gods in different phases of the sexual act. Although

mystical experience and contemplation is an important element in Indian religion, the artists at least were not prepared to deny the joys of the human world. In general, as we
might expect, the more exotic and extrovert works of art are
associated with Hinduism, the more withdrawn and contemplative works with Buddhism. But the two overlap and
intermingle to a remarkable extent, and are evidence of the
complex pattern of man's mental development in the region.

Except in its most primitive technological form, science
was almost unknown in India until the region became influenced by western civilisation. Religious hopes and desires
being the basis of life, and the climate itself being uncondu-
cive to intellectual effort, there was little opportunity for
reason to flower. According to their natures men preferred
sensual experience or religious devotion to thought, and
scientific or philosophical speculation based on a critical examination of evidence hardly occurred at all. The main intellectual achievements of India in the scientific field were in
the building of temples and palaces which, quite apart from
their aesthetic magnificence, show a considerable mastery of
the principles of construction. But in the more advanced
forms of science and technology, which require a wide understanding and correlation of abstract principles, the civilisation stood practically still for the whole five thousand years of
its history.

The early development of Chinese civilisation is as difficult
to unravel as that of India. Its creators were of Mongoloid
stock, and their emergence from the Neolithic occurred in the
valleys of the Hwang-Ho, Yangtze and Si rivers probably
sometime towards the end of the third millennium B.C. However, neither archaeological nor written evidence gives us any
picture of this process, nor of the early centuries of China's
characteristic civilisation. All we can say with certainty is
that agriculture, and particularly the growing of rice, millet,
and perhaps some imported wheat, was the basis of the early
Chinese economy; that this was supplemented by sericulture,
or the production of silk from the cocoons of the silkworm,
which bred prolifically in the mulberry trees of the region;
and that Chinese civilisation grew up in the fertile river
valleys by a process comparable to that which had caused

parallel developments of riverine communities in Egypt, Mesopotamia and India.

Lack of detailed information about China before the first millennium B.C. makes it necessary for us to deal with the historical background of her cultural development in extremely generalised form. The first organised communities in the river valleys were probably small city states similar to those found in the most ancient, or Sumerian, phase of civilisation on the Euphrates and the Tigris. Pigs, horses, dogs, fowl, sheep and cattle had been domesticated well before 1000 B.C., and the wheel and the art of metal-working had already developed at this time alongside the more primitive Neolithic crafts. However, all these discoveries were made much later than in the Middle East, and iron did not come into general use until well after 500 B.C. This has led some scholars to suggest that Chinese culture was the result of cultural diffusion from the more ancient western centres, but the theory is extremely unlikely. Biological precedent shows that parallel emergences of species commonly occur in roughly comparable environments, and there is no reason to doubt that the same process can apply to civilisation. Cultural interchange between China, India and the Middle East certainly went on well before the dawn of the Christian era, but this only occurred after the civilisations in each region had become independently established.

In spite of the vastness of China, which occupies an area of some one and a half million square miles, there seems to have been an early tendency towards centralised government. Large tracts of the country were unified under successive dynasties of emperors, and a well-organised civil service controlled the administration of the various provinces. Decrees were passed back and forth with the help of an elaborate form of picture-writing directly ancestral to modern Chinese. A powerful army, divided into both infantry and cavalry units, was equipped first with bronze and eventually with iron weapons, and may have had bronze chariots as early as the Shang Dynasty (c. 1766–1122 B.C.). The centre of these developments was at first the valley of the Hwang-Ho, but by 210 B.C. the ruler Shih Huang of the Ch'in dynasty (from which the name China is derived) had extended the control of the central government to the whole country and laid the foundations of the Chinese Empire.

The course of events in the historical China from the Ch'in dynasty onwards cannot concern us here, and we must limit ourselves to discussing some of the main characteristics of Chinese civilisation as a whole. As in Egypt, Mesopotamia, and particularly in India, the religious ideas of the first civilised communities in China had an extremely important effect on their cultural development. Before the first century A.D., when the Buddhism of India began to have an increasing effect on the Chinese mind, these ideas were largely comprised in two great religious systems which had themselves emerged from the magic, animism, and nature and ancestor worship of primitive China. These early Chinese religions sprang from the teachings of two men, the probably legendary Lao-Tse, who according to tradition was born in 604 B.C., and the more solidly human Confucius, who lived some fifty years later than his rather nebulous predecessor, and whose teaching has influenced the practical moral behaviour of millions of Chinese right down to this day.

Taoism, as Lao-Tse's teaching is called, has many similarities to Buddhism, which later largely replaced it through the activities of foreign missionaries. It is a vague and mystical faith based rather on negative values than any criteria of positive action. An unchanging unity, known as *Tao,* is alleged to underlie every manifestation of the unstable material world, and a power known as *Te,* based on a resigned quietude and yogic breathing exercises, is regarded as the Eternal Way to realising the nature of *Tao.* The role of the individual, it was believed, was to express through his life a code of unassertive effortless behaviour, known as *wu wei* (literally 'inactivity'), which would lead eventually to an understanding of the fact that *Tao* 'is ever inactive, yet there is nothing that it does not do'. It is easy to ridicule such an apparently contradictory and negative philosophy, and indeed when expressed in the extreme form of Taoism it was entirely unproductive. On the other hand the virtues of contemplation and reflection are recognised in every religious faith, and even form an important element in the creative thought propagated by pure science. Pure Taoism remains an interesting example of an evolutionary cancer at the mental level – a kind of proliferation of the cells of idleness. But the fact that in its undisciplined form it led to a disastrous retardation of thought does not invalidate the value of contemplation as an aid to human awareness. What the disciples of Taoism lacked at the period of its heyday in China was the capacity to integrate its attitudes into a wider philosophy which included also an understanding of creative action.

By contrast with Taoism, the doctrines of Confucius were esentially practical. Confucianism in fact embodied a common-sense moral code aimed at regulating the relationships between man and man. Confucius, like most intelligent men, had confidence in the essential goodness of human nature. He believed that man's misfortunes sprang less from hard hearts than thick heads, and he also had a compassionate understanding of the limitations of the human mind. His followers in ancient China were enjoined to recognise the value of propriety, courtesy and reverence in their personal and public dealings. He had a profound belief in human dignity, and felt that the organisation of human society must be based on mutual respect. His philosophy did not include the mystical flights of Buddhism or Taoism; it aimed rather at achieving harmonious relations in this world between ruler and subject, master and servant, and friend and friend. Its inspirational content may not have been high, but it provided a valuable antidote to the more extravagant fantasies of the mystics, whose heads were so constantly in the clouds that they quite lost sight of the fact that their feet stood on the earth.

Unlike the civilisations we have previously discussed, China shows no evidence of a close link between her religion and her art. This is largely because Taoism was extremely hostile to physical representation of the Universal Spirit, or anything connected with it, regarding it as too impersonal to be realised in concrete shape, while Confucianism, being less of a religion than a practical philosophy, provided no inspiration for religious art. Respect for ancestors, which was such an important feature of Chinese religion, required only comparatively simple rites, and therefore the creation of temples and all the sculptures and other works of art associated with them received much less attention than in other lands. In fact one of the main characteristics of Chinese art, which in the long run has been a cause of its timeless appeal, is that it is largely secular. It finds its expression in landscapes, and in pictures of animals and men going about their everyday tasks, rather than in heroic or pious representations of the gods. The reason is simply that a people whose metaphysical beliefs were rooted in the mystical contemplation of Taoism or the moral code of Confucianism had no gods in

FIG. 32. A Chinese dragon from the Imperial flag
of the Manchus

the Egyptian, Mesopotamian or Indian sense. Their nearest approach to a symbolic representation of a powerful personage was the dragon, but this was a concept that had evolved from primitive nature worship, and was never tied to a theistic interpretation of the universe. Everyone can enjoy pictures of Chinese dragons just as much, and in the same spirit, as those who first painted or looked at them. To the Chinese, of course, they have a special significance according to such points of anatomy as the number of their claws, the arrangement of their scales, and the colour of their eyes, but this in no way destroys the universality of their aesthetic appeal. The Chinese dragon, like so much of Chinese art, is not an expression of narrow religious bigotry but a gay expression of the artistic imagination of men.

Turning finally to science, we find that the Chinese were

as backward both in technology and rational speculation as their Indian neighbours. Once they had mastered such comparatively simple technological inventions as were common to all the early civilisations, their progress in the scientific field was so small as to be almost negligible. As recently as the sixteenth and seventeenth centuries A.D. such evidence of technological progress as could be found in China can be almost entirely traced back to the importation of western ideas. Neither did the Chinese make any significant contribution to the more abstract sciences of mathematics, astronomy and physics. It seems that the dead hand of Taoism and Buddhism so completely paralysed the minds of the Chinese that their intellectual evolution stopped for all practical purposes well before the dawn of the Christian era. Only in the last few decades have western influences awakened this vast and populous country to a new sense of urgency in scientific matters. The present attempt by the more enlightened Chinese leaders to transmute ancient habits of thought, and to encourage their countrymen to make a new and constructive contribution to the progress of all mankind, is therefore greatly to be welcomed.

To sum up, what can be said from an evolutionary standpoint of the role of the two great eastern civilisations in the human adventure? They represent in general a most remarkable example of the growth of two similar but distinct organisms in an isolated environment. Behind the immense barriers of rock, sea and sand which once separated southeastern Asia from the rest of the world they were for long cut off from the main stream of progress. It was an environment where a moderately congenial climate and the exceptional fertility of six great river valleys allowed the evolutionary energy expressed in all forms of organic development to discharge itself up to a certain point. A reasonably high level of material culture was achieved, but the urge towards its expansion was then lost through the influence of a mystical philosophy which held that no present disturbance of mind was ultimately worth while, as the purpose of man was to lose himself in the quietude of a harmony which intellectual effort could only destroy. This allowed the individual to support a degree of personal suffering and frustration that might otherwise have proved intolerable, and for more than four thousand years the civilisations of the East lived by this code. Now at last in the twentieth century the physical barriers which had previously isolated Far Eastern civilisation from the evolutionary challenges confronting western man have been broken down. India and China are once again becoming integrated with the forward march of consciousness which it is apparently the destiny of our species to express. The form of this advance was hammered out in the eastern Mediterranean region in what are known as the civilisations of Greece and Rome. It is to this great episode in the history of mankind, which saw the forging of the modern world, that we must now turn our attention.

Chapter Seventeen

CLASSICAL CIVILISATION

In the two previous chapters we have dealt with four major manifestations of civilisation. Each represented an independent emergence from the Neolithic level in different regions, and each followed its own characteristic course. At the same time, as the chapter grouping indicates, these four civilisations can be logically divided into two pairs: (1) the foundation civilisations of Egypt and Mesopotamia, which were to pass on important cultural legacies to the main stream of human advance, and (2) the comparatively isolated civilisations of India and China, which were to proceed at a much slower pace and have only recently begun to be reintegrated into the general pattern of progress. We must now consider yet a third pair of civilisations, which evolved not in parallel but in succession, and played the most vital role of all in bringing man to his present condition. These are, of course, the classical civilisations of Greece and Rome.

Although classical civilisation was greatly affected by cultural developments in Egypt and Mesopotamia, absorbing many of their ideas and transmitting them forwards, it is important to realise that in its essence it represents a quite individual growth. Greece was not the child of either Egypt or Mesopotamia, but their precocious cousin, the product of its own physical environment and genius. Rome likewise evolved in her own individual way. Although her civilisation never reached the supreme creative level achieved by the Greeks, the stability she imposed on the ancient world enabled the achievements of eastern Mediterranean culture to be passed on to modern times.

Both Greek and Roman civilisations are much more recent than the civilisations of the Middle East. The climax of Greek

233

civilisation did not occur until the fifth century B.C., and at that time Rome had hardly embarked on the period of her greatness. No significant events are recorded about the ancestry of either civilisation before the first millennium B.C., and even our knowledge of the first centuries of that millennium depends more on tradition than established fact. Compared with the age of life on earth, or even the million-odd years of hominid history, the time between Greek civilisation and ourselves seems almost too short to be measured.

The Greeks and Romans themselves were members of the same Indo-European stock that invaded the Indus valley. The ancestors of all these people probably belonged to nomadic tribes roaming the steppes and forests of central Eurasia some four thousand years ago. In the second millennium B.C. they were advancing in successive waves into the peninsulas of southern Europe we now know as Italy and Greece.

In this southward advance the northern nomads came into contact with a civilised world that had already been long established. Apart from the two major civilisations of Egypt and Mesopotamia, which we have already described, other organised societies had developed in Persia and on the island of Crete. A Semitic people known as the Phoenicians, whose homeland corresponded roughly with the Lebanon of today, were opening up maritime commerce throughout the whole of the Mediterranean, and establishing trading posts as far west as Carthage and the modern Cadiz. Concerned as we are only with the major features of human evolution, we cannot pursue the fascinating story of these developments here. The main point to emphasise is simply that the Greeks and Romans did not create their world in a psychological vacuum. The southern coasts of Europe some 3,000 years ago were not a virgin territory, but already supported a population of active and striving human beings who from the beginning formed an important element in the environment of classical man.

Now what are the major contributions of classical civilisation to the story of man's evolving mind? To answer this question we shall deal first with Greece and then with Rome along the lines followed in the last two chapters. That is to say, we shall begin with a synoptic account of the social organisation which provided each society with its basic stability and then briefly describe the main features of its material and metaphysical culture.

The social organisation of ancient Greece, as of all civilised communities, was very much a product of the region's topography. In Egypt, we have seen, a single desert-fringed river was the sole source of life, and the need for co-operative effort as an essential technique of survival therefore imposed on the land an exceptionally rapid realisation of the virtues of unity. In Mesopotamia, with a broader territory watered by two rivers, instead of one, and a less intensely specialised environment, unity came more slowly but was nevertheless achieved within a fairly short period as a result of comparable environmental pressures. The Greek peninsula provided by contrast a quite different set of physical controls. No single river unified the land, either as a channel of communication or a source of fertilising water. Greece is essentially a land of geographical compartments – narrow valleys and small plains cut off from easy communication with neighbouring areas of habitation by mountain barriers or maritime inlets. Although seasonally arid it is far from being a desert, and an adequate rainfall removes the need for widespread irrigation. It was natural, therefore, that the migrating tribes which settled the peninsula should establish themselves in small and comparatively self-sufficient city states which had little material need for communication with their neighbours over the hill.

How then can we explain the unity – the essential 'Greekness' – of Greek civilisation? It seems that in the main this was based on shared traditions. The southward-moving tribes came from the same environment, and their patterns of thought and feeling had therefore evolved under roughly the same conditions. Although they spread and established themselves in different geographical niches they retained an emotional bond. This was expressed in a similar attitude to moral and ethical questions, a shared mythology (later to be expressed in the Hesiodic and Homeric poems), and a common Pantheon. The accidents of geography caused a fragmentation of Greek society, but could not destroy its underlying *ethos*.

We must now look more closely at the organisation of the individual city states as they became established in the first half of the first millennium B.C. It should first be emphasised that all the states were extremely small by our standards, their size being comparable to that of a modern English county. The total population of a typical state was less than that of most country towns in modern America and Europe, and the whole army of some of the smaller states could have been carried by half a dozen double-decker buses. These ancient Greek communities therefore resembled large clans or families rather than states in the modern sense of the word. The leading citizens were often closely related to one another, and the society was administered very much on family lines.

Each state was ruled by a council of its most prominent men, who were elected by all members of the community possessing the status of citizens. The idea of a 'pharaoh' with divine attributes, or even of a priest-king on Mesopotamian lines, was quite foreign to Greek thought. The Greek rulers were either aristocrats who had acquired their status by birth, or rich men whose wealth gave them the power they could not claim by their lineage. The citizens, who were the only members of the community with the right to vote, were nearly all members of the leading families, although in some states wealthy farmers and merchants who had shown evidence of social responsibility were granted the same status. Below this level the population consisted of unenfranchised artisans and slaves without any recognised power to influence the administration of the state.

This type of social organisation, depending on the intelligence and integrity of a privileged class, would not be suitable to the populous and rapidly evolving technological world of today, but in classical times it ensured a stability appropriate to the stage of evolution that had been reached. This was largely due to the responsible attitude of the ruling class, who in general governed wisely and fairly for the benefit of the whole community. Any tendency to corruption could be checked by the main body of citizens who, being educated men, were capable of weighing the issues without hysteria. Both rulers and citizens were also greatly influenced in their concept of their duties by the pronouncements of the Greek philosophers. In the Greek state, unlike the modern world, thinkers were among the most respected members of the community, and therefore had considerable power over men's minds and actions. They were in effect secular priests using reason instead of magic as a technique of persuasion, and through their agency Greek civilisation benefited perhaps more than any other in history by the application of intelligence to practical affairs. The exceptional importance to mankind of the Greek philosophical attitude will shortly be discussed, but we must first briefly enumerate some of the characteristics of material culture under the régime of the city states.

Probably owing to the existence of a large body of slaves, applied technology did not make great advances in classical times. Small communities, adequate sources of food, and a plentiful supply of cheap labour, did not encourage mechanical invention, and the Greek achievements in this field were mainly intellectual playthings and 'gadgets' with little practical value. For instance, Ctesibius of Alexandria, who flourished in this important Greek colony in the second century B.C., invented a slot machine, an hydraulic organ, and a number of devices operated by air pressure, including an airgun and a pneumatic pump. The water screw developed by Archimedes of Syracuse at about the same time is perhaps the most famous example of a Greek machine. This device enabled water to be lifted from one level to another by rotating a helix inside a cylinder, and is still used today for irrigation in Egypt and elsewhere in the Middle East.

Apart from such isolated inventions the material culture of the Greeks was essentially an extension of Neolithic and Bronze Age practices. The traditional crafts continued to flourish, and pottery showed a greatly increased refinement, both in technique and decoration. Buildings were at first simple, and the most ancient Greek temples were of mud brick with a thatched timber roof. Later magnificent edifices of stone were erected, and such buildings as the Parthenon at Athens are among the glories of Greek civilisation. But the greatness of Greek buildings lies in their design and aesthetic quality rather than any innovation in methods of construction. Little was achieved in the material culture of the Greeks that was not already present in the earlier civilisation of Egypt.

It is above all in metaphysical culture that the unique contribution of the Greeks to human progress is to be found. This will now be summed up under four heads, namely religion, philosophy, pure science, and art. But such divisions are, of course, entirely arbitrary; in every civilised society the contribution made by each to the growing awareness of mankind shades into the next, so that the four in conjunction form the single spearhead of man's mental and spiritual advance.

In religion *per se* the Greek contribution was not large. Or perhaps it would be truer to say that religion in Greece remained an instrument of social stability and did not provide any special inspiration leading to new levels of experience. The gods of the Greek Pantheon were essentially large-scale human beings, indulging in petty squabbles, wars and jealousies just as men do. Their chief was Zeus, who was supposed to live on Mount Olympus on the borders of Macedonia and Thessaly, accompanied by a large assemblage of other gods and goddesses each related to some different aspect of nature or human affairs. These included Helios, the god of the sun; Apollo, the god of music, athletics and prophecy; Ares, the god of war; Poseidon, the god of the ocean; Artemis, the goddess of the moon; and Aphrodite, the goddess of love and beauty. The Greek gods are thus comparable to the gods of other early civilisations, especially those of ancient Sumer and India, and their chief value lay in the unifying effect they had on the geographically separated city states.

Far more important than religion in the Greek contribution was their philosophical thought. Philosophy, or 'love of wisdom', was a very important concept to the Greeks, and they were the first members of our species to make a reasoned and sustained attempt to understand the nature of the universe as a whole. Formerly men had pursued knowledge solely for their own needs, and their awareness of the external world had been restricted to emotional reactions, such as feelings of pleasure at the sun or fear at the storm. They personified the forces of nature as benevolent or hostile gods, and considered other forms of life, and even other men, mainly for the effect they had on themselves. The supreme achievement of the Greek mind was to emancipate the personality from an attitude centred on the self, and to encourage the investigation of first causes and principles. The philosophers maintained that only by a disciplined attempt to understand the laws governing all phenomena in nature, whether these were physical, mental or spiritual, could wisdom be achieved.

The main tool of this method of investigation, as it has been of all later investigations of a scientific or philosophical kind, was reason. Reason is simply a method of thought which holds that true knowledge about any phenomenon must be based not on emotion, desire, or appeals to magical authority, but on demonstrable proof. The Greek philosophers looked at the whole world in this spirit, and refused to set any limit to the range of their speculations. Unfettered by any sacred books or rigid priestly doctrines, their minds were free to explore the fundamental questions with which man at his highest level of evolution is inevitably concerned. In this way they initiated an attitude quite distinct from that associated with magic and revealed religion on the one hand and applied science and technology on the other. This was the attitude of pure science, which ranks with philosophy itself as the most noble activity of the human mind. In fact in ancient Greece the pure scientist and the philosopher were one.

Whereas priests and myth-makers always offer an essentially magical account of the origins and nature of the universe, the Greek philosopher-scientists tried to explain natural phenomena in a natural way. Some of their theories show a remarkable anticipation of some currently respected doctrines of modern science. For instance, Heraclitus of Ephesus, who was born in the sixth century B.C., maintained that the universe had no beginning and no end but was in a condition of constant change. Several aspects of his doctrine are very similar to the views which have been put forward at different times in the twentieth century A.D. by Henri Bergson and Fred Hoyle. Again Leucippus and his successor Democritus of Abdera, who both lived in the fifth century B.C., held that matter consists of minute particles so small that they cannot be subdivided. Although the true nature of atoms as revealed by recent research was not understood by these early Greek scientists, their theory obviously fore-shadowed modern concepts. Even those Greek philosophers and scientists who were much further astray had arrived for the first time in history at the idea of an orderly universe which changed from one state to another by natural law and not by the whim of some mythical or divine personage. Of course the men who even discussed such matters were exceptionally advanced and intelligent members of the community, and the rank and file continued to hold to the ideas of primitive mythology and religion. But Greek science and philosophy nevertheless pioneered the attitude, and some of the theories, which are embodied in the most advanced modern thought.

It was not only in cosmology and pure scientific speculation that the Greek thinkers pointed the way to the future. Such philosophers as Socrates, Plato and Aristotle attempted to apply reason to the social organisation and everyday relationships of human life. It is true that their ideas only slowly took root, and Socrates was even condemned to death for his attempt to corrupt the Athenian youth with his allegedly subversive views, but once they were established their influence was never afterwards entirely lost. Thus the Greeks led the way not only in intellectual speculation about the universe as a whole, but in all those departments of knowledge which may lead ultimately to the greater happiness of mankind. Their most fundamental inquiries concerned the nature of matter and life, but they were also profoundly interested in the principles that should govern the ideal state, the proper place of law, morals and religion in the social scheme, and even the validity of the special kind of emotional exaltation we experience in art. There is scarcely a field they did not explore in their passionate and disinterested search for truth.

The speculation of Greek thinkers on these topics was aided not only by the special quality of their minds, which we may call the genetic component, but also by a greatly enlarged environment. The Greek peninsula lay at the crossroads of the civilised world, and its inhabitants travelled widely into other lands. The Greeks established colonies throughout the length and breadth of the Mediterranean, and under Alexander the Great their knowledge and influence extended eastward to the Indus and even beyond.

Travellers such as Herodotus gave graphic accounts of the life and thoughts of the peoples of north Africa and Egypt, while Greek geographers used the reports of the daring Phoenician navigators to build up the first map of the known world. The stimuli of these new geographical discoveries, coming from so many different sources, gave a continual impetus to the lively curiosity of the Greeks and provided fuel for their intellectual endeavours.

Apart from the ferment of ideas initiated in pure science and philosophy, in sociology and politics, and in the study of their geographical environment, the Greeks also produced the greatest works of art since the paintings in the Palaeolithic caves. Moreover, the best of their art had become emancipated from magical or religious associations and was now practised for its own sake. They strove to reveal in their art a vision of grandeur and beauty, a visual representation of that same order and harmony in the universe which they sought in their scientific and philosophical speculations. Nothing was represented in an exaggerated or disproportionate way; sculptures, reliefs, decorations on pottery and buildings, all show a preoccupation with balance of form and mood. The artists excelled especially in their representations of the human body, and no art before or since has so completely expressed an ideal concept of the beauty and dignity which man can attain.

The literature of the Greeks, being written in a dead language, is unfortunately less accessible to most people than their art. However, the great works of Greek literature have maintained their influence on the modern world through numerous excellent translations which are still widely read. The earliest important works were the Homeric poems, dating from about the ninth century B.C. Apart from being exciting adventure stories, recounting the exploits of the Greek gods and heroes, these contained profound moral truths comparable to those expressed in the finest of Shakespeare's histories. A still higher level of expression was achieved by the tragic dramatists Aeschylus, Sophocles and Euripides, whose works, even in translation, still produce the authentic spine-chilling sensation associated with all great poetry. The literature of the Greeks, no less than their philosophy, marks the beginning of a cultural tradition which has led directly to nearly all the major intellectual, artistic, and moral achievements of the modern world.

Compared with the Greeks, the Romans made a less original contribution to man's mental and spiritual growth, but it was nevertheless of vital importance. Before discussing its particular nature we must summarise a few historical facts. The ancestors of the Romans, we have seen, were members of a vast complex of Indo-European nomadic tribes which some four thousand years ago were moving southwards from their central Eurasian homeland into the Indus valley and the southern European peninsulas. While the Greeks were organising themselves in their city states and building the glittering civilisation we have just described, other tribes were moving in successive phases through the Alpine passes on to the Plain of Lombardy. From there they fanned out into different regions of the modern land of Italy, where they established themselves in the most congenial geographical environments between the Mediterranean and Adriatic coasts. One of these tribes, which settled along the banks of the Tiber on the 'shin' of Italy, founded the city of Rome – a city which was to become mistress of the whole western world, and the centre of an empire stretching from the Atlantic seaboard to the banks of the Euphrates, the Tigris and the Nile.

Rome was built by a tribe known as the Latins on a ford across the Tiber sometime in the early part of the first millennium B.C. To the north was the land of the Etruscans, a Mediterranean people who had probably arrived in this area by sea from the Middle East, and were well established when the nomads began to come down from central Europe. To the east and south other nomadic tribes, such as the Sabines and Samnites, occupied different regions of the Apennines, while in the toe of Italy and in eastern Sicily was the flourishing Greek colony of Magna Graecia.

The history of Rome from the time of her foundation until the second century B.C. is mainly concerned with a struggle for supremacy between the Romans and their Italian and Etruscan neighbours. Rome also came into conflict with Carthage, an important Phoenician trading post on the northern coast of Africa near the modern Tunis, and with the barbaric tribes of France, known as Gauls. In all these struggles she emerged ultimately as the victor, and in the second century B.C. she began to advance still further on the path of conquest. The fall of Carthage in 202 B.C. gave her domination not only of much of north Africa, but also of the Carthaginian colonies in Sicily and Spain. She then moved eastward, absorbing Macedon and Greece, and establishing colonies in Asia Minor. Eventually, under Julius Caesar and his grandnephew and successor Octavius, the foundations of the Roman Empire were laid. This period in European civilisation begins roughly at the same time as the Christian era, and saw Rome extend her influence to every part of Europe except the barbarian north, to the whole of Africa north of the Sahara, and to many of the most prosperous and fertile lands of western Asia. The stability of this Empire was to last for nearly five centuries, and its effect on the later history of mankind can still be felt today.

The immense stability which Rome imposed on the world is her supreme contribution to civilisation. Unlike the Greeks, who were responsible for an extraordinary episode of explosive evolution in the development of the human mind, the Romans had little of supreme originality to offer in the higher expressions of metaphysical culture. Some of their paintings and sculptures were excellently observed and executed, and their literature includes many noble and readable works; but on the whole it must be admitted that none of their contributions to art, science or philosophy can compare with the achievements of the Greeks. Yet we must remember that without the Romans these very achievements might have been lost to mankind. If Rome did not create a civilisation, she was certainly extraordinarily efficient in transmitting the creations of her predecessors. She provided man with a long period of assessment and reflection in which the achievements of the past could be assimilated and synthesised for the benefit of future generations.

Although the ideas which came down the great pipeline of Rome to the modern world originated mainly in Greece, many other influences became embodied in the stream. The cultures of ancient Egypt, Mesopotamia and Persia had already interacted with the Greek genius, particularly after the conquests of Alexander the Great, and the Roman Empire now gave these different elements in human thought a chance to fuse. The influence of Christianity likewise became incorporated in the general pattern after the Christianisation of the Empire, and the new religion brought with it a full cargo of ideas from its Hebraic past. These various cultural streams, interacting and intermingling in Roman civilisation, and being later reinforced by the contribution of the Arabs, were the source of the intellectual energy which created the civilised western world.

Now what was the form of social organisation which enabled Rome to sustain her long period of unchallenged supremacy? This question cannot be simply answered, for during the period of her greatness her form of government went through many transformations. Beginning as a small city state, intensely nationalistic, and bent solely on protecting her own frontiers, she grew first into a powerful Republic, ruling over most of the Mediterranean world, and then into a vast Empire. The detailed ebb and flow of events in these transformations cannot concern us, but as we look at the overall pattern we may feel that the stability of Roman society throughout the period of its greatest influence was based on two main characteristics: (1) a general recognition by the governing power that there must be some safeguard for human rights; and (2) a corresponding recognition by the individual of the necessity for discipline and law.

It would be wrong to imply, of course, that a recognition of this twofold principle, which lies at the root of every stable society, was made instinctively and automatically by either rulers or ruled. Oppressive acts by the government and anarchic movements by the governed were as much a part of Roman society as of any other. However, it seems that some special quality in the Roman character made it possible for the wilder excesses on either side to be avoided. This can doubtless be partly accounted for by the Roman military tradition, with its special emphasis on responsibility and duty, which from the earliest times permeated the thinking strata of the community. The innate conservatism of the Romans was also a factor which helped to keep their civilisation stable, even if it also inhibited any exceptional creative daring in the intellectual field. Whatever influences determined their nature, the Romans in their greatest period under the first centuries of the Empire were characterised by a special gravity in their attitude to their society and to their personal responsibilities. This diminished the likelihood of any frivolous adventure disturbing the poised state of their civilisation, which in fact did not begin to disintegrate until the growing decadence and autocracy of the Emperors undermined its basic character.

The sense of order and responsibility which was so typical of Rome at the height of her greatness was embodied in a legal code which is one of her most valuable legacies. Roman law was transmitted forward long after the Empire had died, and still lies at the heart of the legal systems of western Europe. It originated in the days of the simple peasant society which lived along the banks of the Tiber long before Rome became a world power, and throughout its later transformations retained the innate conservatism of a peasant people. In its formal expression, however, it can be said to date back to the famous Twelve Tables, written down about 450 B.C., which first codified a system of conduct which should regulate human relationships for the greater good of the community as a whole. As Rome extended her influence over foreign lands the scope of the law was broadened to include the differing customs of the conquered peoples, and Greek influences began to be incorporated. For instance, the Stoic emphasis on man's natural equality exercised a humanising influence on the legal code, and contributed much to its effective application to alien societies coming under Roman rule. This basic legal tradition was further modified as a result of Christian teaching which, in spite of a totally different intellectual basis, was working towards the same liberal and egalitarian end. Thus when the Roman law of the Empire was finally codified by the Byzantine emperor Justinian in A.D. 527 it represented, by and large, a fairly reasonable and practical concept of what men could and could not do if society was to survive.

The stabilising influences of discipline and law operating over a vast area are undoubtedly the most important contributions of Rome to the evolution of our species. Certainly nothing of a more creative kind stems directly from Roman civilisation. However, to conclude this chapter we must briefly describe a few representative facets of other human activities as they were practised under Roman rule.

In material culture, or technology, Rome's main achievements lay in the field of what one would now call civil engineering. In building the bridges and roads which were essential to communication between the different parts of their huge Empire, the Romans showed an exceptionally competent and original talent. This same emphasis on large-scale engineering was apparent in the public works which are such a characteristic feature of their cities. Their public drainage systems and the aqueducts they built to carry water to the main centres of their population were superior to any produced by previous civilisations, and were not surpassed in later times until the Industrial Revolution of the nineteenth century. By contrast, Roman domestic and public architecture showed fewer innovations. It largely followed Greek models, although everything was built on a grander, and indeed heavier, scale. Roman buildings are of formidable size, strength, and solidity, but generally lack the grace of their Greek prototypes. However, mechanical problems were solved with great efficiency, and stone buildings of several storeys were often built to house the poorer members of the community. The public baths, arenas and theatres which played such a large part in the life of the Roman citizen when off duty were also conceived on an exceptionally grand scale, and executed with supreme technical skill.

Rome's contribution to metaphysical culture was particularly disappointing. The earliest Roman religion was simply a development of the nature worship of a primitive agricultural people, modified by concepts inherited from the Greeks. The gods and goddesses were at first thought of simply as spirits, such as Silvanus, the spirit of the wild woods, Vesta, the spirit of the hearth, and Jupiter, the controlling principle of nature. But as a result of Greek influence these were later personalised and given human shape. Statues and images of the gods were then made, and many of them were identified with the gods of the Greek Pantheon. These extremely primitive religious concepts persisted throughout the whole period of Rome's greatness, and were not superseded until the Christianisation of the Empire under the Emperor Constantine in the fourth century A.D.

Roman art shows a great falling off after the magnificent achievements of the Greeks. Its best features are realistic portrait sculpture and the lively mosaics which often decorated Roman homes and public buildings. In other respects it was often heavy, uninspired and tasteless. We nevertheless owe a great deal to Roman sculptors for their exceptionally competent copies of Greek masterpieces. It is not generally realised that only a tiny handful of original Greek sculptures have survived, and nearly the whole of our knowledge of this great artistic age comes from the work of Roman copyists.

Turning from visual art to literature we find the scene still more depressingly bleak. The Romans excelled in history and biography, and such writers as Livy, Tacitus and Plutarch have left enthralling factual accounts of their age and the men who fashioned the Roman world. The campaign records of Caesar and the animated correspondence of Cicero likewise give us a fascinating insight into Roman life. But of works of great imaginative literature in either prose or verse there are none. The nearest approach is made in Virgil's *Aeneid,* but even this splendid poem cannot be compared in either vision or technique with the majestic utterances of Homer.

In pure science the Romans had none of the immense curiosity about the natural world that characterised the Greek philosophers and scientists. They were content to take their knowledge second-hand from books, and especially from such encyclopaedic compilations as Pliny's *Natural History.* Pliny himself was a cavalry officer and a gentleman (a disastrous combination from a scientific viewpoint) and his book simply transmits, without criticism or analysis, the statements of earlier authorities with all their inaccuracies intact. Such practical aspects of natural science as medicine appealed to the Romans, but they added nothing to the earlier discoveries of the Greeks. In fact the two most reputable scientific workers in any field under Roman rule were both Greeks. One was the geographer Strabo, a wandering scholar who produced a vast geographical description of the known world in

seventeen volumes; the other was Claudius Ptolemaeus, generally known as Ptolemy, a Greek astronomer working in
Alexandria. Ptolemy produced an encyclopaedia known as
the *Megale Syntaxis,* or 'Great Synthesis', which largely determined human thought in mathematics as well as astronomy
for many centuries. But neither he nor Strabo was a scientist
in the modern sense. Although their work includes a certain
amount of original speculation they were mainly content to
transmit and comment on the more important Greek discoveries.

Finally we come to philosophy, and here again Roman
civilisation reveals an intellectual bankruptcy. Such Romans
who studied philosophy at all based their ideas almost entirely on a few particular facets of Greek thought. The most
important of these was Stoicism which, as we have already
seen, played a part in formulating the Roman concept of
government and law. Stoicism may be defined as the philosophy of virtue, which is regarded as the sole good. Health,
happiness and possessions are of no account; our only duty
is to live in accord with nature and to recognise the brotherhood of man. Such a doctrine appealed greatly to the more
serious and austere members of Roman society, but it never
made much headway with the masses. The practical mind of
the average Roman had in any case no interest in abstract
thinking, which seemed to have little obvious application to
material needs.

From a modern point of view one of the most interesting
contributions to thought to come out of the Roman world is
the work of the poet-philosopher Lucretius, who died about
55 B.C. In his poem *On the Nature of the Universe* Lucretius
rejects the old beliefs about the gods, immortality, and even
the eternal ideas of Plato, and holds that life is nothing but a
fortuitous combination of atoms. In Book V he gives a remarkable, if somewhat fantastic, account of the origin and
evolution of life, the early development of man, and the history of civilisation. No one interested in the theme of human
development as a part of nature should neglect to read these
speculations by an early thinker of the Roman world.

What can we say to sum up in a few sentences the role
of classical civilisation in human evolution? One thing, I

think, is clear: the Greeks were a people of genius – perhaps the greatest genius which the extraordinary primate called man has so far displayed. If, as we said in Chapter 12, the late Pleistocene epoch saw an explosion of the human mind, Greek civilisation saw an explosion of the human spirit. A fire was lighted in ancient Athens which has flickered and wavered through the centuries but has never been finally extinguished. The fuel for this fire came from ancient Egypt, from Crete, from distant Babylon and Persia, and even from the primitive nomadic tribes who crossed river and mountain and plain to settle in the Greek peninsula; this fuel was ignited and fanned by the genius of Hellas. But when at last it seemed to have burned itself out, and to be in danger of extinction, it was resuscitated by Rome and preserved to influence the whole future development of mankind. Compared with the genius of the Greeks, the Romans may appear to be only a people of talent. But they paid the tribute which men of talent have so often paid to men of genius: they took the responsibility for keeping their ideas alive.

Chapter Eighteen

ANCIENT AMERICA

So FAR in this Part we have discussed the cultural characteristics and possible evolutionary significance of six ancient
civilisations. We have seen how a parallel development of
human society occurred in both Egypt and the valleys of the
Euphrates and the Tigris and how, somewhat later, a third
emergence occurred in the Indus valley. We have seen also
how the nomadic tribes occupying central Eurasia in late
Pleistocene and early Holocene times eventually fanned out
into new environments on the southern borders of the land
mass. Mongoloid immigrants, perhaps mingling with an
aboriginal population, were responsible for the ancient civilisation of China, while Caucasoids from a more westerly continental centre moved into the Greek and Italian peninsulas
to found the civilisations of Greece and Rome. The eastern
civilisations of India and China, we have stated, evolved
largely in isolation behind the great natural barriers of the
Himalayan range and the Gobi Desert, and for this reason, it
seems, acquired a special character based on the nature of
the geographical setting. The civilisation of Egypt, Mesopotamia, Greece and Rome, on the other hand, occupied a much
smaller area, and as a result of interaction between them important elements from each passed naturally into the main
stream of western civilisation, which is today the dominant
civilisation on earth. An account of this process, emphasising
the special importance of the Christian and Moslem contributions, will form the subject of the next chapter. But meanwhile we must deal with one other complex of civilisations
which, although essentially a side branch of the evolutionary
progress of man as a whole, provides an exceptionally interesting example of parallel evolution at the cultural level. I refer,

of course, to the emergence of Maya and Inca civilisation in ancient America.

At some uncertain period in the late Pleistocene (probably between 20,000 and 10,000 years ago) successive waves of men were moving from their evolutionary centres in central and northern Asia into the American continent. Some of these had strongly Mongoloid features; others were more generalised in physical type and may have been descended from the common ancestors of both the Mongoloids and the American Indians. In any case, as the waves of immigrants came in, they would have multiplied and blended to a considerable extent. Later, as they became more settled in different habitats, they would also have shown new differentiations. This process of constant mixing, of convergence followed by divergence, is sufficient to account for the many variations of physical type observed among the American aborigines when western Caucasoids first met and described them.

The migration of these people from Asia to America would not have been difficult. It is believed that in late Pleistocene times a land bridge joined eastern Siberia with Alaska across the present Bering Strait, so the immigrants could probably have made the whole of their journey on dry ground. Even today the two continents are separated only by some fifty-three miles of sea, being sometimes in sight of one another. At no time would it have been difficult to negotiate this obstacle, either in skin boats or even by walking across winter ice.

Some of the newcomers moved east across the desolate northern plains of North America to settle along the north-eastern seaboard of Canada and the coast of Greenland. These people had many Mongoloid characteristics and, perhaps with some Nordic admixture from early Norse adventurers who sailed across the Atlantic from northern Europe, were the ancestors of the modern Eskimoes. Other invading Asiatics moved further south and settled in many parts of what is now the United States, where their 'Red Indian' descendants still live to this day. Others again migrated further afield to establish themselves in the jungles of Central America and Brazil, the snowy heights of the Andes, and the rolling pampas of the Argentine. In fact almost the whole

American continent was soon occupied by the invading hominids from the west. It was an extraordinary example of radiation by a dominant species over a vast new territory in a comparatively short space of time.

When these Asian peoples reached America we can be reasonably certain that they all belonged to hunting tribes at a Palaeolithic level of development. One reason for this belief is that no single domestic plant or animal from the Old World is known to have reached the New before the arrival of Columbus from the east in 1492. They relied for their food supply on the big game of the American plains and forests, including many species now extinct. Mammoths, mastodons, several different kinds of wild horses, and enormous ground sloths were all among their prey, as well as the more familiar deer and bison still found on the American continent today.

But this hunting phase was only the beginning of the story. The cultural evolution of the immigrants went on at a considerable pace, paralleling in some regions – although at a later date – the achievements of the early civilisations of the Old World. So remarkable did this development seem to the first archaeological investigators that they felt it must have been the result of cultural diffusion from some Old World centre. This view has long been abandoned, however, and it is now clear that the cultural development of America before the arrival of European influences from across the Atlantic was entirely independent. It was another example of the well-established biological principle of parallel evolution, which also accounts for the independent emergence of civilisation in Egypt, Mesopotamia, and the Indus valley. Human society in the continent moved from Palaeolithic beginnings, through a Neolithic phase, to civilisation by the same logical steps as had been followed in the Middle East and south-east Asia several thousands of years before.

A detailed account of the growth of pre-Columbian American society is irrelevant to our story, for it could really only be a restatement of the processes operating in Eurasia, which have been described in previous chapters. I therefore propose to deal only with the end-products of its various transformations as represented by Maya and Inca civilisation.

The earliest New World break-through from the Neolithic

to civilisation occurred in Central America and southern Mexico sometime about 1000 B.C. It was made by a group of American Indians known as the Mayas, who established flourishing centres in the Yucatan peninsula and its immediate hinterland. The culture of these people grew up from an agricultural economy based on maize, but lacking domestic animals except the dog and the turkey. Compared with the development of the Eurasian civilisations the progress of the Mayas was slow, and when Old World influences, as represented by the Spaniards, spread to this part of America early in the sixteenth century A.D. their society was completely destroyed. Nevertheless we must briefly summarise a few of the major aspects of their cultural evolution before it was so rudely interrupted by the Spanish invaders.

The high degree of social organisation required for city life had been developed by the Mayas well before the dawn of the Christian era. In the ancient cities of Yucatan, craftsmen flourished and interchanged their goods much as they did in the civilised centres of the Old World. Pottery reached a very high standard of excellence, and the richer vessels were often decorated with elaborate polychrome designs. Weaving was also widely practised, and representations on Maya monuments suggest that many different kinds of fabrics were made, ranging from simple cottons to elaborately embroidered brocades. There was very little progress in metal culture, however, owing partly to the lack of raw materials in Yucatan and partly to a failure to realise their potentialities when they were found. No metal objects are associated with the most ancient Maya sites, although for some centuries before the Spanish conquest ornaments of gold, copper and even bronze are occasionally found. A remarkable feature of the material culture of ancient Central America is that it scarcely emerged at all from a Stone Age technology.

Each Maya city had its king, its nobles, and a powerful priesthood, and at different phases enjoyed either a largely autonomous condition, or was absorbed in successive confederations and empires similar to those found in ancient Mesopotamia and other regions of the Old World. Although conditions between the cities were peaceful in earlier times,

253

the closing centuries of Maya civilisation saw numerous disastrous outbreaks of civil strife. The Spanish are often criticised for their ruthless obliteration of ancient Central American culture, but in fact they only completed a process that a self-destructive militarism had already initiated from within.

Although destined to make no ultimate contribution to the progress of our species, the Mayas conducted several intellectual experiments comparable to the more successful innovations made by the men of the Old World. For example, they repeated the ancient Egyptian inventions of hieroglyphic writing and the calendar. Maya hieroglyphs lack the sophisticated development of their Egyptian counterparts, and were never even arranged in an alphabet, but they do show a parallel type of mental development from simple picture-writing to formalised symbols. The Maya calendar likewise evolved on the same lines as that of the ancient Middle East. A solar calendar was substituted for the old lunar reckonings as early as the eighth century B.C., when the year was already recognised as consisting of 365 days plus about six hours. This six-hour fraction was corrected against the true duration of the solar year by periodical computations, leading to a change in the dates of festivals and other significant days.

The science of the Mayas was extremely primitive by the standards of even the most ancient Old World civilisations. Except in their architecture, to be referred to later, the application of scientific principles to everyday life was greatly neglected. The wheel, for example – that symbol of technological progress which forms such an important element in the civilisations of other lands – was never effectively used by the Mayas. Intellectual matters were mainly in the hands of a superstitious priesthood, and even the astronomical observations necessary for the invention of the calendar were practised almost entirely for magical ends. However, the Mayas did make some progress in mathematics, having a system of numerals based on the number twenty, which they represented by a figure of the moon. They also understood the principle of the zero – a very real advance in abstract thought – which they usually depicted in the form of a shell or an open human hand. These concepts enabled them to think in terms of large numbers of several millions.

But however much we try to single out the more positive achievements of Maya civilisation we must recognise that, compared with its Old World counterparts, it was intellectually a failure. One of the main reasons for this may well be that it never succeeded in freeing itself from the shackles of a particularly savage and primitive religion in which human sacrifice played a prominent part. The heart of the living victim was cut out with a knife, and the effigies of the gods were anointed with warm blood. This was thought to propitiate the god and to encourage him in acts of benevolence to the community.

Irrational religious beliefs are, as we have seen, associated with every early manifestation of civilisation, but the degree to which they have dominated the intellectual stratum of society has varied greatly in different regions. In India, for example, Hinduism kept the human mind in a state of mental retardation from which it has only recently emerged as a result of western influences. In ancient Greece, on the other hand, religious superstition did not effectively impede the more intelligent and realistic speculations of the philosophers. Maya religion seems to have so permeated every stratum of society that no effective body of thought could resist its stifling influence. This may well have been due to a certain lack of vitality (perhaps based on environmental factors) in the society as a whole, but it in any case prevented the Mayas from fulfilling a vital creative role in the advance of the human mind. They repeated in a different environment, and with a less lively spirit, certain discoveries already pioneered elsewhere, but they failed to contribute anything original to man's progress up the evolutionary ladder.

The main destructive force in Maya religion sprang from its esoteric character. Its gods and goddesses were essentially comparable to the nature deities of other primitive faiths, but it was administered by an inner band of initiates whose interpretations could not be questioned by ordinary men. Although extreme authoritarianism in religion, as in any other department of life, may produce temporary stability it also causes intellectual death. The rigid formulae of the Maya faith, imposed by fear on an ignorant and superstitious populace, stultified all genuine creative endeavour and were an important contributory cause of the civilisation's inner decay.

Finally a word must be said about the art of the Mayas, particularly their architecture and sculpture. Both these were inspired very largely by their religious beliefs, and if considered in isolation represent a considerable achievement, at least in the technical sense. What they did not do was to add any new ingredient to the earlier and more integrated manifestations of metaphysical culture produced some three to four thousand years previously by the Egyptians. Like the Egyptians, the Mayas built pyramids and temples of stone which showed a considerable mastery of building techniques, and carved figures of their gods which well revealed the nature of their spiritual aspirations. Truncated step pyramids surmounted by temples were a characteristic feature of their architecture and they also erected enormous monolithic stelae to mark the completion of calendrical cycles. Some of these stelae exceeded twenty feet in height, and the figures of priests and deities, often in elaborate head-dresses and costumes, were engraved on them in high and low relief. Unfortunately, however, the achievements of Maya art were not of universal evolutionary significance, for they only repeated, in somewhat different form, the earlier concepts of another age. If Egyptian civilisation had never existed, the Mayas might indeed have one day opened up new horizons for mankind. But their discoveries had in fact been antedated and surpassed in the Nile valley several thousands of years previously.

From about the sixth century A.D. new influences were beginning to operate in Central America which were to have an important effect on the later phases of its civilised development. Aggressive Indian tribes were moving down from the north and establishing themselves in what is now southern Mexico. After the so-called Toltec phase of culture in the region, which lasted from about A.D. 700 to 900, and a chaotic period when autonomous city states were battling for supremacy, there emerged in the fourteenth century a new unified civilisation to the north-west of the old Maya lands. This is what has become known as Aztec civilisation, a cultural complex which, stabilised by a powerful military junta, remained intact until the arrival of the Spaniards. The capital was at Tenochtitlan (the modern Mexico City) from which a reasonably effective military government administered an empire extending from the Gulf of Mexico to the Pacific.

In the Aztec twilight of ancient American civilisation society seems to have been organised largely on feudal lines. A privileged aristocracy demanded tribute and military service from a subservient class of freemen, who in turn were supported by an enormous body of serfs, civil malefactors, military prisoners, and children sold into slavery by their parents. Religion remained esoteric and priest-ridden, and such barbarous practices as human sacrifice did not diminish but increased. The Aztecs had a calendar which in some ways resembled that of the Mayas, and they also used the same system of numerals. The key figure 20 was represented by a flag, 400 (or twenty squared) by a feather, and 8,000 (or twenty cubed) by a purse. Writing resembled the Maya hieroglyphs, but was more phonetic in character, and both this and arithmetic were taught in the temple schools. But still there was no sign of advance in metal culture, and when the Spaniards entered the Aztec cities they remarked that in the barbers' shops men were still being shaved with obsidian razors.

Stone was still the main building material (although mud brick was used for simple huts), and the Aztecs, like the Mayas, used to erect great pyramid temples. These were often associated with trophy platforms for the display of human heads. The main artistic achievements of the Aztecs were in three-dimensional sculpture. Grotesque figures of the gods, often more than life-size, stood in the temples and showed a high standard of workmanship. They were sometimes gruesomely conceived, however, often having skulls for faces and wearing necklaces of human hearts and hands. Aztec art, like almost the whole of ancient American culture, often seems to be the product of a fevered, half-insane, and essentially decadent imagination. It lacks the grandeur of ancient Egyptian statuary and, when compared with the masterpieces produced by the Greeks, it is difficult to realise that it was created by men of the same species.

Apart from the Maya-Aztec complex, the only large-scale civilisation to evolve in the ancient New World was that of the Incas of Peru. These people, like the Aztecs in Central America, did not establish their rule until nearly the middle of the fifteenth century A.D. They also resembled the Aztecs in being a small militaristic group who established their sway over a civilisation which had already been in existence for many hundreds of years. The roots of this Inca civilisation are even more difficult to trace than those of the corresponding Maya phase in Central America, but we can nevertheless make some reasonable assumptions.

In the second half of the first millennium B.C., probably three or four centuries later than the Mayas were beginning to build their civilisation in Yucatan, it seems that another group of Indian tribes was embarking on a similar process on the slopes of the Peruvian Andes. The members of these tribes were descended from the Asiatic peoples who, many millennia before, had crossed the Bering Strait to Alaska and gradually filtered southwards through Central America and the Isthmus of Panama to the South American continent. At first hunters and food-gatherers, these people had gradually taken to an agricultural life. From about 2500 B.C. they supplemented their fishing and hunting with a limited amount of cultivation, and by 1000 B.C. were already growing maize on a large scale. At the same time they were domesticating animals, the duck and the guinea pig being used as a source of food, and the dog adopted as a pet. The Peruvians also had the advantage of their Central American cousins in having two large mammals available for domestication. These were the llama, which was widely used as a beast of burden, and the related alpaca, which was chiefly reared for its wool.

The stages by which our species has evolved from the hunting and food-gathering phase, through Neolithic farming, to the higher manifestations of culture have been roughly the same in every region where civilisation has developed. In the present context it would therefore be tedious to relate in detail how such traditional primitive crafts as basketry, weaving and pottery emerged in Peruvian society. This would only be to duplicate a story with which we are already familiar. There is, however, one point that should be stressed. Metallurgy in Peru reached a much higher level than in any other ancient American civilisation, and the products of the crafts-men were by no means inferior to those found in the early civilisations of the Old World. Gold was probably the first metal to be used, for it was readily available and easy to work. Silver and copper came later, and in the later phases of the civilisation we see the growth of a genuine Bronze Age culture. In one respect ancient Peru even anticipated metallurgical developments in the Old World. This was in the making of platinum ornaments, which have been discovered at a number of coastal sites. Platinum was not used in the Old World, either for adornment or practical purposes, until the beginning of the eighteenth century. However, neither the Peruvians nor the Mayas and Aztecs of Central America ever created an iron culture. Although it is possible that they would have done so if their evolution had continued undisturbed, the arrival of the Spaniards destroyed their civilisation before the event occurred.

By the closing centuries of the pre-Christian era a civilised urban society was well established in Peru, both on the coast and in high mountain valleys in the Andes. In the so-called 'Florescent Period' which followed (A.D. 400–1000) this civilisation reached a very high level of achievement. Its major centres at this time were on the coast, and the cities were characterised by enormous civic buildings, temples and forts, as well as comfortable dwelling houses of sun-baked brick for the richer members of the community. The engineering skill of the Peruvians at this time is comparable with that of the Romans. Irrigation works were carried out on a large scale, and aqueducts and canals brought water from distant sources to the great centres of population.

Fascinating as it would be to detail stage by stage the later developments of this civilisation, we must restrict ourselves here to its culminating phase under the Incas. This lasted only for a brief hundred years before the Spanish conquest in A.D. 1532, but saw the highest level of development attained by any New World civilisation. The Incas, or 'children of the sun', were a militant group of Indians who established their rule over the whole of the Peruvian Andes. They were ruled by a dynasty of semi-divine emperors, whose role resembled that of the pharaoh in the history of ancient Egypt. The emperor was regarded as the descendant of the great sun god, Inti, of Inca religion and the physical embodiment of Viracocha, the Lord of all Creation. To preserve the purity of this line his consort was normally his sister – another custom reminiscent of the Egyptian pharaohs. In addition he was allowed a large harem of secondary wives, who made his clothes, prepared his food, and carried out the domestic duties of his palace. His court consisted of nobles, most of whom were the sons either of the emperor himself or earlier members of his line by such secondary wives.

The emperor, his court, and the large body of priests who administered Inca religion, were maintained by a heavy tribute in the form of labour from the mass of the peasant population. Although essentially authoritarian, this system seems nevertheless to have worked well, and many aspects of its organisation remind us of modern Soviet communism. For example, there was no private property, and the cultivable lands, the mines, and even the llama herds were regarded as the property of the state. To work these 'means of production' the rank and file of the people were rigorously disciplined and regimented, but in return were protected by the state from unnecessary hardship, exploitation and want. However, it is unlikely that they would have had the same opportunities for rising to senior positions under the Inca régime as are made possible under the more advanced systems of communism and socialism practised today.

Limitation of space makes it impossible to deal even briefly with every major aspect of late Peruvian culture, so I propose to single out three of special relevance to my main theme. These are the architecture of the Incas (especially as expressed in their public works), their religion, and their general intellectual and artistic development. I have already briefly alluded to the earlier architectural achievements of the Florescent Period, and these were fully equalled in Inca times. The chief building materials were adobe, or mud brick, and stone, although timber was also used in regions where it was plentiful. The ordinary dwelling house was a simple rectangular structure without windows or chimney, the smoke from a central hearth finding its way out through the chinks in a thatched roof. Public buildings were much more elaborate, however. These were normally built of stone, with either thatched or stone roofs. They were financed from government funds and built with government labour; presumably also a state architect was responsible for the designs. Peruvian civilisation never developed paper or a system of writing, so the architects worked from small clay models. Many of these have been recovered, and give us valuable information about buildings that were later destroyed.

The truncated pyramids of Maya and Aztec civilisation were not characteristic of the late Inca period in Peru, although great pyramidal structures were built in coastal regions in the earlier Florescent Period. The most remarkable stone structures of the Incas occur in the Cuzco region, and of these the great fort of Sacsahuamán is perhaps the most impressive. This is more than a third of a mile in length, and its triple-terraced walls rise to a height of over 60 feet. Some of the enormous stones used in its construction are comparable in size with those found in the Egyptian pyramids, and some individual blocks weigh between 100 and 200 tons. To transport these stones from the nearest quarry, nine miles from the site, and then to raise them into position, shows that the Incas must have had a sound knowledge of the roller, the lever, and perhaps even the windlass. Labour must also have been deployed on a pharaonic scale for several years before the structure was completed.

In other public works and engineering projects the Incas made equally impressive progress. Irrigation had been widely practised from very early days in Peru but now reached a new level of efficiency. Canals followed the contours of the hills, and the flow of water through sluices into the subsidiary channels in the fields was controlled by stone slabs. Streams running through towns and other settlements were also harnessed to bring a private water supply to individual houses through conduits lined and roofed with stone.

The Inca road system reminds us strongly of that of the Romans, although the total lack of wheeled vehicles removed the need for elaborate surfacing. In flat country the roads ran absolutely straight in the traditional Roman manner, and were between ten and fifteen feet wide. In hilly country they were narrower, usually only between three and four feet, but this was still adequate to take a llama train in single file. The surfaces were paved with stone in bad terrain, and in marshy regions were carried on raised causeways. If a ravine or river had to be traversed, bridges of several different types were constructed. In fairly level country the road would be carried across a river by laying logs or slabs of stone on top of masonry piers; if the current was not too swift these piers would be replaced by rafts or small boats to form a pontoon. The most elaborate Inca bridges, used for spanning deep ravines, were of the suspension type, the footway being supported by thick cables of twisted fibre. However, these bridges must have sagged dangerously in the middle, for the Incas never discovered how to suspend a level footway from two main cables in the manner used in modern suspension bridges.

Compared with this impressive progress in material culture, the religious idea of the Incas remained at a primitive level. Their chief god, Viracocha, although deeply venerated and regarded as the divine analogue of the emperor, was of less importance in everyday affairs than the various gods of nature. Of these by far the most highly revered was Inti, the god of the sun, who has already been alluded to as the ancestor of the emperor, and to whom numerous temples were erected in different parts of Peru. Like Viracocha he was thought to have human shape, but was often represented as a flat gold disk with a man's face surrounded by a halo of rays. He was served by a band of women known as the Virgins of the Sun, sworn to perpetual chastity, and a second group, known as the Chosen Women, who formed a convenient sacred harem for the emperor and his nobles. Other important gods were Illapa, the god of thunder, Mamaquilla, goddess of the moon, and the earth and sea goddesses, named respectively Pacamama and Mamacocha. Innumerable holy objects, sites and shrines, known collectively as *huacas,* also played an important part in Inca beliefs, and witchcraft and sorcery were widely practised.

As in most primitive religious systems, sacrifice was thought to be an exceptionally effective way of obtaining the favour of the gods. Domestic animals, particularly guinea pigs, were the most common sacrifices. Llamas were too valuable to be used for the purpose by any but the richest individuals, but were offered in important public ceremonies from the communally owned state herds. At moments of exceptional crisis, disaster or rejoicing, a human sacrifice would be made, although this practice was rare compared to the Central American holocausts. The victim was usually a boy or girl of about ten years old, although occasionally adults were offered. The children were almost always the sons or daughters of the Chosen Women of the sun god; less frequently a family seeking to avoid some dire misfortune would offer up one of their own sons. An elaborate ceremony preceded the sacrifice, which was then usually performed by throat-slitting or strangulation. Alternatively, as in Maya and Aztec society, the heart might be cut from the still-living body and placed, while still beating, on the sacrificial altar.

A great deal is known about the religion of the Incas from the early chronicles of the Spanish invaders, but enough has already been said to show its general character. We shall therefore turn next to a few characteristic aspects of their intellectual and artistic development.

Ancient American civilisation in both its main centres is remarkable for its failure to develop any really effective system of writing. We have already seen that the Central American hieroglyphs were extremely primitive compared with developments in Egypt, but in Peru not even the simplest type of written communication was achieved. However, at least one, and possibly two, devices were used to aid the memory. The first, known as a *quipu,* was an arrangement of different coloured strings in which knots of various kinds could be tied in various positions. By judicious combinations of knots, spacings, and string colours, a great number of symbolic arrangements could be built up for the keeping of records and other purposes. The second device was the *abacus,* or counting-box, which enabled calculations to be made by moving pebbles or other small objects from one compartment of the box to another. There is, however, no definite archaeological evidence for the use of the *abacus,* and the possibility still rests on the accounts of the Spanish chroniclers and on the single picture reproduced on page 265.

The absence of writing ruled out the development of a written literature, but traditional Inca folk tales, dramas and religious works were recorded by the Spaniards. They resemble, as might be expected, similar compositions by other societies at a corresponding level of development, and have little interest except to students of folklore. Inca visual art is also disappointing, and represents a decline from an earlier artistic flowering. Stone sculptures of the gods were characteristic of this earlier Peruvian art, and included great monolithic figures sometimes more than twenty feet high.

The comparatively primitive nature of all American civilisations would not suggest that the human mind in this region was yet capable of the abstract thought necessary for pure science. This indeed proves to be the case, and the astronomical observations associated with the different phases of the agricultural year, and with omens, is the highest activity we can claim for the Incas in the proto-scientific field. Even these were not applied to the invention of a properly organised solar calendar, and it is probable that throughout Peruvian history time was always reckoned in terms of sunrise and sunset, the rotation of the seasons, and the phases of the moon. Apart from their technical achievements in architecture and civil engineering, the Incas' applications of science were only impressive in one field. This was in surgery where, considering the retarded state of their culture in many other respects, they achieved amazing progress. Amputations, trepanning, and even possibly bone transplants, were carried out by the Inca surgeons, probably with the use of vegetable drugs as primitive anaesthetics. Skulls showing the marks of trepanning with obsidian, copper or bronze instruments have frequently been found, and archaeological evidence shows that forceps, bandaging, and the tourniquet were all used. Great attention was also paid to hygiene, and the 'operating theatre' was disinfected before the surgeon went to work by burning maize flour sprinkled on the floor.

The summing up of the role of ancient American civilisation in the evolution of mankind is much easier than that of its Old World cousins. We need not consider the influence it had on man's future development for the simple reason that it had no influence at all. Ruthlessly destroyed in both its

FIG. 33. Two primitive counting devices probably used by the ancient Incas. The man in the picture holds a *quipu*, consisting of a main cord to which are attached a number of strings; different colours, knottings and groupings of the strings served as an aid to memory in counting. In the bottom left-hand corner is an *abacus*, or counting-box; it was used for making calculations by moving pebbles or other small objects from one compartment of the box to another. *After Mason* (*1957*), *p. 229*

evolutionary centres by the Spaniards in the fifteenth and six-teenth centuries, it survived only as a subject for study by curious archaeologists. The descendants of the proud Aztec and Inca war-lords drifted into squalor and misery as subject peoples, and even today, particularly in Peru, have become one of the most pathetic and degraded societies in the world. Ancient American civilisation was an experiment which came entirely to nought, leaving no legacy to the future of man-kind.

Although we may deplore the senseless destruction of these interesting cultures, this outcome was predictable on the basis of evolutionary principles. At that particular phase in human history the advance of technology had not yet made it neces-sary for mankind as a whole to co-operate or perish, and violent competition between different groups of men was still possible without the destruction of both parties. Ancient American civilisation, growing up in isolation at a slower rate and in a later period than the civilisations of the Old World, resembled an animal species which had branched off from the main evolutionary stream to develop along its own lines in a special environment. This environment provided fewer challenges and fewer opportunities for the interplay of minds than the great crossroads of Old World civilisation in the eastern Mediterranean. It was even more isolated by the Atlantic and Pacific Oceans than the Indian and Chinese communities behind their natural screen of mountain and desert. In these circumstances, as in organic nature, the arrival of a more powerful competitor was bound to lead to the elimination of its more backward cousin. In the contem-porary world, as we shall hope to show, the destruction or suppression of one society by another is no longer an effec-tive, or indeed a possible, technique of survival. Four hun-dred years ago, however, it still worked very well, as is shown not only by the Spanish liquidation of Aztec and Inca civilisa-tion, but by the extraordinary success of the British, Dutch, French, Belgians and Portuguese in the building of empires. We shall return to this whole question at some length in Part 5, but meantime we must consider some salient aspects of western civilisation between the fall of Rome and the present day.

Chapter Nineteen

WESTERN CIVILISATION

WE COME NOW to the origins and evolution of western civilisation which, during the last fifteen centuries, has grown to be the dominant civilisation on earth. By comparison with such civilisations as Egypt, Mesopotamia and India, which arose directly from Neolithic beginnings, the origin of western civilisation is much more complex. It is not a 'foundation' civilisation as the others were, but a channel in which many cultural streams converged and intermingled, to be carried forward in what has proved to be an exceptionally effective way. The cultural attitudes of western civilisation gradually spread over the whole surface of the earth, at first imposing themselves on peoples at a lower level of development, and then leavening these societies into a progressively more homogeneous whole. Today every region where earlier civilisations once flourished is permeated by western ideas. In the Middle East, India, China, and Central and South America the ancient civilisations have been radically transformed, while in such regions as North America, Australia and Africa south of the Sahara, which never produced major indigenous civilisations, western ideas have led to the development of new and progressive societies on western lines.

The manifold origins of western civilisation make it a phenomenon exceptionally difficult to define. We cannot say that it began at such and such a date in such and such a region. It is essentially a complex of thought patterns to which many previous and parallel civilisations contributed to a greater or lesser extent. Egypt, Mesopotamia and, above all, Greece were the dominant influences in its genesis, while even before the dawn of the Christian era important side streams were flowing in from such peoples as the Hebrews and the Persians. This cultural complex was transmitted forward first by the Romans and then, as we shall shortly see, by the Arabs. Resisting at least two major attempts at its destruction by Mongoloid peoples from the east, it gained a new stability through the influence of doctrinaire Christianity in the Middle Ages, and then flowered again with renewed vigour in the Renaissance. Finally, in the nineteenth century, the development of scientific ideas gave it a fresh impetus, and today it is the universal civilisation of all mankind.

In the context of the last million years, which must reduce the whole of this complex story to a chapter, we can do nothing more than indicate main trends, without reference to any but a few major events. We shall begin our sketch at the collapse of the Roman world, a time when the whole of human cultural progress was in a condition of the greatest peril. At this period Rome was one of the five major civilisations spread across the face of the earth, the other four being those of India, China, Central America and Peru. But, as we have seen, all of these were vastly more backward than the classical civilisation of which Rome was now the sole legatee. India and China behind their vast natural barriers were already becoming living fossils, and their culture held out little hope of further independent advance. Central America and Peru represented specialised side branches of the main evolutionary stream, and had already lagged far behind the parallel development of civilisation in the Old World. Rome alone, therefore, seemed to hold the key to the whole future progress of human evolution.

When we reflect on the events of the fourth century A.D. we may well give a retrospective shiver at the narrow margin by which man avoided a relapse into barbarism. At this time the Roman Empire was assailed by enemies on every side. Barbarian tribes were pressing down on its northern frontiers, and a renascent Persia was advancing from the east. A stronger, more vital Rome, such as had existed under the Caesars, would have resisted these threats with ease, but now the Empire had become flabby with its own success. The growing autocracy of the emperors, the decadence of the aristocracy, and a neglect of the interests of the common people, had sapped the inner strength of Roman society. Early in the

fourth century the Emperor Constantine was compelled by
barbarian pressure to move the capital to Byzantium, which
was now renamed Constantinople, and the empire was thus
effectively divided into east and west. In the second half of
the fifth century barbarian invaders, who had for long robbed
and plundered the western Roman territories, brought this
part of the empire to an ignominious end.

Henceforward three main forces were responsible for preserving the cultural legacy of earlier civilisations. The first,
and in some ways the most influential, of these was Christianity. The Christianisation of the empire had occurred
early in the fourth century, and a great system of teachers and
missionaries had been built up to administer the faith. In
spite of the collapse of the western part of the empire as a
political unit, its members still preserved in their minds and
hearts the powerful traditions of the Catholic Church. When
the barbarians destroyed the brittle and decadent fabric of
secular Rome this spiritual force at its centre stood mankind
in good stead. Gradually Christianity permeated the attitudes
of the barbarian conquerors and was incorporated as a vital
stabilising influence in the new societies that grew up on the
ruins of Rome. At least equally important from the point of
view of man's cultural evolution was the role of Catholic
monks and scholars in preserving the legacy of classical
antiquity. In the Middle Ages they became the custodians not
only of Christian doctrine but of the whole cultural tradition
of Greece and Rome, and their carefully guarded manuscripts
were the data without which the new intellectual attitudes of
the Renaissance could never have been framed.

The second force which transmitted human culture forwards was Byzantium itself. Unlike its western counterpart,
this section of the empire was destined to preserve its identity
for a further thousand years. The reasons why it remained
comparatively stable while the western empire fell to the barbarians have long been discussed by scholars and no final
conclusion has been reached. The answer possibly lies in its
geographical position in the eastern Mediterranean, where
the ebb and flow of different ideas offered a constant stimulus
and challenge to everything that was most vital in the human
mind. Although originally a part of the vast territories ruled

from Rome, its main language was always Greek. Greek traditions in art and thought were carried on here even more effectively than in Italy and the west, and flourished vigorously under the protection of the Roman order. At the same time it was directly exposed to eastern influences, particularly those of the Sassanid Empire in Persia and the spectacular development of Mohammedanism, shortly to be described. The constant challenge of these pressures from neighbouring cultures, combined with the stabilising effect of a powerful Christian tradition, must certainly have contributed to the long survival of Byzantium as a cultural unit.

Within this framework, however, the manifestations of its thought processes sometimes took contradictory forms. Under the Emperor Justinian there was a great flowering of art and architecture, particularly in the creation of works inspired by Christian ideas, and Roman law was organised into a code which is still the basis of our law today. But this same Emperor was also responsible for closing the philosophy schools at Athens which had flourished since the time of Plato, and thus temporarily cut off the human mind from the vitalising influence of disinterested philosophical speculation. Science likewise made little progress under the Byzantine régime, for rational examination of phenomena in the light of evidence is not an activity that is normally encouraged in a Christian society. In Byzantium, as in the west, the irrational dogmatism of formalised religion, although it provided a valuable stabilising force, did much to stifle the fire of intellectual curiosity in all but a few dedicated individuals. Byzantium undoubtedly formed a cultural bridge between Rome and the Renaissance, but its character was expressed in Christian art and architecture rather than the reaching out of the human mind towards new concepts.

The third and most important channel by which the ideas of classical civilisation were carried through the troubled centuries following the fall of the western Empire was Arab scholarship. Although the indigenous culture of the Arab world fell behind that of western Europe after the Renaissance, it was one of the main agencies which made the Renaissance possible. Moreover Arabic civilisation was not only effective in preserving and diffusing the culture of earlier times, but was much more resourceful than either Christianity or the Byzantine state in creating new forms of cultural expression.

The driving force behind Arabic civilisation was the Moslem, or Islamic, faith. This was based on the teaching of the prophet Mohammed, who was born at Mecca about A.D. 570. At this time Arabia was inhabited by a number of nomadic tribes which were constantly bickering and raiding each other's encampments. There was no single religious faith, nor even a common language, and each tribe reverenced a different set of native deities. These were associated with trees, springs, wells and other natural phenomena, and their worship was characterised by all the magical and superstitious paraphernalia of the primitive faiths of earlier times. Mohammed was a religious fanatic with a passion to unite the Arab people in a common faith. Like the ancient Hebrew prophets he preached an uncompromising anthropocentric monotheism, insisting that Allah, the One True God, was the ruler of the world, and that Mohammed himself was the chosen messenger of Allah to reveal the truth to men. In this fervid insistence on his prophetic role and his direct channels of communication to the Almighty, Mohammed closely resembled Christ. In fact Christianity and Islam are examples of parallel evolution operating at the religious level; both were symptomatic of the phase through which human consciousnes was passing at the time, and their differences are much less apparent than the disciples of either are even now prepared to admit.

One of these differences did lie, however, in the aggressive crusading zeal with which the earlier followers of Mohammed sought to spread the gospel through the world. This was never equalled even by the militant Christianity of the Middle Ages. Under his immediate successor, Abu Bekr, the Arabs embarked on a career of conquest that made them the masters of the whole eastern Mediterranean. In the seventh and eighth centuries the armies of Islam carried the Moslem faith and Moslem ideas over vast tracts of the Old World. The whole of Egypt and north Africa came under their dominion, and the tide of conquest flowed onward through Spain into

western and southern France. They liquidated the new conquests of the eastern emperors in Syria, and pushed back the
boundaries of Byzantium deep into the mountains of Ana-
tolia. In the east they conquered Persia and carried their rule
to beyond the Indus in India and the Oxus in western Turk-
estan. In biological terms this eruption of the Arabs was an
example of explosive evolution among the human species as
momentous in its scope and effects as any that has occurred
in history.

The Arabs themselves, even after achieving religious unity
under Mohammed, were not characterised by an advanced
native culture. But their restless and active minds were
quickly fertilised by the culture of the lands they conquered.
In Egypt they came into contact with the Greek cultural
tradition as preserved by Roman rule, while in Persia also they
could study Greek literary works, both in the original language
and in Syrian translations. In Syria they were influenced by
Christian doctrines, and further east by the beliefs and customs of many Asiatic peoples, including even the Indians and
Chinese. Perhaps most ironically of all when one considers
the present rivalry and hatred existing between Jews and
Arabs, they absorbed many elements of the Hebrew tradition,
not only in its eastern Mediterranean homeland but from
Jewish emigrants in distant Spain.

Inexperienced as they were in the arts of government and
administration, the Arabs were not destined to preserve their
Empire for very long as a single unit, but in the early years of
their rule they established an intellectual brotherhood which
was to survive all the political changes and uncertainties of
the next five centuries. Under the impact of new ideas from
so many sources, intelligent Arabs either abandoned the
authoritarian dogmas of the Koran or relegated them to a
purely formal and domestic status. They studied, reflected
and speculated, and began to look with a new daring at the
world. The works of the Greek philosophers widened the
intellectual horizon of these desert Semites and, for the first
time since the great days of Hellas, original and exciting discoveries began to be made in many branches of science.
Mathematics, medicine and physical science in particular
made great progress. Roman numerals gave place to the

VI. Man in the twentieth century

In the twentieth century the physical and psychological problems created
by a highly industrial society and intense urbanisation are still being
worked out. **84** Industrial scene, Yorkshire, England. **85** Modern New York.

Organised warfare and political and racial murder have attained a unique
degree of efficiency and horror in the twentieth century. **86** Dead soldier,
Ypres, 1917. **87** Destruction caused by a German air-raid on London, 1941.

88 Murdered Jews and their murderer, Belsen concentration camp, 1945. **89** A British soldier sweeping bodies into the communal grave, Belsen concentration camp, 1945.

90 (*overleaf*) An American atomic cannon test. The atomic cannon is a typical destructive weapon of the nuclear age.

Twentieth-century man, like most of his primate cousins, is a highly
social animal. **91** Music-making is a common social activity of our species.
92 Faith in supernatural cures still motivates the annual pilgrimages to
the grotto of Saint Bernadette at Lourdes, France. **93** Football, no
less than music and religion, arouses strong emotions in the human heart.

94 Adam, by Jacob Epstein, powerfully expresses the spiritual aspirations of earth-bound man. *Reproduced by kind permission of Lady Epstein.*

Arabic numerals we still use today, and scientific principles were applied to such varying activities as the manufacture of alloys and dyes, dentistry, pharmacology, sanitation, cartography, and the design of lenses and other forms of optical glass. The very word algebra (*al-jebr*) is of Arabic origin, while the whole science of chemistry owes the origin of its name to the Arabic *al-kimia,* meaning 'the art of pouring'. Through the vitalising influence of Arab scholarship the human intellect was once again astir in the Mediterranean world.

When we consider the characters of these three main transmitters of ancient culture after the fall of Rome their respective roles can perhaps best be assessed as follows. The main contribution of Christianity was to provide a moral stabiliser for western Europe and the Byzantine Empire when the Roman order collapsed before the barbarian invasions. Apart from the elaborate religious system which still survives in Roman Catholicism and the various schismatic Christian sects, Christianity was also of importance in its fostering of visual art, architecture and music. It was, however, hostile to science and scientific philosophy, and in this respect has been on many occasions a destructive anti-evolutionary force.

The role of Byzantium, which itself owed a great deal to the stabilising influence of Christianity, was to provide a bulwark between east and west, where men's minds were bubbling furiously as in a cauldron but had not yet produced reasonably stable social conditions in which these ideas could become fully effective. Byzantium provided, in fact, a kind of blueprint for an orderly and well-administered society. Being Christian in faith it was hostile to science, but it did make an important contribution to the preservation of artistic traditions. Still more important, however, was its role in carrying forward the Roman concept of law and government, and thus providing future generations with the basic principles of organised society.

Finally, the main role of the Arabs was undoubtedly in transmitting, and also originating, scientific ideas. In addition they produced valuable art and architecture, but this was not a unique function of their society. In science, on the other hand, at this particular juncture in human history, they stood almost alone. Had it not been for Arab scholars, the hostility of Christianity and of Byzantine society to the quest for scientific truth might have still further retarded the development of the human mind.

The religious, artistic, social and scientific concepts transmitted forward through these three main channels met, but did not always blend, in the Renaissance. Beginning in fourteenth-century Italy, the significant cultural changes associated with this phase in the growth of civilisation had spread to the rest of Europe by 1600. The Renaissance marked the beginning of western civilisation as we know it today.

No glib hypothesis can convincingly account for every aspect of this remarkable outburst of creative energy. Certainly the Renaissance was not, as was once thought, a total rebirth of civilisation after a period of bigotry and intellectual darkness. Such a concept does less than justice to the very real achievements of the Middle Ages, both in the Christian societies of western Europe and Byzantium, and the Moslem societies of north Africa and the Middle East. Rather it was a period of profound reassessment concerning the whole nature of the external world and the meaning of human life. The need for this reassessment was forced on western man by the growth of his knowledge, which was now becoming too great to be contained within the comforting framework of ancient doctrines. Doubt and wonder were returning to the world, and western society was entering a period of emotional and intellectual ferment. Not only were two great religious systems, Christianity and Islam, competing for men's emotions, but the discoveries of explorers, astronomers, and scientific thinkers generally were making it apparent that both the earth itself and the universe as a whole were far larger and more complex in their organisation than anyone since the time of the Greeks had been prepared to recognise. The challenge of these discoveries was immense, and the attempt to meet it initiated a new period of explosive evolution in the development of the human mind.

In a general survey of this kind it would be out of place to detail item by item the stages by which western civilisation has evolved between the Renaissance and today. The period, being so close to us in time, is extraordinarily well documented, and it is beyond the compass of any one brain to take in and correlate all the relevant facts. Moreover, the very richness of the evidence tends to obscure the main features of the story. There is a temptation for the student to concentrate on one or two manageable aspects of the period and draw from these a number of totally erroneous conclusions. I therefore propose to limit myself here to an approach at once more general and more bold. Without more than a passing reference to individual events, I shall attempt to define the outlines of the process as a whole.

First, between the Renaissance and today we have seen the final triumph of western civilisation over all other human cultures. I do not mean by this, of course, that western man has himself dominated the rest of his species. This was indeed the case in the great age of empire building which began with the Renaissance itself and continued with undiminished vigour right down to the early years of the present century. But this was essentially a transitional phase in which western ideas were spread over the earth's surface to transform and 'westernise' other communities. Today it is obvious that western man is not the ruler of the world, and in fact in many regions he is in retreat. Nevertheless, the communities which are now challenging his supremacy are doing so with ideas and a technology which they themselves learnt from the west. Western society no longer enjoys its former political dominance, but western civilisation is still the basis of all man's vital intellectual processes, whether the society in which these operate be in China, central Africa or Peru.

Now what are the main features of the extraordinarily successful cultural complex which we term western civilisation? These can best be considered under three heads. First, the factors in the civilisation making for social stability, comprised mainly in its political and economic organisation; second, its technical achievements, leading to its material progress; and third, its intellectual and spiritual aspirations, as reflected in its religious and artistic attitudes, its development of pure scientific thought, and its philosophical speculations. In each of these fields we can, of course, only be concerned with the most general examples and the main trends

275

that have conditioned their development. The method may well cause students of conventional history to shudder, but to see the record of the last six hundred years in the vaster context of human evolution as a whole the focus cannot be further reduced.

Under the first head, a considerable range of political and economic systems have operated within the general framework of western civilisation. The last half-millennium has seen numerous experiments in different forms of government practised by different societies within the cultural group. The historian can point to innumerable examples of autocracy, oligarchy and democracy, which have all operated with a greater or lesser degree of success within the period. Squabbles between rival communities have proceeded with the same wasteful abandon that characterised the tribal communities of former times, except that in this latest phase the tribal units have expanded into the more complex societies known as nations. Nevertheless, even the suicidal tendencies exhibited by our species in two major twentieth-century wars did not prove completely fatal, and at the moment of writing western civilisation remains intact.

Whether or not it continues to do so must depend on a number of factors, of which the ability of men to organise the economic basis of their society will be one of the most important. Until the second decade of the twentieth century it was still widely believed that personal property was a guarantee of security and power. This instinct was natural, but only in an extremely primitive sense, for it represented a survival of the combative instincts of a much earlier phase of evolution. As the record of man's first million years has amply shown, the success of our species has depended not on the aggrandisement of the self, nor the survival of individuals, but on the communal achievements of human society as they have been transmitted by intelligent but flexible traditions from one generation to the next. This has inevitably demanded a diminishment of the personal power conferred by property, and an acceptance of the fact that individual survival, and the only reasonably secure kind of human happiness, must be related to the survival and happiness of the species as a whole.

There are, of course, certain kinds of property which must

always remain entirely personal. No reading of the lessons of evolution would suggest that the possession of such things as clothes and toothbrushes, or of an individual home and the financial means to travel and enjoy the beauty of the world, is in any way reactionary. But at the present advanced stage of human development it is becoming increasingly clear that other kinds of property formerly enjoyed by individuals as a source of security and power must come under the general control of society if abuses are to be avoided. Western civilisation is, in fact, moving towards this end, and even in the highly individualistic society of Britain it is coming to be accepted that such essential utilities as mines, railways and airlines should be controlled by the people as a whole instead of being exploited for personal gain.

The main advocate of this concept in recent western civilisation was Soviet Russia, a nation which has been much criticised for its repression of individual liberty. However, this repression was one of degree rather than kind, for all societies that regard liberty as a high ideal accept without question many quite irksome curtailments of their freedom. Any extreme liberal who doubts this fact might try the experiment of driving his car down the wrong side of the street, attempting to go abroad without a passport, or lying naked in the park on a hot day. It might be charitable to consider whether the initial repression of liberty in Soviet Russia, however open to criticism it may seem in the different social context of western Europe and America, might not have been regarded by the creators of that system as an essential responsibility. The growth of liberalism in Russia as the country's economy becomes more stable certainly suggests that the harsh repressive measures employed in the early years of the régime were not intended to be permanent.

To sum up the present political and economic situation of western civilisation, both in its place of origin in western Europe and in other parts of the world to which it has spread, we may say that after more than five hundred years of experiment its individual members now subscribe to one or other of two basic attitudes. These attitudes can be roughly equated with the capitalism and communism of basic Marxist theory, although the extreme differences between the two have been much diminished by the growth of socialism in capitalist countries and of liberalism in Russia. In many regions of the world these differences of opinion cut across national boundaries, but broadly speaking the communities officially supporting one or the other can be divided into two main groups. The first group consists of the United States, most nations of western continental Europe, and the allies and disciples of these societies in other continents. The second group consists of Russia and eastern continental Europe, with their allies and disciples in Asia, Africa and South and Central America. The differences between the groups are based primarily on their attitude to property and their concept of freedom. In terms of biological and social evolution they can be regarded as two great tribal confederations facing each other across the world. Not only the stability of civilisation but the very survival of man as a species will depend on whether they can agree on common definitions of freedom and social justice or resort to the futile alternative of self-annihilation by war.

We come now to our second head: the development of technology in western civilisation which has led to its material progress. Increasing refinement of extra-corporeal equipment is one of the most characteristic manifestations of human evolution, and the new curiosity about the world which began with the Renaissance gave a tremendous spur to technological development. The opening up of new lands required the invention of improved methods of transport and better instruments to guide the ships of the early adventurers across the uncharted oceans. At the same time, population pressure led to the need for an increasingly integrated economy based on more efficient means of production and distribution, and in achieving this the development of machines played a vital part. The whole tempo of technological progress was stepped up to a spectacular extent in the nineteenth century, when the application of scientific principles to large-scale industrial projects reached new heights of efficiency. This process has continued up to today, when the very survival of the species depends on the technical progress necessary to support ever larger numbers of individuals.

Distressing as it must be to moralists, the destructive wars conducted by individual societies within western civilisation were a particularly important stimulus to technological progress. Each warring group had to achieve maximum efficiency if it was to overcome its neighbour, and this required sustained inventive power on the part of its scientists and technologists. Emotion may sometimes suggest that it was the courage and fighting spirit of the troops that eventually gave the victory, but in fact the winning side usually proved to be the one with the better weapons. Even in the last war the stimulus to technology created by the need to destroy the enemy led to a rapid increase in the output of inventions which, when peace came, could be applied to the more efficient running of society and the greater happiness of mankind.

The fact that war has proved in the past to be a stimulus to human progress but could now easily wipe our species from the face of the earth may seem on the face of it an odd paradox. However, the explanation is quite simple. While weapons had a moderately limited effect, and at worst could only cause the death of a few hundred thousand people, it was still possible for physical conflict to achieve positive, and even desirable, results. Since the development of atomic weapons, however, this is no longer the case. Western civilisation is in the interesting situation where the very excellence of its technological equipment has made its total destruction possible for the first time in history. Inventions largely inspired by war, if now used for conflict instead of being transformed for peaceful purposes, could totally eliminate life from our planet. The outcome of this situation is that all-in atomic war became obsolete as an instrument of policy at the very moment that the possibility of conducting it was achieved. This is not, of course, to say that a war of catastrophic proportions cannot be touched off by the folly of some reckless and ignorant politician, but it does now seem more likely that man will in future concentrate on producing less universally devastating weapons. This at least offers the hope that a few reasonably thoughtful and active people will be permitted to escape destruction, and may therefore eventually be able to persuade their more backward fellows that war is a stupidly wasteful, as well as cruel, way of attempting to settle human differences.

To sum up the progress of western civilisation under our second head, we can say that technology has now reached such a point of refinement that it can offer men almost infinite potentialities for good or evil. As the species grows in numbers, technology is able to provide the means by which human society can be physically maintained, at least for several centuries to come. Shortly also it will make possible the piping off of large numbers of the surplus population to other planets where, in an artificially created environment, they will be able to explore new modes of life. At the same time, if intraspecific destruction is regarded as a preferable alternative, technology will continue to provide effective weapons for limited wars, thus allowing the population of the planet to be kept within reasonable bounds without totally eliminating mankind from the cosmic scene. To compassionate and intelligent men it is, of course, a macabre thought that the second alternative can even be contemplated, but it is a possibility that cannot be ruled out.

We come now to our third head, the intellectual and spiritual aspirations of western civilisation as reflected in its religious, artistic and philosophical attitudes. These are, of course, very closely related, and grade into each other at many points, but for ease of description we shall first consider them one by one.

The very concept of religion still leads to great confusion in the minds of men. The confusion has mainly occurred because the word is open to a wide variety of subjective definitions according to the particular emotional and intellectual make-up of the individual. To consider these in detail would not be possible in the space available, but the two main attitudes that have led to difficulty must be briefly defined.

To one type of person religion is nothing but emotional folly, and a religious man is one who unthinkingly supports authoritarian dogmas which cannot stand up to rational analysis. This type of person maintains, not without reason, that more stupid, destructive and downright wicked acts have been carried out in the name of religion than any other department of human thought. Those who support the alternative view insist that religion, properly understood, is an entirely valid form of experience which extends, but does not contradict, the findings of science. To understand how these attitudes originated we must briefly consider the historical perspective.

Primitive religion was born, as we have seen, from the wonder and fear which man felt when his increased cerebral powers first enabled him to reflect on the universe around him and his own position in the environment of nature. Since then, however, religious thinking has evolved like any other type of thinking, and throughout history a number of specially insighted persons have described religious experience with a remarkable degree of unanimity. These men claim to have recognised, by a type of knowledge which for want of a better word we may term 'spiritual', that the universe is controlled by an, as yet, imperfectly understood power or principle, and that a special mental approach must be adopted, particularly in the field of morality, if this principle is to be understood. So far there is nothing in this attitude from which any reasonable man could possibly dissent. In fact it does not even contradict the most austere concepts of modern science, being based on a conviction that the universe works by law and not by chance, and that disciplined procedures must be followed if we are to understand its nature.

However, parallel with this profounder attitude to spiritual questions, more dogmatic expressions of religious belief have periodically gained currency. The formal observances associated with primitive magic have been adopted by well-meaning but woolly-minded disciples of the religious seers, and imposed on their utterances so that genuine religious experience has often become debased into a formalised ritual. This type of mental fossilisation is, of course, widely divergent from the creative thinking of the more enlightened scientists, or even of ordinary intelligent men. During the twentieth century particularly western civilisation has seen a great widening of the gulf between so-called religion on the one hand and leaders of rational and scientific thought on the other.

I shall have more to say about this dangerous dichotomy in Part 5 of this book, but meanwhile it would be only fair to mention one aspect of established religion which has been of very real benefit to our species. The survival of any civilised society depends on the degree to which the forces of order triumph over the forces of disintegration and, as we have seen, the maintenance of western civilisation throughout the last fifteen hundred years has been largely due to the stabilising effect of the two great religious systems of Christianity and Islam. It seems, in fact, that there is an initial period after the inspiration of a sage or visionary has led to the establishment of a religious ideal when the formal organisation of an ecclesiastical system leads to positive good. It is only when the system becomes so rigid and authoritarian that it resists the pressure of environmental change that it becomes a handicap to progress rather than a benevolent force.

Turning now to art, we find fortunately that there has been rather less of a split between the scientific and artistic viewpoints in western civilisation than there has been between science and religion. Art operates at many different levels, and the experiences it describes are often much more familiar to ordinary men than the experiences of the religious sage. Very broadly speaking, it may be defined as a description of the universe in which the organisation of an emotional element forms part of the description. In a word, it can add beauty to truth just as religion can add goodness to truth. Thus, like religion, it deals with a wider field than science, and in consequence becomes an indispensable additional tool for gaining a fully rounded picture of the universe as a whole. There is no space to treat the contribution made by art to western civilisation at length, but it is certainly true that it is maintaining a far greater influence on the great mass of people than organised religion now seems able to achieve. We shall return to this subject in Chapter 21 when we consider the reciprocal relationship of science, art and religion, and their relevance to the problems of the individual.

The role of philosophy in western thought is another subject too vast to be considered adequately here, and I shall therefore only offer a personal comment on its present condition. There was a time when philosophy was a noble word that could be literally interpreted in its Greek sense of 'love of wisdom'. Philosophers in those days attempted to correlate data from every department of knowledge and to relate their conclusions to problems of individual action. Western civilisation right down to the time of Bergson and Whitehead produced a large proportion of men of this kind, but today, with certain honourable exceptions, philosophers have very largely restricted their field of inquiry to epistemology, or the theory of what can be known. Although it is admirable to apply criticism to this subject it seems to me fatal to overdo it, and this many modern philosophers have certainly done, especially by an excessive preoccupation with the meaning of words. I do not mean by this that reasonable discipline in the use of words must not be observed. But it is essential that the symbol should not be mistaken for the reality. Words are a rough and ready way of representing speech in visual terms, and speech itself is only a sound symbolism for ideas. Moreover the symbolism of both speech and words varies from year to year and, in even more obvious ways, from place to place. The present impasse of philosophy in its original and best sense is due to its failure to recognise that its prime concern is not with symbols, which can be adequately systematised by successive generations of linguistic artisans according to their constant shifts of meaning, but with the ideas for which they stand.

How, then, can we sum up the present position of western civilisation – the complex of emotional and intellectual attitudes which characterise our species in the second half of the twentieth century? First we see a society torn between the primitive instincts of its animal past and the aspirations that can eventually bring it into a fully self-conscious relationship with the universe as a whole. Second, we see a society which this conflict has so confused that it still regards its major techniques of thought and experience as expressed in religion, art and science as antagonistic instead of parallel and compatible aspects of the same quest. Third, and perhaps most immediately tragic, we see a society whose technology has so far outstripped its wisdom that it must either destroy itself entirely, or wastefully conform to the pattern of limited conflicts which characterised the primitive hominids of a million years ago.

To the aware but faint-hearted person the attempt to alter this pattern may seem predestined to failure. But with the opportunities conferred on us by our evolutionary heritage it would certainly be ignoble to persist in so defeatist a view. If man has survived for a million years it seems reasonable to hope that he may survive still longer, provided he is prepared to make sufficient intellectual effort. One of the main parts of this effort must consist in standing back from the immediate condition of mankind, and particularly from preoccupations with the self, and attempting to see the possible role of our species in the grander context of space and time. The second must consist in translating thoughtful conclusions into positive actions which are open to every member of the species to make according to his talents. In the final part of this book I shall ask the reader to accompany me into these difficult and dangerous waters and see how far it may be possible to reach some tentative conclusion.

Part 5

MAN'S PLACE IN NATURE

Chapter Twenty

MAN, EVOLUTION AND THE
COSMOS

IN THE MAIN body of this book, now completed, I have told
in outline the story of the brief million years in which the
species *Homo sapiens* and his closest ancestors and collaterals
have inhabited the planet earth. Some aspects of this story,
based on evidence that is now accepted by most reasonable
people, have been treated with a certain assurance. Others,
where there are gaps in the record, or where the significance
of certain events is open to doubt, have required a more tentative approach, for interpretation is a field where dogmatism
is especially out of place. What I hope has emerged is a reasonably balanced account of human history in relation to its
immediate setting in nature, open naturally to many criticisms on points of detail, but generally accurate so far as its
basic facts are concerned.

However, any author foolhardy enough to embark on such
a project at all must obviously be concerned with interpretation at an even more general level than has so far been
attempted. It will already have become apparent to any
reader who has followed me so far that my view of the development of mankind, and particularly of the growth of
civilisation, is very different from that of the specialist historian. Indeed I do not believe that human history can be
properly understood and interpreted unless it is regarded
as an extension of natural history, obeying the same laws
which govern the whole process of organic evolution. In this
and the following chapter I propose to broaden the context
still further and give my personal views concerning man's
relationship to the universe as a whole.

To begin with I must make it clear that I entirely reject

any anthropocentric interpretation of the nature of the universe and of human destiny. It is not, in my view, any longer possible for rational people to regard man as the spoiled child of the cosmos, eternally protected by a benevolent personal Creator, and occupying in the earth a favoured antechamber to Heaven. The majestic prospects opened up by science have revealed the parochialism, and indeed the unseemliness, of this limited concept of man, and offered him a new challenge. We have to face the fact that, far from being the special recipients of some magical divine favour, we are only a tiny part of the totality of nature, and that our earthly home is merely a speck of interstellar dust in one of the infinitely numerous galaxies spread through the immensity of space.

The implications of these facts may come at first as a rude shock, even to thoughtful men, but it then becomes apparent that they open up new possibilities for courageous thought and creative action. Science has cut the apron-strings tying us to the father-figure of a personal deity and allowed us to venture forth into the universe with adult minds. It can lead us through a new humility to a grander concept of the world and of our own nature than any that our species has hitherto known.

If the reader agrees that enlightened people must now give up all magical explanations of man's place in nature he has a right to ask what alternative approach can be made to the problem. To me there is no doubt whatever that our basic attitude must be scientific, but here again there is a danger of semantic confusion. The word science, like the word God, has been narrowed down to a special meaning, which in many people's minds is entirely separate from religious or artistic experience, and is indeed hostile to these other means of knowing. If I say that the basic approach to the problems of the universe and of man should be scientific, I do not mean that religious and artistic experience must be rejected as invalid. They should, indeed, be extensions of the scientific method, which enable the scientific picture to be enormously expanded and enriched. Their different approaches are not in the slightest degree contradictory, and each can gain enormously by an understanding of the methods of the others.

The ability to harmonise the findings of these three techniques of knowing is in fact an apt and concise definition of wisdom – a state of mind which is generally regarded as the most desirable which man can attain.

If this attitude finds any acceptance, I need make no excuse for first considering human history from the scientific point of view, with special attention to its place in the general pattern of organic evolution. To begin with it will be necessary to amplify some of the statements already made in Chapter 2 about the evolutionary process itself. As we saw there, the break-through from non-living to living matter probably occurred rather more than 2,000 million years ago. At that time comparatively simple inorganic compounds of carbon and hydrogen were interacting with each other, as well as with water vapour, ammonia, hydrogen sulphide, and other gases in the primeval atmosphere, to produce the first life-stuff in the world. The transition was very gradual, muddled and indirect, depending entirely on the chance availability of the necessary ingredients in a suitable environment at the right time. Nevertheless this random and wasteful process did produce after many long millennia the extra degree of complexity associated with living things. Most probably, also, the break-through did not just occur in one place, from which it was later diffused, but on a broad front along the intertidal beaches of the tropic seas.

The next stage was the elaboration of the biosphere by equally random stages until living things were spread over almost the whole face of the earth. The most congenial environments were naturally the first to be exploited, but as these were filled, and life continued to spread, special adaptations became necessary to achieve survival. Organisms were forced into new regions and became specialised by natural selection to fit widely contrasted habitats. In responding to each new challenge their bodies became more and more divergent in shape and size, and more and more complex in organisation. Adapt or perish was the law of life, and the evolutionary lines that failed to find an answer to the environmental challenge became extinct.

But it was not only the physical environment that encouraged this constant differentiation and complexification of life.

As each physical niche was filled with organisms, the organisms themselves formed in effect part of the environment for new life forms emerging in the same region. Thus life could only progress there if its new manifestations were able to deal not only with the environmental challenges of geography, climate, and so on, but also with the challenge of organisms already in occupation. The sheer pressure of numbers in a given habitat thus often led to grim struggles for survival between its occupants, and to the continual selection of new evolutionary lines which replaced the previously dominant forms. This replacement of one group of animals by another more efficient group within a single habitat is an even more significant feature of organic evolution than adaptive radiation into new geographical settings. The challenge of geography and climate can often be met by physical specialisation alone, but to achieve dominance in a defined region where existing life forms are already well established, and therefore themselves form part of the environment, requires mental growth as well as physical specialisation. To take only two examples from the evolutionary record, the triumph of the teleost fishes over earlier marine vertebrates, and of the mammals over the reptiles, was not mainly the result of a migration and a new start in a virgin area (although examples of this also formed part of the process). It was typically achieved by superior adaptations within the same environment, and in the mammals particularly this was correlated with greatly improved mental ability.

Since the triumph of the mammals some fifty-eight million years ago the two major stages in the growth of mind have been, first, the development of conceptual thought by the hominid primates at the beginning of the Pleistocene epoch and, second, the triumph of *Homo sapiens* in the last Glacial Phase of the Great Ice Age. In the later stages of this process the limiting factor encouraging evolutionary energy to flow into this ascending channel was no longer a single restricted environment, but the whole physical surface of the earth. When *Homo sapiens* emerged, mammals had already radiated into nearly every part of the world, and were dominant everywhere they went. The further development of life had therefore to be entirely in the mental sphere, and the break-through occurred with our own species. The particular nature of man is thus due to a principle that has operated throughout the whole history of life: namely, the tendency of evolutionary energy to press organisms into regions where new possibilities can still be realised and, when further growth through these channels is prevented, either by the physical or biological environment (or, we should add, by excessive and irreversible specialisations in the organisms themselves), to overflow into mental channels. Moreover, man represents a unique and special organisation of this overflow in that he is now the only animal on this planet capable of reflecting on his own origins, nature, and destiny. As Sir Charles Sherrington, Teilhard de Chardin and Julian Huxley were among the first to point out, in man for the first time evolution has become conscious of itself.

Now what are the main characteristics of this new 'psychozoic' era in the history of life? One of its most interesting features is that physical and cultural divergence within the species has been brought to an end. The formation of the human races described in Chapter 11 was the last example of purely physical divergence, and since that time there has been a growing tendency for men to draw closer together. The reason for this is that culture, unlike physical characteristics, can be passed very easily from one contemporary group to another, so that as communications improve there is a tendency for society to become continually more homogeneous. With this convergence the ideas that bind men together begin to flow more easily from group to group, and the old taboos and social prejudices of primitive tribal societies are gradually broken down. Intermarriage then begins to occur on an increasing scale, and the trend to physical divergence which occurs in isolated communities is reversed. Already today the spread of western civilisation to nearly every part of the earth, and the prowess of such Mongoloid peoples as the Japanese in applied science, has destroyed once and for all the fiction of a Caucasoid 'master race'. It seems certain that, within a few centuries at most, physical as well as cultural differences between Negroids, Mongoloids, and Caucasoids will have become much diminished through interbreeding, and the world's population will be very largely of one physical and cultural type.

Another characteristic feature of the psychozoic era, closely related to racial and cultural convergence, has been the tendency for human society to organise itself into larger and larger units. The first family units combined to form tribes, then groups of tribes joined together to form states, and then states themselves formed larger confederations based on mutual interest. The survival value of this evolutionary trend is clearly shown by the success of the large confederations existing in the world today, such as the United States of America and the Union of Soviet Socialist Republics. Even the conservative and intensely individualistic national communities of Europe are now beginning to realise that they must form a closer association if their society is to be effective. There is little doubt that a common economic market will soon lead to a Federated States of Europe comparable to the federations of America and Russia, and that a similar process of integration will proceed equally rapidly in other parts of the world. The last stage will, we must hope, be a purposefully controlled community of all mankind, although this will depend on whether the grave dangers discussed at the conclusion of the last chapter of Part 4 can be successfully avoided.

The third, and most exciting, characteristic of the psychozoic era at its advanced human level has been the astonishing development in man of science, art, and religion. These matters have been dealt with in detail in Part 4, but a word must now be said about their evolutionary significance. If the totality of man is regarded as evolution becoming conscious of itself, then science can be defined as the technique of thought by which this consciousness is critically ordered. Its role is to describe and classify phenomena as they impinge on the mind, and so far as possible to ascertain the laws that govern them. But when we turn to art and religion we are confronted by much greater difficulties of definition. In their highest form (and by this I mean when they have cast off the shackles of primitive superstition) it seems reasonable to suggest that they give a greater insight into the nature of the universe and of man than can be provided by science.

This is not due to any esoteric quality in these techniques of knowing the world, but simply because their domain includes a much wider range of perception. Beauty and goodness, for instance, cannot be described by science, and by leaving out these attributes of phenomena even the truths which science can reveal must always be limited. An example will help to make the matter clear. It is quite possible for a scientist to give a certain account of, say, Beethoven's Ninth Symphony in scientific terms. He can measure the frequency of each individual note, he can analyse and describe the mathematical structure of the melodies and harmonies, and even relate these data to such external factors as distance, the acoustics of the concert hall, and so on. What he cannot do is to give any account whatever of the symphony's beauty, or whether the performance is good or bad. The inability of science to include any account of value in its descriptions means that it can never tell the whole truth about any phenomenon it studies.

The function of art and religion in human evolution seems to be to provide a key to the additional aspects of phenomena with which science is incompetent to deal. They are concerned not with material objects, nor even the atoms that compose them, but with vision. They are thus highly subjective, and the direct apprehension of either beauty or goodness is not something that can be communicated from one mind to another by logical or rational means. Artistic and religious experience is, however, so common and so consistent in its manifestations that only an exceptionally rash and foolish scientist would deny that it, too, obeyed certain laws. To those who have had such experience it seems extremely probable that art and religion are the keys to a new level of awareness in human consciousness, even though this cannot be 'rationally' described. The world to which they give access has bigger horizons than the world of science but is not at all in conflict with it. It seems to be a natural continuation of the evolutionary sequence that has already led from inorganic matter to the mind of *Homo sapiens*.

Leaving these propositions on one side for the moment, we return now to the question of man's possible relationship to the universe as a whole. One of the major achievements of science has been in astronomical research, which has been much stimulated during the past few decades by the construction of the giant optical telescopes at Mount Wilson and Mount Palomar in America and, more recently, the radio telescopes at Jodrell Bank and Cambridge in Great Britain. Some of the findings of science in this field were alluded to in the first chapter of this book, but it is now necessary to reflect on them again. Particularly I would commend to the poetic imagination of my readers the sheer size of the universe, in which grand star cities, themselves so vast that the intellect cannot begin to appreciate their magnitude, are scattered like handfuls of dust throughout the still greater immensity of space. The number of stars in this beautifully ordered system can no longer be reckoned in millions or even tens of millions, but is at least 1,000,000,000,000,000,000,000,000. That is, using the British billion, a thousand million billion, or, using the American and continental billion, a hundred thousand million billion. Moreover, many of these stars are certainly ringed like our sun by a family of planets, and it is unlikely indeed that none of these planets provides an environment as suitable for life as does our own earth.

The relevance of these facts to any speculations about the role of man in the cosmos is too obvious to be laboured. It is overwhelmingly likely that life is not unique to earth, and must be following a course of parallel evolution in at least a few of the planetary bodies circling distant suns. This is not to say, of course, that this life will have conformed to exactly the same pattern as is found on earth, for we have already stressed the random nature of evolution, and referred to the evidence which shows that our present bodies and minds are the end-products of a series of accidents. But there is no reason to doubt that comparable processes have been going on in other parts of the universe while life on earth has been pursuing its upward struggle. Even though this proposition cannot yet be scientifically proved, the findings of astronomy and evolutionary biology already suggest that it is much more likely to be true than false.

To assist our speculations on the role of life, and especially of man, in the cosmos we must now briefly set out the findings of science concerning the nature of the stellar universe.

Two major theories on this subject at present occupy the minds of cosmologists. Both seek to devise a cosmographical model which will take account of a major observable fact – that the universe is in a state of rapid expansion. The causes for believing this statement to be true, which are based on comparisons of the behaviour of radio and light waves between bodies at a constant distance and in recession, need not concern us here; it will be sufficient to say that most astronomers now accept that the star cities scattered throughout space do not maintain a constant distance, but are rushing away from each other at enormous speeds. Very briefly, the first of these theories, generally known as the 'evolutionary' or 'big-bang' theory, suggests that the recession of the galaxies is due to the explosion of a primeval atom into which all the stuff of the universe was once compressed. It is estimated, according to different interpretations of the data, that this explosion occurred at least 9,000 million and at most 60,000 million years ago. The alternative theory, known as the 'steady-state' or 'continuous-creation' theory, denies the occurrence of the 'big bang' altogether. It maintains instead that new matter in the form of hydrogen atoms is actually being created in interstellar space and gradually condensing into galaxies. As the old galaxies recede from each other, leaving greater and greater spaces in between, these new galaxies take their place. The new galaxies then recede in their turn, and so on *ad infinitum*.

Both theories have extremely interesting implications. According to the evolutionary theory the physical universe has a finite past but an infinite future; it began with a bang and will now gradually run down until its energy is so evenly distributed that no further change can occur. According to the steady-state theory, the universe has had no beginning and will have no end. Its individual parts are constantly being replaced, but the general picture remains the same. This model offers us a universe that has always been of indefinite extent in space and time. One of the most interesting aspects of both theories is their reliance on the principle of creation. In the steady-state theory this is quite explicit, for it is based on the assumption that entirely new hydrogen atoms are continually coming into existence. In the evolutionary theory the creative principle is less obvious, but must be invoked when we consider the origin of the primeval atom itself.

Observational evidence does not yet finally confirm either of these theories, and it is not within my competence to comment on the data so far produced in support of each. However, the role of life in a universe of either kind is of extreme interest, and may even throw some light on the cosmological arguments. Let us begin with a summary of the main facts of organic evolution as they may possibly illuminate our speculations on man's cosmic significance.

First, we have seen that life on earth is simply matter at a higher level of organisation, and does not represent a separate order of nature. Second, we have seen that mind has evolved as naturally from the biological envelope enclosing the earth as life evolved from the physical elements preceding it. Third, we have seen in man an extreme heightening of mental ability, expressed characteristically in the power of conceptual thought, which has given him dominance over all other organisms. Fourth, we have suggested that in the purest forms of artistic and religious experience man himself may be in process of breaking through still further, and entering a layer of consciousness beyond the rational understanding of mind itself. Fifth, and finally, we have suggested that it is much more likely than not that a similar pattern of evolution is widespread throughout the universe on planets where a suitable environment occurs.

Before asking how the ideas summed up in these five points can be most reasonably related to the two proposed cosmographical models, it is necessary to emphasise the special importance of points four and five. The fourth point will allow us to introduce an extra dimension into our speculations, for we may invoke the existence of a realm of experience not contained within the strict framework of science as conventionally understood. The fifth point shows that the process of organic evolution on our local planet which has led to *Homo sapiens* is unlikely to be unique, and that an anthropocentric interpretation of biology in relation to the universe as a whole can be misleading. Evolution on earth must be regarded as only a local example of a widespread process which also manifests itself in other suitable environments throughout space.

Let us first consider the possible significance of the cosmic development of life in terms of the evolutionary theory of the universe. This theory, as we have seen, involves a basic assumption: namely, the existence of a primeval atom whose origin cannot be explained by science, nor even lies within the realms of scientific investigation. In fact the most eminent exponent of the evolutionary theory, the Belgian astrophysicist Georges Lemaître, is himself in Holy Orders, and the whole model depends on the acceptance of an extra-scientific creative principle.

Now if we accept this concept, what followed the disintegration of the primeval atom between 60,000 million and 9,000 million years ago? Details of interpretation vary here with the mathematical leanings of cosmologists, but in general the picture is reasonably consistent. We must imagine the stuff of the primeval atom disintegrating with unimaginable violence, probably as a result of radioactive decay, and then radiating out into space as a great cloud of gas. After many millions of years this expanding cloud began to condense into galaxies which, by the force of the original explosion, continued to race away from the original centre at enormous speed.

According to this theory the whole energy controlling the evolution of the universe came from the 'big bang' and, as time has gone on, the energy reserves available for the performance of work have become less and less. In other words, the entropy of the universe (which, simply put, is the measure of its running-down process) has constantly increased.* On the evolutionary theory a stage will therefore one day be reached where the whole universe will have run down like a clock and, after this point, no further events will be able to occur.

Now it does not seem to me entirely fanciful to believe (as Teilhard de Chardin has already suggested) that life may be the means by which the increasing entropy of this particular model of the universe is counteracted. We have already

---

*A full discussion of entropy would take us beyond the scope of this book, and the interested reader is referred to Eddington (1935), Chapter 4, and to Dampier (1961), pp. 234, 300, 407 and 481-8.

described the process by which increased environmental pressure on our local planet has led eventually to self-conscious mind and spiritual awareness, and we have stressed that similar processes are almost certainly going on in the satellites of other suns. The highest manifestations of awareness in man carry us beyond purely scientific means of knowing and, through art and religion, have opened up to numerous insighted persons visions of a world unlimited by conventional concepts of space and time. It seems to me most likely that as more and more men evolve into this new sphere of knowledge the whole cosmological picture will become clearer. The laws now supposed to be leading to the running-down of the universe on the evolutionary theory will be recognised as belonging only to a limited system within the totality of nature. Although true enough within their own context, the addition of the new dimension revealed by artistic and religious experience will enormously increase our understanding of their principles of operation. This awareness will also allow us to integrate the creative principle implicit in the primeval atom into a much grander system of nature than our present limited human minds can possibly grasp.

Turning now to the steady-state theory, we find it demands a somewhat different concept of life's place in the cosmos. Although, like the evolutionary theory, it begins by postulating a creative principle, this principle is more diffuse. It is manifested not through a primeval atom, but through the constant appearance of new hydrogen atoms in interstellar space. According to the steady-state theory, therefore, the universe is not living on the capital of one initial supply of energy, but is receiving a regular income from the continuous creation of hydrogen. This creation is itself constantly counteracting increasing entropy, and therefore life is not the only anti-entropic force. Nevertheless, it is still consistent with this model to suppose that man and his collaterals elsewhere in the universe are moving into a fifth dimension of experience. Moreover, according to both models, it seems certain that only with the perspective provided by this new dimension will it be possible to integrate the creative principle, whether expressed in a primeval atom or through the continuous production of hydrogen, into the general pattern.

When at last this happens, both the present models will certainly be transcended; they are only a temporary scaffolding erected by man's evolving mind to aid its growth into awareness.

I am very conscious that the last few pages have taken us to the limits of intelligible communication, and it would certainly be inappropriate to the main theme of this book to pursue such speculations here. To conclude this chapter, however, I would like to reiterate one point that seems to me to lie at the heart of any discussion of man's place in nature. It is that science as at present defined cannot, on its own admission, give a complete description of the physical universe, of life, or of man. The province of science is to investigate and codify secondary laws, and such ultimate questions as the significance of value or the nature of creation lie beyond its scope. It is an odd irony that scientists, who have so often attempted to eliminate a creative God from the universe in the interests of truth, are now finding that they can ultimately explain nothing at all unless they are prepared to put Him back.

Chapter Twenty-one

HUMAN DESTINY AND THE
INDIVIDUAL

IN THE LAST chapter of a book we arrive at the stocktaking. As best we can we must sum up the major features of what has gone before and consider our own individual predicament in the modern world. Our theme has been man, and throughout the study of this vast subject we have established, I think, that the nature of man can be understood only by relating him so far as our limited vision will allow to his context in space and time. It is impossible to understand the human phenomenon except by considering it as an aspect of the universe as a whole.

The object of our inquiry can thus be briefly summed up, as the subtitle of this book suggests, as an attempt to tell the story of man as a part of nature. We began with a picture of man's home on the planet earth, spinning through space in a universe so vast that no effort of the unaided human intelligence can hope to grasp its magnitude. We continued with a brief account of the origin and evolution of life on earth, the principles that seem to have governed it, and the nature and early history of the primate order from which we sprang. We watched the evolution of man as he groped his way upwards through his early trials and difficulties to the phase of co-operative effort known as civilisation, and we attempted to relate the development of civilised societies to the principles of biological growth that had gone before. Particularly here we tried to show how, through the spread of western civilisation, our species has now become part of a single cultural group. In the last phase of our account we began to see that the whole of this majestic process must form part of an even more universal and magnificent whole, and suggested that the purest and highest forms of artistic and religious experience are probably the only means by which a vision of our universal role can eventually be attained. Man, we have agreed, through an imaginative understanding of previous intuitions by members of our species, now represents a phase of life in which evolution is becoming aware of itself. We have gone even further, and hinted that man and his collaterals on other planets may actually represent the means by which the growing entropy of the physical universe will be counteracted.

I have stated in the previous chapter that further speculation about these questions cannot be entered into here. Although I hope to return to them in another book, the finale to *A Million Years of Man* must be less ambitious. In this concluding chapter I shall be concerned only with some of the problems of the individual who, like myself, has to live a life in the immense, and as yet inexplicable, context of the spatio-temporal scene.

The universe is large and evolution long, but the individual man is small and his direct experience of the earth is restricted to only the minutest fraction of the process of which he forms a part. Nevertheless, when we consider the marvellous record of events described in this book, it seems that his role may not be so insignificant as it might at first appear. Man alone among living organisms on earth has the potential ability to construct his own philosophical and moral scheme, and thereby consciously contribute his small quantum of energy to the future evolutionary course of nature.

In examining the implications of this statement I shall necessarily have to venture to some considerable extent beyond the stricter disciplines of conventional science. As will already be clear to the reader who has followed me so far, I do not believe that science as at present defined can give more than a partial account of the nature of the universe or of man. The intuitional techniques of the advanced primate psyche must also be used if we are to arrive even at an approximation of the truth. Scientists who may be dismayed by this approach will need no warning to cease their reading at this point. To those who stay with me I promise to observe as disciplined a method as the subject will allow, and to show if possible that a consideration of these ultimate problems may extend, but does not necessarily contradict, the findings of science.

Any discussion of the role of the individual in evolution must necessarily involve the question of values. The majority of animals, including subhuman primates, do not make self-conscious creative actions; they simply behave. Many men also only behave, but as evolution has proceeded, their behaviour has been more and more controlled by value judgements. Their actions, whether positive or negative, show a greater or lesser awareness of the existence of the good, the beautiful and the true.

In considering the values, I propose to start with goodness, which, although correlated with beauty by certain poets, seems to me to have an even more fundamental significance. Goodness may perhaps be defined as beauty in action – a process by which an awareness of something greater than the individual mind is translated into terms of creative movement. The awareness of this value, like that of beauty and, to a lesser degree, of truth, is intuitional. It is something heightened by experience, but experience alone cannot give it. It is comparable to a genetic mutation transferred to the level of psychosocial evolution.

Now the special importance of goodness in action is that it affects a large number of other organisms. Man being a social animal this is of profound importance. To be compassionate, ungreedy and virtuous is not simply of selfish benefit to the individual because it stores up some hypothetical reward in an equally hypothetical heaven; it makes for the survival of the species. Even by conventional scientific standards this result must be regarded as desirable.

By comparison with goodness, beauty has less immediate impact. It is a contemplative value, an awareness of which can be a spur to action, but it is not action itself. Thus ugliness, although representing a failure to organise the environment, is less seriously destructive than evil behaviour. Ugliness cannot provide inspiration or creative stimulus, but nor does it normally produce positively harmful results. Of course, if ugliness at any phase of human development so dominates beauty that the latter's spur to good actions is greatly reduced, then ugliness can be said to cause harm. In the general context of evolution, however, it is of less vital importance as a value.

Truth has already been incidentally discussed in previous chapters. Contrary to the majority view it seems to me the most relative of the values. Within any frame of reference where scientific discipline rather than emotionalism is predominant, certain laws can be said to be true. For example, the laws of Newtonian physics are entirely true within a Newtonian frame. It is only when an Einsteinian frame is introduced to extend that of Newton that they become untrue. The limitations of truth as a value, as opposed to the values of goodness and beauty, are that the framework of law can be indefinitely extended as new discoveries are made. What is a whole truth to one generation may therefore be only a partial truth to the next, whereas goodness and beauty are much less susceptible to change. Ultimate truth can probably never be known by the purely human mind, and it is therefore necessary to assess this value most critically every time it is adduced in argument.

Now even if we agree that man is evolving to some apprehension of value, transcending both reason and desire, the problem of translating this new-found knowledge into action still remains. What should each one of us do to make our groping aspirations effective at the present phase of our evolutionary development? The answer to this question is of particular importance, even to the most self-centred person, as it also contains the key to that most desirable state which we recognise as individual happiness.

Let us first consider the social context on which the very survival of the individual depends. In Chapter 19 we considered as dispassionately as possible the present condition of western civilisation, and came to some tentative and not altogether encouraging conclusions. Man, it seems, in the second half of the twentieth century, is intent not only on destroying his individual potential for happiness, but even on the much more ambitious task of wiping out his species as a whole. We have suggested, perhaps somewhat optimistically, that this final disaster is unlikely to occur, but we must nevertheless bear in mind that even the continuance of limited wars must be a serious disadvantage to the collective advance of man. The first conscious application of values to human affairs can therefore well be made most constructively to social behaviour.

The lessons of human history show beyond any possibility of doubt that co-operative effort is the only valid survival technique remaining to our species. As we have seen countless times in this book, 'adapt or perish' is a fundamental law of nature. When evolution was still proceeding at the physical level, adaptations for survival were likewise mainly physical. But the combination of an upward stance and the development of brain in the early primates enabled a breakthrough to be made. In this new psychosocial phase of evolution the development of co-operative mind became the main technique of survival and, in spite of the new penetrations now being made into what we may call psychospiritual awareness, it still remains so. Unless man learns to co-operate with his fellows his local dominance on this particular evolutionary centre in the universe is liable to cease.

Now co-operation operates at two levels: first, in the everyday relationships between man and man; second, in the relationship between organised groups of men, known as nations, which at present represent the highest state of human aggregation. On the personal level the major obstacles to co-operation depend on both economic and psychological factors. These are closely interrelated, but the second is the key to the first. Men crave security to face what they have often had reason to feel is a cold and hostile universe. The search for security means also to most people the search for power, and economic dominance is one major method by which this power-security is often achieved. People seek wealth as an answer, unconscious as they may be of their motives, to their animal insecurity in the world around them.

The immense fallacy implicit in this attitude is made clear by history. Even without bringing in the moral aspects of economic greed, it is clear that any society based on exploitation of the earth's resources for individual gain is destined to destruction. As the earth's population grows, the need for co-operative effort in making our planet's riches available for all becomes increasingly essential. If this is neglected, population pressure will ultimately lead to physical strife, with all the anti-evolutionary destruction that this entails. It is therefore most desirable that every man should use his intelligence, as well as his moral intuitions if he possesses them, to limit his instinct towards personal gain. It is perhaps too much to expect at the present phase of evolution that individuals will make this limitation voluntarily because they believe in goodness as a moral force; they may perhaps accept, however, that personal greed is not in the long run effective in obtaining the ends they desire, and must lead ultimately to the destruction of themselves and their children.

The security principle works in much the same way at the level of national groups as it does at that of the individual. The tribal systems of former times have now fortunately given place to only two major confederations of mankind, so the problem is somewhat simplified. However, the weapons of destruction possessed by both these groups are now so powerful that the danger of fear overtaking intelligence can have much more universally disastrous consequences than was formerly possible. One of the most constructive lines that can be followed by the individual is therefore not only to understand the issues that must lead to his own abandonment of the power-security principle, but to persuade others in his community that it must also be abandoned, at least at the national level. Again in this context it would be too much to hope that goodness itself will be a sufficient motivating force. The major appeal to sanity must be based on the realisation that aggressive acts by the world's two major power groups cannot hope to achieve the ends that every man desires. This appeal will be effective only when, by a study of evolution in relation to human destiny, a majority of individual men and women reach an intelligent appreciation of the processes at work.

We cannot develop further here the application of evolutionary and cosmological studies to the destiny of humanity as a whole, but something must be said about the more personal fears and desires which stand between the individual and the achievement of happiness. Apart from the social insecurities which lead to aggression and greed, many of us are much concerned with the more immediate problem of our possible fate as individuals. Our lives on earth are short, and even if by a proper use of our intellects and imaginations we avoid the atomic war that will make them even shorter, the problem of our individual fate still remains. There was a time when it was possible to evade the issues of suffering and death by an appeal to a personal Father in Heaven who, it was hoped, would compensate for present misery by an infinitude of bliss in the hereafter. But I believe that most thoughtful people would now accept that the mental and spiritual evolution of mankind has carried us far beyond the point where such a view is tenable. The immense beauty and grandeur of the universe around us, and the wonderful intricacy of the process that has led us to our present state, cannot be circumscribed by such limited aspirations. More and more we have to see ourselves not as individuals but as part of the whole complex of nature. Straining our imaginations to the utmost we must attempt to break the barriers of space and time and relate our individual personalities to the whole cosmic scene.

Man, we have said, has the high privilege of carrying evolution to an awareness of itself on the planet earth. By intellectual effort, intuition, and the pursuit of value, he has the possibility of reaching such a state of wisdom that the self-centred problems of the individual must dissolve. In saying this, we approach once more the fringes of rational communication, and begin to trespass into the realms of religion and art. But even the strictly scientific study of evolution cannot suggest that our individual egos can be of any special account unless they contribute to a wider understanding of our place in nature.

Already at the present limited stage of human development I feel it is possible to glimpse through the darkness and hesitations of our ignorance a grander prospect for humanity than any that we have hitherto known. It it not beyond our powers to bring about a situation on our local planet where insecurity, greed and fear have given place to an intelligent and imaginative awareness of what man can be. Instead of being torn by dissensions and anger, and being carried like driftwood on the tide of change, we could rise to the challenge of reflecting on our origins, our development, and the contribution each of us can make to understanding the cosmos as a whole. In this condition of man there would no longer be wars and rumours of wars and the ruthless pursuit of economic or political power. Embraced in one family, and invested with a new dignity, our species would become fully conscious of its evolutionary destiny and its special role in the universal scene.

I have no doubt whatever that this vision can be realised if enough individuals can convince themselves of the need for effort. The beginning of the road has already been mapped by science, which has also done much to tear down the walls of wishful thinking, ignorance and superstition. Art and religion, re-orientated in the new context of the scientifically revealed universe, can carry the process still further. Reflective people will doubtless agree with Goethe, when he said that 'the greatest happiness of thinking man is to have searched into what is open to his methods of research and to reverence in quietude that which is not open to these methods'. But today they will wish, I believe, to carry their aspirations still further. They will be ready to extend and ennoble the restricted scientific view of the universe with daring new perspectives, so that the relationship between art, science and religion – between beauty, truth and goodness – can be better understood. However long and arduous the quest, I do not believe that there is any other road by which man can hope to arrive at a true picture of the universe and of himself.

BIBLIOGRAPHY

NOTE. – For obvious reasons a book with the present title cannot have a fully comprehensive Bibliography; the following list therefore includes only those works which I have actually consulted in preparing the manuscript. I hesitated whether to classify the books under different subject headings, but this would have required so much duplication and cross-referencing of entries that I eventually decided on a straightforward alphabetical presentation. On page 321, however, the reader will find some *Suggestions for Further Reading* in which a selection of standard general works from the Bibliography appear in classified form.

R.C.

ATIYAH, E. (1955): *The Arabs*. Pelican Books, A.350. Penguin Books: Harmondsworth. pp. 242.

BARNETT, A. (1957): *The human species: a biology of man*. Pelican Books, A.341. Penguin Books: Harmondsworth. pp. xiv, 351.

BARROW, R. H. (1953): *The Romans*. Pelican Books, A.196. Penguin Books: Harmondsworth. pp. 224.

BERGSON, H. (1911): *Creative evolution*. Authorised translation by A. Mitchell. Macmillan: London. pp. xvi, 425.

BERNAL, J. D. (1957): *Science in history*. 2nd ed. Watts: London. pp. xxiv, 984.

BIRDSELL, J. B. *See* COON, C. S.

BOULE, M., and VALLOIS, H. V. (1957): *Fossil men: a textbook of human palaeontology*. With a new introduction by K. P. Oakley. Translated by M. Bullock from the revised enlarged fourth French edition of *Les hommes fossiles,* with additional information supplied by Professor Vallois. Thames and Hudson: London. pp. xxvi, 535.

BOUQUET, A. C. (1941): *Comparative religion: a short outline*. Pelican Books, A.89. Penguin Books: Harmondsworth. pp. x, 239.

BOURLIÈRE, F. (1955): *The natural history of mammals*. Translated from the French by H. M. Parshley (i.e. L. Harrison Matthews). Harrap: London. pp. xxii, 363, xi.

BOWRA, C. M. (1958): *The Greek experience*. History of Civilisation. Weidenfeld and Nicolson: London. pp. xiv, 211.

BREASTED, J. H. (1916): *Ancient times, a history of the early world: an introduction to the study of ancient history and the career of early man*. Ginn: Boston, New York, etc. pp. xx, 742.

BREASTED, J. H. (1956): *A history of Egypt from the earliest times to the Persian conquest*. 2nd ed. fully revised. Hodder and Stoughton: London. pp. xxxii, 634.

BRITISH MUSEUM (NATURAL HISTORY) (1958): *A handbook on evolution*. Trustees of the British Museum: London. pp. x, 110.

BROAD, C. D. (1925): *The mind and its place in nature*. The Tarner Lectures delivered in Trinity College, Cambridge, 1923. Routledge and Kegan Paul: London. pp. x, 674.

BRODRICK, A. H. (1948): *Prehistoric painting*. Avalon Press and the Central Institute of Art and Design: London. pp. 40.

BRODRICK, A. H. (1960): *Man and his ancestry*. Hutchinson: London. pp. 256.

BROOM, R. (1950): *Finding the missing link*. Watts: London. pp. vi, 104.

BROOM, R., and ROBINSON, J. T. (1952): *Swartkrans ape-man* Paranthropus crassidens. Transvaal Museum Memoir No. 6, March 1952. Transvaal Museum: Pretoria. pp. xii, 139.

BROWN, G. B. (1928): *The art of the cave dweller: a study of the earliest artistic activities of man*. Murray: London. pp. xx, 280.

BUSHNELL, G. H. S. (1956): *Peru*. Ancient Peoples and Places, Vol. 1. Thames and Hudson: London. pp. 207.

CARRINGTON, R. (1956): *A guide to earth history*. Chatto and Windus: London. pp. xvi, 240.

CHILDE, V. G. (1936): *Man makes himself*. The Library of Science and Culture, No. 5. Watts: London. p.p. xii, 275.

CHILDE, V. G. (1942): *What happened in history*. Pelican Books, A.108. Penguin Books: Harmondsworth. pp. 288.

CHILDE, V. G. (1951): *Social evolution*. Watts: London. pp. viii, 184.

CHILDE, V. G. (1958): *The prehistory of European society*. Pelican Books, A.415. Penguin Books: Harmondsworth. pp.185.

CLARK, G. (1957): *Archaeology and society: reconstructing the prehistoric past*. 3rd ed. revised and reset. Methuen: London. pp. 272.

CLARK, G. (1961): *World prehistory: an outline*. University Press: Cambridge. pp. xvi, 284.

CLARK, J. D. (1959): *The prehistory of southern Africa*. Pelican Books, A.458. Penguin Books: Harmondsworth. pp. xxvi, 341.

CLARK, W. E. LE GROS (1955): *The fossil evidence for human evolution: an introduction to the study of palaeoanthropology*. The Scientist's Library. University of Chicago Press: Chicago. pp. x, 181.

CLARK, W. E. LE GROS (1959): *The antecedents of man: an introduction to the evolution of the primates.* Edinburgh University Press: Edinburgh. pp. x, 374.

CLARK, W. E. LE GROS (1960): *History of the primates: an introduction to the study of fossil man.* 7th ed. Trustees of the British Museum: London. pp. viii, 119.

CLARKE, S., and ENGELBACH, R. (1930): *Ancient Egyptian masonry: the building craft.* Oxford University Press, Humphrey Milford: London. pp. xvi, 242.

COLBERT, E. H. (1955): *Evolution of the vertebrates: a history of the backboned animals through time.* Wiley: New York; Chapman and Hall: London. pp. xiv, 479.

COLE, S. (1954): *The prehistory of east Africa.* Pelican Books, A.316. Penguin Books: Harmondsworth. pp. 301.

COLE, S. (1959): *The Neolithic revolution.* Trustees of the British Museum: London. pp. vi, 60.

COLLIER, D. *See* MARTIN, P. S.

CONTENAU, G. (1954): *Everyday life in Babylon and Assyria.* Translated from the French by K. R. and A. R. Maxwell-Hyslop. Arnold: London. pp. xvi, 324.

COON, C. S. (1955): *The history of man: from the first human to primitive culture and beyond.* Cape: London. pp. xxii, 438, xiii.

COON, C. S., GARN, S. M., and BIRDSELL, J. B. (1950): *Races: a study of the problems of race formation in man.* American Lecture Series, Publication No. 77; a monograph in American Lectures in Physical Anthropology. Charles C. Thomas: Springfield, Illinois. pp. xiv, 153.

CORNWALL, I. W. (1960): *The making of man.* Phoenix House: London. pp. 63.

COULBORN, R. (1959): *The origin of civilised societies.* Princeton University Press: Princeton, New Jersey; Oxford University Press: London. pp. xii, 200.

CRAIG, D. *See* DART, R. A.

DAMPIER, W. C. (1961): *A history of science and its relations with philosophy and religion.* 4th ed. reprinted with a postscript by I. B. Cohen. University Press: Cambridge. pp. xxviii, 527.

DART, R. A., with CRAIG, D. (1959): *Adventures with the missing link.* Hamish Hamilton: London. pp. xvi, 251.

DARWIN, C. (1871): *The descent of man, and selection in relation to sex.* 2 vols. Murray: London. Vol. 1: pp. viii, 423; Vol. 2: pp. x, 475. (The 2nd ed., revised and augmented, appeared in 1883.)

DAVISON, D. (1951): *The story of prehistoric civilisations.* Watts: London. pp. xiv, 266.

DAWSON, C. (1957): *The dynamics of world history.* Edited by J. J. Mulloy. Sheed and Ward: London. pp. xiv, 489.

DERRY, T. K., and WILLIAMS, T. I. (1960): *A short history of technology from the earliest times to* A.D. *1900*. Clarendon Press: Oxford. pp. xviii, 782.

DICKINSON, G. LOWES (1909): *The Greek view of life*. 7th ed. revised. Methuen: London. pp. xvi, 261.

DOBZHANSKY, T. (1951): *Genetics and the origin of species*. 3rd ed. revised. Columbia Biological Series, No. 11. Columbia University Press: New York. pp. xii, 364.

DOBZHANSKY, T. (1962): *Mankind evolving: the evolution of the human species*. Yale University Press: New Haven and London. pp. xiv, 381.

DUNBAR, C. O. (1949): *Historical geology*. Wiley: New York; Chapman and Hall: London. pp. xii, 573.

DURY, G. H. (1959): *The face of the earth*. Pelican Books, A.447. Penguin Books: Harmondsworth. pp. xiv, 223.

EDDINGTON, A. (1935): *The nature of the physical world*. Introductory note by E. F. Bozman. Everyman's Library, No. 922. Dent: London. pp. xii, 345.

EDWARDS, I. E. S. (1961): *The pyramids of Egypt*. Revised ed. Parrish: London. pp. xiv, 258.

ENGELBACH, R. *See* CLARKE, S.

FARRINGTON, B. (1953): *Greek science: its meaning for us*. Pelican Books, A.142. Penguin Books: Harmondsworth. pp. 320.

FIRTH, R. (1938): *Human types*. Discussion Books, No. 11. Nelson: London, Edinburgh, Paris, Melbourne, Toronto, New York. pp. 207.

FLINT, R. F. (1958): *Glacial and Pleistocene geology*. Chapman and Hall: London; Wiley: New York. pp. xiii, 553.

FRANKFORT, H. and H. A., WILSON, J. A., and JACOBSEN, T. (1949): *Before philosophy: the intellectual adventure of ancient man; an essay on speculative thought in the ancient Near East*. Pelican Books, A.198. Penguin Books: Harmondsworth. pp. 275.

FRAZER, J. G. (1933): *The golden bough: a study in magic and religion*. Abridged ed. Macmillan: London. pp. xiv, 756.

GALLENKAMP, C. (1960): *Maya: the riddle and rediscovery of a lost civilisation*. Muller: London. pp. x, 219.

GARN, S. M. *See* COON, C. S.

GARRATT, G. T. (Ed.) (1937): *The legacy of India*. With an introduction by the Marquess of Zetland. Clarendon Press: Oxford. pp. xviii, 428.

GATES, R. R. (1948): *Human ancestry from a genetical point of view*. Harvard University Press: Cambridge, Mass. pp. xvi, 422.

GELLNER, E. (1959): *Words and things: a critical account of linguistic philosophy and a study in ideology*. With an introduction by Bertrand Russell. Gollancz: London. pp. 270.

GERARD, R. W. *See* SPUHLER, J. N.

GILLISPIE, C. C. (1960): *The edge of objectivity: an essay in the history of scientific ideas.* Princeton University Press: Princeton, New Jersey. pp. x, 562.

GLANVILLE, S. R. K. (Ed.) (1957): *The legacy of Egypt.* Clarendon Press: Oxford. pp. xx, 424.

GLOVER, T. R. (1957): *The ancient world: a beginning.* Pelican Books, A.120. Penguin Books: Harmondsworth. pp. 350.

GRANT, M. (1960): *The world of Rome.* History of Civilisation. Weidenfeld and Nicolson: London. pp. xxii, 322.

GRAZIOSI, P. (1960): *Palaeolithic art.* Translated from *L'arte dell'antica età della pietra,* 1956. Faber: London. pp. xii, 278.

GRUNEBAUM, G. E. VON (1961): *Islam: essays in the nature and growth of a cultural tradition.* 2nd ed., with an appendix. Routledge and Kegan Paul: London. pp. xvi, 266.

GUILLAUME, A. (1954): *Islam.* Pelican Books, A.311. Penguin Books: Harmondsworth. pp. vi, 208.

HALL, A. R. *See* SINGER, C.

HARGREAVES, F. J. (1948): *The size of the universe.* Pelican Books, A.193. Penguin Books: Harmondsworth. pp. 175.

HARLOW, H. F. *See* SPUHLER, J. N.

HARRISON, R. J. (1958): *Man the peculiar animal.* Pelican Books, A.412. Penguin Books: Harmondsworth. pp. 307.

HILL, W. C. OSMAN (1953–): *Primates: comparative anatomy and taxonomy.* A monograph (with a bibliography). Edinburgh University Publications, Science and Mathematics, No. 3, etc. University Press: Edinburgh. (Work in progress.)

HILL, W. C. OSMAN (1954): *Man's ancestry: a primer of human phylogeny.* William Heinemann Medical Books. Heinemann: London. pp. ix, 194.

HILL, W. C. OSMAN (1957): *Man as an animal.* Hutchinson University Library. Hutchinson: London. pp. 176.

HOCKETT, C. F. *See* SPUHLER, J. N.

HOEBEL, E. A. (1958): *Man in the primitive world: an introduction to anthropology.* 2nd ed. McGraw-Hill Series in Sociology and Anthropology. McGraw-Hill: New York, London, Toronto. pp. xvi, 678.

HOFER, H., SCHULTZ, A. H., and STARCK, D. (Eds.) (1956–61): *Primatologia: handbook of primatology.* Vols. 1–4. Karger: Basel, New York.

HOLMES, A. (1937): *The age of the earth.* New Nelson Classics. Nelson: London. pp. 263.

HOLMYARD, E. J. *See* SINGER, C.

HONIGMANN, J. J. (1959): *The world of man.* Harper: New York. pp. xiv, 971.

HOOTON, E. A. (1946): *Up from the ape.* 2nd ed. revised. Macmillan Company: New York. pp. xxiv, 788.

HOWELLS, W. (1960): *Mankind in the making: the story of human evolution.* Secker and Warburg: London. pp. 382.

HOYLE, F. (1951): *The nature of the universe.* A series of broadcast lectures. Blackwell: Oxford. pp. vi, 121.

HÜRZELER, J. (1960): 'The significance of *Oreopithecus* in the genealogy of man'. *Triangle: the Sandoz Journal of Medical Science.* Vol. 4, No. 5, April 1960, pp. 164–74. London.

HUSSEY, R. C. (1947): *Historical geology: the geologic history of North America.* 2nd ed. McGraw-Hill: New York, London. pp. xii, 465.

HUXLEY, J. S. (1942): *Evolution: the modern synthesis.* Allen and Unwin: London. pp. 645.

HUXLEY, J. S. (Ed.) (1961): *The humanist frame.* Allen and Unwin: London. pp. 432.

HUXLEY, T. H. (1906): *Man's place in nature and other essays.* Everyman's Library. Dent: London. pp. xx, 372.

JACOBSEN, T. *See* FRANKFORT, H.

JAMES, E. O. (1956): *History of religions.* The Teach Yourself Books. English Universities Press: London. pp. x, 237.

JAMES, W. W. (1960): *The jaws and teeth of primates.* Pitman Medical Publishing Co.: London. pp. 328.

JASTROW, M., JR. (1915): *The civilization of Babylonia and Assyria: its remains, language, history, religion, commerce, law, art and literature.* Lippincott: Philadelphia, London. pp. xxvi, 515.

JONES, F. WOOD (1916): *Arboreal man.* Arnold: London. pp. x, 230.

KEPHART, C. (1961): *Races of mankind: their origin and migration.* Owen: London. pp. xvi, 566.

KITTO, H. D. F. (1954): *The Greeks.* Pelican Books, A.220. Penguin Books: Harmondsworth. pp. 256.

KOENIGSWALD, R. VON (1956): *Meeting prehistoric man.* Translated by M. Bullock. Thames and Hudson: London, New York. pp. 216.

KÖHLER, W. (1957): *The mentality of apes.* Translated from the second revised edition by E. Winter. Pelican Books, A.382. Penguin Books: Harmondsworth. pp. 286.

KRAMER, S. N. (1956): *From the tablets of Sumer: twenty-five firsts in man's recorded history.* Falcon's Wings Press: Indian Hills, Colorado, pp. xxvi, 293.

KROEBER, A. L. (1948): *Anthropology: race, language, culture, psychology, prehistory.* New ed. revised. Harrap: London, Bombay, Sydney. pp. xii, 856, xxxix.

LATOURETTE, K. S. (1946): *The Chinese: their history and culture.* 3rd ed. revised. Macmillan Company: New York. pp. xvi, 847.

BIBLIOGRAPHY

LEAKEY, L. S. B. (1951): *Olduvai Gorge: a report on the evolution of the hand-axe culture in beds I–IV*. With chapters on the geology and fauna by the late Professor Hans Reck and Dr A. T. Hopwood. University Press: Cambridge. pp. xvi, 164.

LEAKEY, L. S. B. (1953): *Adam's ancestors: an up-to-date outline of the Old Stone Age (Palaeolithic) and what is known about man's origin and evolution*. 4th ed. completely rewritten. Methuen: London. pp. xii, 235.

LEAKEY, L. S. B. (1959): 'The first men: recent discovery in East Africa'. *Antiquity*, Vol. 33, pp. 285–6. With an additional note by Dr K. P. Oakley, pp. 286–7. Gloucester.

LEAKEY, L. S. B. (1960): 'Recent discoveries at Olduvai Gorge'. *Nature*, Vol. 188, No. 4755, 17 December 1960, pp. 1050–2. London.

LEAKEY, L. S. B. (1961): 'New finds at Olduvai Gorge'. *Nature*, Vol. 189, No. 4765, 25 February 1961, pp. 649–50. London.

LIPS, J. E. (1949): *The origin of things: a cultural history of man*. Harrap: London, Sydney, Toronto, Bombay. pp. 420.

LOVELL, A. C. B. (1959): *The individual and the universe*. The B.B.C. Reith Lectures, 1958. Oxford University Press: London. pp. viii, 111.

LUCAS, H. S. (1953): *A short history of civilisation*. 2nd ed. McGraw-Hill Series in History. McGraw-Hill: New York, Toronto, London. pp. xii, 1002.

LUCRETIUS (1951): *On the nature of the universe*. Translated and with an introduction by R. Latham. The Penguin Classics, L.18. Penguin Books: London, Melbourne, Baltimore. pp. 256.

LYELL, C. (1863): *Geological evidence of the antiquity of man with remarks on theories of the origin of species by variation*. Murray: London. pp. xii, 520.

MACGOWAN, K. (1953): *Early man in the New World*. Macmillan Company: New York. pp. xviii, 260.

MAHLER, J. G. *See* UPJOHN, E. M.

MARINGER, J. (1960): *The gods of prehistoric man*. Translated from the German by Mary Ilford. History of Religion. Weidenfeld and Nicolson: London. pp. xviii, 219.

MARINGER, J., and BANDI, H.-G. (1953): *Art in the Ice Age: Spanish Levant art; Arctic art*. In execution of a plan by H. Obermaier. Translated by R. Allen. Allen and Unwin: London; Holbein Publishing Company: Basel. pp. 168.

MARTIN, P. S., QUIMBY, G. I., and COLLIER, D. (1950): *Indians before Columbus: twenty thousand years of North American history revealed by archaeology*. 4th imp. University of Chicago Press: Chicago. pp. xxiv, 582.

315

MASON, J. A. (1957): *The ancient civilizations of Peru*. Pelican Books, A.395. Penguin Books: Harmondsworth. pp. xx, 330.

MEDAWAR, P. (1961): *The future of Man*. New American Library: New York. pp. xii, 13-125.

MILLER, W. J. (1952): *An introduction to historical geology: with special reference to North America*. 6th ed. Van Nostrand: New York, Toronto, London. pp. xii, 555.

MONTAGU, M. F. ASHLEY (1960): *An introduction to physical anthropology*. 3rd ed. Charles C. Thomas: Springfield, Illinois; Blackwell: Oxford. pp. xvi, 771.

MONTET, P. (1958): *Everyday life in Egypt in the days of Rameses the Great*. Translated from the French by A. R. Maxwell-Hyslop and M. S. Drower. Arnold: London. pp. xvi, 365.

MOORE, R. C. (1958): *Introduction to historical geology*. 2nd ed. McGraw-Hill: New York, Toronto, London. pp. ix, 656.

MORLEY, S. G. (1946): *The ancient Maya*. Stanford University Press: Stanford, California; Oxford University Press, Geoffrey Cumberlege: London. pp. xxxii, 520.

MUIR-WOOD, H. M. *See* OAKLEY, K. P.

MUMFORD, L. (1957): *The transformations of man*. World Perspectives, No. 6. Allen and Unwin: London. pp. 192.

MURRAY, MARGARET A. (1949): *The splendour that was Egypt: a general survey of Egyptian culture and civilisation*. Sidgwick and Jackson: London. pp. xxiv, 354.

NAPIER, J. (1961): 'Human origins: recent discoveries at Olduvai Gorge'. *The Lancet*, 30 September 1961, pp. 767–8. London.

OAKLEY, K. P. (1961): *Man the tool-maker*. 5th ed. Trustees of the British Museum: London. pp. vi, 98.

OAKLEY, K. P., and MUIR-WOOD, H. M. (1959): *The succession of life through geological time*. 4th ed. revised. Trustees of the British Museum: London. pp. viii, 94.

OSBORN, H. F. (1910): *The age of mammals in Europe, Asia and North America*. Macmillan Company: New York. pp. xx, 635.

OSBORN, H. F. (1919): *Men of the Old Stone Age: their environment, life and art*. 3rd ed. With new notes and illustrations on the archaeology of Spain and North Africa. Bell: London. pp. xxx, 559.

PALMER, L. S. (1957): *Man's journey through time: a first step in physical and cultural anthropochronology*. Hutchinson: London. pp. xv, 184.

PRITCHARD, J. B. (Ed.) (1958): *The ancient Near East: an anthology of texts and pictures*. Princeton University Press: Princeton, New Jersey; Oxford University Press: London. pp. xx, 380.

QUIMBY, G. I. *See* MARTIN, P.S.

READ, H. (1949): *The meaning of art.* Pelican Books, A.213. Penguin Books: Harmondsworth. pp. 197.

READE, W. (1872): *The martyrdom of man.* Trübner: London. pp. viii, 544.

ROBERTSON, J. M. (1937): *A short history of Christianity.* 3rd ed. revised and condensed. Thinker's Library, No. 24. Watts: London. pp. viii, 248.

ROBINSON, C. A., JR (1958): *Ancient history from prehistoric times to the death of Justinian.* Macmillan Company: New York. pp. iv, 738.

ROBINSON, J. T. *See* BROOM, R.

ROE, A., and SIMPSON, G. G. (Eds.) (1958): *Behaviour and evolution.* Revision of papers presented at the 1955 and 1956 conferences sponsored by the American Psychological Association and the Society for the Study of Evolution. Yale University Press: New Haven. pp. viii, 557.

ROMER, A. S. (1941): *Man and the vertebrates.* 3rd ed. University of Chicago Press: Chicago. pp. x, 405.

ROMER, A. S. (1945): *Vertebrate paleontology.* 2nd ed. University of Chicago Press: Chicago. pp. x, 687.

ROMER, A. S. (1959): *The vertebrate story.* University of Chicago Press: Chicago. pp. viii, 437. (The revised and largely rewritten fourth edition of *Man and the vertebrates (q.v.).*)

RUSSELL, BERTRAND (1949): *The scientific outlook.* 2nd ed. Allen and Unwin: London. pp. 285.

RUSSELL, BERTRAND (1961): *History of western philosophy and its connection with political and social circumstances from the earliest times to the present day.* New ed. Allen and Unwin: London. pp. 842.

SAHLINS, M. D. *See* SPUHLER, J. N.

SARTON, G. (1927–47): *Introduction to the history of science.* 3 vols. Vol. 1: From Homer to Omar Khayyam, pp. xi, 839 (1927). Vol. 2: From Rabbi Ben Ezra to Roger Bacon, 2 pt., pp. xxxv, xvi, 1251 (1931). Vol. 3: Science and learning in the fourteenth century, 2 pt., pp. xxxv, xi, 2155 (1947–8). Carnegie Institution Publication, No. 376. Carnegie Institution: Washington.

SCHULTZ, A. H. *See* HOFER, H.

SHAPLEY, H. (1958): *Of stars and men: the human response to an expanding universe.* Elek Books: London. pp. viii, 145.

SHERRINGTON, C. (1955): *Man on his nature.* The Gifford Lectures, Edinburgh, 1937–8. Pelican Books, A.322. Penguin Books: Harmondsworth. pp. 312.

SILCOCK, A. (1947): *Introduction to Chinese art and history.* 3rd ed. revised. Faber: London. pp. 252.

SIMPSON, G. G. (1945): 'The principles of classification and a classification of mammals'. Vol. 85 of the *Bulletin of the American Museum of Natural History*, pp. xvi, 350. New York.

SIMPSON, G. G. (1950): *The meaning of evolution: a study of the history of life and of its significance for man.* Oxford University Press, Geoffrey Cumberlege: London. pp. xvi, 364.

SIMPSON, G. G. (1953): *The major features of evolution.* Columbia Biological Series, No. 17. Columbia University Press: New York. pp. xx, 434.

SINGER, C. (1959): *A short history of scientific ideas to 1900.* Clarendon Press: Oxford. pp. xx, 525.

SINGER, C., HOLMYARD, E. J., HALL, A. R., and WILLIAMS, T. I. (Eds.) (1955–8): *A history of technology.* 5 vols. Clarendon Press: Oxford.

SPAHNI, J.-C. (1954): 'Les gisements à ursus spelaeus de l'Autriche et leurs problèmes'. *Bulletin de la Société Préhistorique Française,* Tome 51, pp. 346–67. Paris.

SPUHLER, J. N., GERARD, R. W., WASHBURN, S. L., HOCKET, C. F., HARLOW, H. F., and SAHLINS, M. D. (1959): *The evolution of man's capacity for culture.* With a summary by L. A. White. Wayne State University Press: Detroit. pp. viii, 79.

STARK, D. *See* HOFER, H.

STIRTON, R. A. (1959): *Time, life, and man: the fossil record.* Wiley: New York; Chapman and Hall: London. pp. xii, 558.

SUMNER, W. G. (1960): *Folkways: a study of the sociological importance of usages, manners, customs, mores, and morals.* With a special introduction by W. L. Phelps. New American Library: New York. pp. xvi, 17–605.

TAX, S. (Ed.) (1960): *The evolution of man: man, culture and society.* University of Chicago Darwin Centenary (1959). Being Vol. 2 of *Evolution after Darwin.* Chicago University Press: Chicago; Cambridge University Press: London. pp. viii, 473.

TEILHARD DE CHARDIN, P. (1959): *The phenomenon of man.* With an introduction by Sir Julian Huxley. Collins: London. pp. 320.

TEILHARD DE CHARDIN, P. (1960): *Le milieu divin: an essay on the interior life.* Collins: London. pp. 160.

THOMPSON, J. E. S. (1954): *The rise and fall of Maya civilisation.* University of Oklahoma Press: Norman. pp. xii, 287.

TOYNBEE, A. J. (1946): *A study of history.* Abridgement of Vols. 1–6 by D. C. Somervell. Issued under the auspices of the Royal Institute of International Affairs. Oxford University Press: London. pp. xiv, 617.

TOYNBEE, A. J. (1957): *A study of history.* Abridgement of Vols. 8–10 by D. C. Somervell. Issued under the auspices of the Royal Institute of International Affairs. Oxford University Press: London. pp. xii, 414.

UPJOHN, E. M., WINGERT, P. S., and MAHLER, J. G. (Eds.) (1958): *History of world art.* 2nd ed. revised and enlarged. Oxford University Press: New York. pp. xx, 876.

VAILLANT, G. C. (1955): *The Aztecs of Mexico: origin, rise and fall of the Aztec nation.* With a postscript by C. A. Burland. Pelican Books, A.200. Penguin Books: Harmondsworth. pp. 333.

VALLOIS, H. V. *See* BOULE, M.

VIAUD, GASTON (1960): *Intelligence: its evolution and forms.* Translated from the French by A. J. Pomerans. Arrow Science Series. Hutchinson: London. pp. 127.

WASHBURN, S. L. *See* SPUHLER, J. N.

WATSON, W. (1950): *Flint implements: an account of Stone Age techniques and cultures.* Trustees of the British Museum: London. pp. viii, 80.

WEBSTER, H. (1940): *History of civilisation.* Heath: Boston. pp. xx, 1051.

WEIDENREICH, F. (1946): *Apes, giants and man.* University of Chicago Press: Chicago. pp. vii, 122.

WELLS, H. G. (1951): *The outline of history: being a plain history of life and mankind.* Revised and brought up to the end of the Second World War by R. Postgate. Cassell: London, Toronto, Melbourne, Sydney, Wellington. pp. xviii, 1260.

WHEELER, M. (1955): *Rome beyond the imperial frontiers.* Pelican Books, A.335. Penguin Books: Harmondsworth. pp. 224.

WHITEHEAD, A. N. (1934): *Nature and life.* The Cambridge Miscellany, No. 13. University Press: Cambridge. pp. 96.

WHITEHEAD, A. N. (1938): *Science and the modern world.* Pelican Books, A.34. Penguin Books: Harmondsworth. pp. 246.

WHITEHEAD, A. N. (1942): *Adventures of ideas.* Pelican Books, A.103. Penguin Books: Harmondsworth: pp. 288.

WIEDEMANN, A. (1901): *The realms of the Egyptian dead, according to the belief of the ancient Egyptians.* Translated by J. Hutchison. The Ancient East, No. 1. Nutt: London. pp. 68.

WIEDEMANN, A. (1902): *Popular literature in ancient Egypt.* Translated by J. Hutchison. The Ancient East, No. 5. Nutt: London. pp. viii, 51.

WILLIAMS, T. I. *See* DERRY, T. K., and SINGER, C.

WILSON, J. A. (1951): *The burden of Egypt: an interpretation of ancient Egyptian culture.* An Oriental Institute Essay. University of Chicago Press: Chicago. pp. xx, 332.

WILSON, J. A. *See* FRANKFORT, H.

WINDELLS, F. (1949): *The Lascaux cave paintings*. Personal note by the Abbé H. Breuil. Preface by C. F. C. Hawkes. Introduction by A. Leroi-Gourha. Text prepared in collaboration with Annette Laming. Faber: London. pp. 139.

WINGERT, P. S. *See* UPJOHN, E. M.

WORMINGTON, H. M. (1957): *Ancient man in North America.* 4th ed., revised. Denver Museum of Natural History: Denver, Colorado. pp. xviii, 322.

YOUNG, J. Z. (1951): *Doubt and certainty in science: a biologist's reflections on the brain.* The B.B.C. Reith Lectures, 1950. Clarendon Press: Oxford. pp. viii, 168.

ZEUNER, F. E. (1958): *Dating the past: an introduction to geochronology.* 4th ed. revised and enlarged. Methuen: London. pp. xx, 516.

ZEUNER, F. E. (1959): *The Pleistocene period: its climate, chronology and faunal successions.* Revised ed. Hutchinson: London. pp. xx, 21–447.

ZUCKERMAN, S. (1932): *The social life of monkeys and apes.* Kegan Paul, Trench, Trubner: London. pp. xii, 357.

ZUCKERMAN, S. (1933): *Functional affinities of man, monkeys and apes: a study of the bearings of physiology and behaviour on the taxonomy and phylogeny of lemurs, monkeys, apes, and man.* Kegan Paul: London. pp. xviii, 203.

SUGGESTIONS FOR FURTHER READING

THE FOLLOWING WORKS, selected from the Bibliography, are specially recommended as supplementary reading on different aspects of human evolution.

The Cosmological Background
Hoyle (1951), Lovell (1959).

The Geological Background
Dunbar (1949), Moore (1958).

Evolution – General
Carrington (1956), Colbert (1955), Huxley (1942), Oakley and Muir-Wood (1959), Romer (1959), Simpson (1950).

The Physical Evolution of Man
Clark (1960), Hooton (1946), Howells (1960).

The Cultural Emergence of Man and the Evolution of Technology
Childe (1942), Cole (1959), Derry and Williams (1960), Hoebel (1958), Oakley (1961).

Civilisation and the Evolution of Ideas
Dampier (1961), James (1956), Lucas (1953), Russell (1949), Singer (1959), Upjohn, Wingert and Mahler (1958), Webster (1940).

Philosophical Aspects of Human Evolution
Bergson (1911), Huxley (1961), Sherrington (1955), Teilhard de Chardin (1959).

INDEX

323

329

Date Due

MY 21 '65			
MAR 4 '70			